Glencoe

Unit 3 Teaching Resources:

# Writing Speaking Reading Listening

**Includes summaries and school-to-home activities in**

- Spanish
- Vietnamese
- Tagalog
- Cantonese
- Hmong
- Haitian-Creole

The McGraw-Hill Companies

 Glencoe

**Note to the Teacher**
There are ten Active Reading Graphic Organizers, on the pages preceding the Answer Key, that students will need in order to complete some of the exercises in this book. Teachers may want to keep a supply of copies on hand for student use.



Send all inquiries to:
Glencoe/McGraw-Hill
8787 Orion Place
Columbus, OH 43240-4027

ISBN: 978-0-07-889243-1
MHID: 0-07-889243-0

Printed in the United States of America.
1 2 3 4 5 6 7 8 9 047 14 13 12 11 10 09 08

# World Literature—Unit 3: Southwest and South Central Asia, 3500 B.C.–Present



## Part 1: Southwest Asia, 3500 B.C.–Present

## Part 2: South Central Asia, 3500 B.C.–Present

# Southwest and South Central Asia: 3500 B.C.–Present *(page 434)*

## Unit Introduction

Most cultures explore basic questions about creation, life, and death. Even the earliest cultures recorded information that focused on these questions. In Southwest Asia, three religions evolved that would influence how people around the world thought about life and death for centuries to come. These three religions—Judaism, Christianity, and Islam—all believe in one God and use sacred texts to guide followers and instill values. Jews and Christians follow the Ten Commandments, a set of laws for daily living and a spiritual relationship with God. Muslims believe that they will find eternal salvation by following the Qur'an.

However, one of the first written collections of laws was produced by Hammurabi, the king of Babylonia (modern Iraq) who ruled from 1792 to 1750 B.C. Hammurabi's Code of Laws was arranged in groups so that all people could easily understand the king's expectations. The code was carved on an eight-foot high monument, which was probably located in a public place. Hammurabi's code was concerned with crime and punishment; lawbreakers were not given an opportunity to explain or defend their actions.

The selections from Hammurabi's code below show the structure of Babylonian society and the consequences citizens could expect if they committed misdeeds.

**3.** If any one bring an accusation of any crime before the elders, and does not prove what he has charged, he shall, if it be a capital offense charged, be put to death.

**5.** If a judge try a case, reach a decision, and present his judgment in writing; if later error shall appear in his decision, and it be through his own fault, then he shall pay twelve times the fine set by him in the case, and he shall be publicly removed from the judge's bench, and never again shall he sit there to render judgment.

**6.** If any one steal the property of a temple or of the court, he shall be put to death, and also the one who receives the stolen thing from him shall be put to death.

**7.** If any one steal cattle or sheep, or an ass, or a pig or a goat, if it belong to a god or to the court, the thief shall pay thirtyfold; if they belonged to a freed man of the king he shall pay tenfold; if the thief has nothing with which to pay he shall be put to death.

Name ______________________ Class ______________ Date ______________

Hammurabi reorganized a legal system that had long been established in Babylonia. Earlier sets of laws have disappeared, but Hammurabi made references that led scholars to believe that they existed.

## ACTIVITY

**Directions** Think about how laws, and the consequences for breaking them, affect modern society. Do you think that establishing specific rules and possible consequences help people to modify and improve their behavior?

Write three new rules that you think would benefit your school. Then write a reasonable consequence for breaking or violating each rule. Finally, write a paragraph that explains how you think your rules and consequences would influence the students in your school.

| Rule 1: | Rule 2: | Rule 3: |
|---|---|---|
| Consequence: | Consequence: | Consequence: |

**How would these rules influence students in your school?**

______________________________________________

______________________________________________

______________________________________________

______________________________________________

______________________________________________

______________________________________________

______________________________________________

______________________________________________

______________________________________________

Name ____________________ Class ____________ Date ____________

# The Big Idea Foldable

## Making a Column Book or Bound Book

Ask your teacher for a copy of the Column Book Foldable template. You can use the template in many different ways. Here are just a few.

### Vertical Tables

**Step 1** Hold a sheet of paper in front of you so that the short side is at the top.

**Step 2** For a two-column table, fold the paper in half lengthwise.

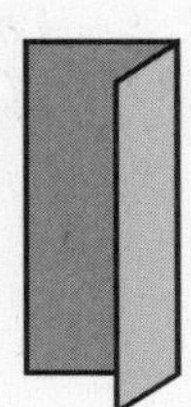

**Step 2a** For a four-column table, fold the paper in half lengthwise, then fold the paper in half again.

**Step 2b** For a three-column table, fold the paper in thirds.

**Step 3** Draw a line along the creases between the columns.

### Horizontal Tables

**Step 1** Hold a sheet of paper in front of you so that the long side is at the top. Follow steps 2 through 3 above to make the number of columns you need.

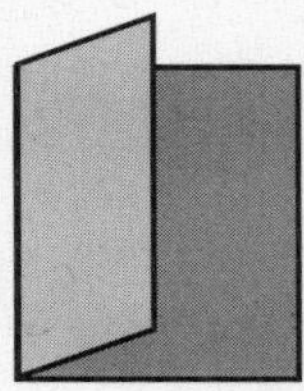

### Bound Book

**Step 1** Decide how many pages you would like in your book. Divide that number by four to find the number of sheets of paper you will need. If you want an eight-page book, you will need two sheets of paper.

**Step 2** Holding the sheets together, follow the directions for a two-column horizontal table. Staple along the fold to make a bound book.

Name ______________________ Class ______________ Date ______________

3-column fold

2-column fold

3-column fold

Name ______________________ Class ____________ Date ____________

# The Big Ideas

## School-to-Home Connection

The exceptionally complex history of South Central Asia, characterized by invasions and colonization, has played a leading role in its vast diversity. Geographical variation throughout the region has further contributed to its heterogeneous culture. This diversity is evident in the different religions and traditions that are practiced throughout the nations of South Central Asia.

## ACTIVITY

**Directions** Think about three of the Big Ideas in Unit 3: The Search for Enlightenment, A Place in Society, and A Complex Heritage. Then interview someone at home about these Big Ideas. Start with the following questions and add more of your own. Make sure that you take notes during the interview. After completing the interview, use your interview notes to write a newspaper article that addresses the Big Ideas.

1. Would you live your life differently if you believed in karma? If so, what behavior(s) would you change?

   ______________________________________________

   ______________________________________________

2. Do you believe reason can be used to achieve contentment? Why or why not?

   ______________________________________________

   ______________________________________________

3. What examples of class divisions have you observed in modern society?

   ______________________________________________

   ______________________________________________

4. What examples of gender divisions have you observed in modern society?

   ______________________________________________

   ______________________________________________

5. What are the benefits of cultural diversity?

   ______________________________________________

   ______________________________________________

Name ______________________ Class ______________ Date ______________

# Ideas importantes

## Enlace entre la escuela y el hogar

La historia excepcionalmente compleja del Asia sudcentral que se caracterizó por las invasiones y colonizaciones, ha desempeñado un papel preponderante en su vasta diversidad. La variación geográfica a través de la región ha contribuido aún más al carácter heterogéneo de su cultura. Esta diversidad se hace evidente en las distintas religiones y tradiciones que se practican en todas las naciones del Asia sudcentral.

## ACTIVIDAD

**Instrucciones:** Piensa en las tres ideas importantes de la Unidad 3: En busca del conocimiento, Un lugar en la sociedad y Una herencia compleja. Luego entrevista a una persona en tu hogar sobre estas ideas importantes. Comienza con las preguntas que están más abajo y añade otras más que sean tuyas. Asegúrate de tomar notas durante la entrevista. Después de completarla, usa las notas de la entrevista para escribir un artículo periodístico que se refiera a las ideas importantes.

**1.** ¿Vivirías tu vida en forma diferente si creyeras en el karma? Si fuera así, ¿qué comportamiento modificarías?

______________________________________________

______________________________________________

**2.** ¿Crees que se puede usar la razón para llegar al bienestar y la paz interior? Explica por qué.

______________________________________________

______________________________________________

**3.** ¿Qué ejemplos de divisiones de clases has observado en la sociedad moderna?

______________________________________________

______________________________________________

**4.** ¿Qué ejemplos de divisiones de género has observado en la sociedad moderna?

______________________________________________

______________________________________________

**5.** ¿Cuáles son los beneficios de la diversidad cultural?

______________________________________________

______________________________________________

Name ______________________ Class ____________ Date ____________

# Các Ý Tưởng Lớn: Kết Nối Gia Đình với Trường Học

Lịch sử đặc biệt phức tạp của Trung Nam Á với những đặc điểm nổi bật là các cuộc xâm lược và quá trình thực dân hóa đã đóng một vai trò quan trọng tạo nên sự đa dạng phong phú của khu vực này. Những vùng địa lý khác nhau trên khắp khu vực cũng góp phần tạo nên nền văn hóa không đồng nhất. Sự đa dạng này thể hiện rất rõ nét trong các tôn giáo và truyền thống khác nhau hiện được duy trì ở khắp các quốc gia Trung Nam Á.

## HOẠT ĐỘNG

**Hướng Dẫn** Hãy nghĩ về ba Ý Tưởng Lớn trong Chương 3: Cuộc Kiếm Tìm Sự Khai Sáng, Một Góc Xã Hội, và Một Di Sản Đa Dạng. Sau đó, hãy phỏng vấn một người trong gia đình về Các Ý Tưởng Lớn này, bắt đầu với các câu hỏi sau và sử dụng thêm các câu hỏi của chính em. Nhớ ghi chép trong quá trình phỏng vấn. Sau khi phỏng vấn xong, sử dụng các ghi chép để viết một bài báo về Các Ý Tưởng Lớn đó.

1. Liệu ………… có sống một cuộc sống khác nếu tin vào nghiệp chướng của Đạo Phật không? Nếu vậy, ………… sẽ thay đổi các hành vi nào?
______________________________________________
______________________________________________

2. ………… có tin rằng có thể sử dụng lý trí để đạt được sự mãn nguyện không? Tại sao có, tại sao không?
______________________________________________
______________________________________________

3. ………… đã chứng kiến ví dụ nào về sự phân biệt giai cấp trong xã hội hiện đại?
______________________________________________
______________________________________________

4. ………… đã chứng kiến ví dụ nào về sự phân biệt giới tính trong xã hội hiện đại?
______________________________________________
______________________________________________

5. Sự đa dạng văn hóa đem lại những lợi ích gì?
______________________________________________
______________________________________________

Name ______________________ Class ______________ Date ______________

# Ang Mga Mahahalagang Kuru-Kuro

## Kaugnayan ng Paaralan sa Tahanan

Ang napaka-komplikadong kasaysayan ng South Central Asia, na markado ng mga pagsalakay at kolonisasyon, ay gumanap ng pangunahing papel sa kanyang malawak na pagkakaiba. Ang pagkakáibá ng heograpika sa rehiyong ito ay lalong nagdagdag sa kanyang halu-halong kultura. Makikita ang pagkakáibang ito sa mga iba't-ibang relihiyon at tradisyon na sinusundan sa mga bansa ng South Central Asia.

## GAWAIN

**Ang Gagawin** Pag-isipan ang tatlo sa mga Mahahalagang Kuru-kuro sa Yunit 3: Ang Paghanap ng Paliwanag, Isang Lugar sa Lipunan, at Isang Komplikadong Pamanang-lahi. Pagkatapos ay interbyuhin ang isang tao sa iyong tahanan tungkol sa mga Mahahalagang Kuru-kurong ito. Magsimula sa mga sumusunod na katanungan at magdagdag ng sarili mong mga katanungan. Siguraduhing magtala habang nag-iinterbyu. Kapag natapos na ang interbyu, gamitin ang iyong mga tala para magsulat ng isang artikulo sa pahayagan na tumutugon sa mga Mahahalagang Kuru-kuro.

1. Babaguhin mo ba ang iyong pamumuhay kung ikaw ay naniniwala sa karma? Kung gayon, anong (mga) ugali ang babaguhin mo?

   ______________________________________________

   ______________________________________________

2. Naniniwala ka bang maaaring gamitin ang katwiran para makamtan ang pagiging kontento? Bakit o bakit hindi?

   ______________________________________________

   ______________________________________________

3. Ano ang mga halimbawa ng class divisions (mga pagkahiwalay-hiwalay ng iba't-ibang katayuan sa lipunan) ang iyong napuna sa modernong lipunan?

   ______________________________________________

   ______________________________________________

4. Ano ang mga halimbawa ng gender divisions (mga pagkahiwalay-hiwalay ng iba't-ibang kasarian) ang iyong napuna sa modernong lipunan?

   ______________________________________________

   ______________________________________________

5. Ano ang mga benepisyo ng pagkakaroon ng iba't-ibang kultura?

   ______________________________________________

   ______________________________________________

# 重要概念

## 學校與家庭的銜接

中南亞極為複雜的歷史，是造成該地區廣泛多元文化的最主要因素，而尤其以遭到入侵和殖民最具代表性。該地區各地在地理上的差異，也更加造成其不同的文化。中南亞各國所具有的不同宗教和傳統，就是這種多元性的證據。

## 活動

**說明** 思考單元3中的三個「重要概念」：啟蒙的尋求、社會中的地位、和複雜的文化遺產。然後針對這些重要概念訪問您的家人。請從下列的問題開始，然後再加上您自己的其他問題。您進行訪問的時候務必要做記錄。完成訪問之後，用您的訪問記錄針對這些重要概念寫出一篇報紙文章。

**1.** 如果您相信因果報應，您會用不同的方式過您的人生嗎？如果會的話，您會改變哪些行為？

______________________________

______________________________

**2.** 您是否相信理性可用來取得滿足？為什麼相信，或是為什麼不相信？

______________________________

______________________________

**3.** 您在現代的社會中，曾觀察到什麼樣的階級區分例子？

______________________________

______________________________

**4.** 您在現代的社會中，曾觀察到什麼樣的性別區分例子？

______________________________

______________________________

**5.** 文化上的多元性有什麼好處？

______________________________

______________________________

Name ______________________ Class ______________ Date ______________

# Gwo Lide

## Koneksyon ant Lekòl ak Lakay

Kokennchenn istwa konplèks Sid Lazi Santral, ki konsène ak envazyon ak kolonizasyon, jwe yon wòl enpòtan nan divèsite laj li. Chanjman jeyografik toupatou nan rejyon an kontribiye nan kilti etewojèn li. Divèsite sa a evidan nan diferan relijyon ak tradisyon ki pratike toupatou nan peyi Sid Lazi Santral yo.

## AKTIVITE

**Enstwiksyon** Reflechi sou twa Gwo Lide nan Inite 3: Rechèch Syèk Limyè, Yon Kote nan Sosyete a ak yo Eritaj Konplèks. Answit, fè antrevi avèk yon moun lakay ou sou Gwo Lide sa yo. Kòmanse avèk kesyon sa yo epi ajoute kesyon pa ou. Asire ou pran nòt pandan antrevi a. Apre ou fin fè antrevi a, itilize nòt antrevi ou pou ekri yon atik jounal ki abòde Gwo Lide yo.

1. Èske ou ta mennen yon lavi yon fason diferan si ou te kwè nan kama? Si w di ou, ki konpòtman ou ta chanje?

______________________________________________

______________________________________________

2. Èske ou kwè rezon ki kapab itilize pou reyalize kontantman? Pou kisa oswa pou ki pa?

______________________________________________

______________________________________________

3. Ki egzanp divizyon klas ou te obsève nan sosyete modèn lan?

______________________________________________

______________________________________________

4. Ki egzanp divizyon sèks ou te obsève nan sosyete modèn lan?

______________________________________________

______________________________________________

5. Ki benefis ki genyen nan divèsite kiltirèl?

______________________________________________

______________________________________________

# Cov Tswvyim Loj

## Tsev Kawm Ntawv-rau-Tsev Kev Txuas Lus

Zaj keebkwm tshwjxeeb covnyom ntawm tebchaws Asia Qab Teb, teev raws kev txeem thiab hauj yuam, tau muab los ua qauv coj rau ntau hom neeg. Tej hajkhawv niam av nthuav raws tej cheebtsam tau muab kev koom kom muaj ntau hom kab li kev cai ntau. Txhua hom kab li kev cai nov yog tim khawv rau ntau hom kev ntseeg thiab kej coj noj haus uas ib txwm muaj thoob plaws txhua haiv neeg ntawm Asia Qab Teb.

## DEJNUM

**Kev Taw Qhia** Xav txog peb Lub Tswvyim Loj hauv Nqe 3: Kev Nrhiav Qhov Chaw Kaj Siab, Ib Qhov Chaw hauv Nroog, thiab Ib Hom Puavpheej Ntxhov. Nug ib tus neeg tom tsev txog cov Tswvyim Loj. Pib nrog cov lus nug nram nov thiab muab nej ib cov lus ntxiv. Nco ntsoov sau tej lus tham cia. Tomqab tham tas, siv cov lus sau cia los teev ib zaj ntawv xovxwm uas qhia txog cov Tswvyim Loj.

1. Nej puas yuav hloov lub neej kom txawv yog nej ntseeg txog karma? Yog hloov, yam cwjpwm dabtsi nej yuav hloov?

______________________________________________________________

______________________________________________________________

2. Nej puas xav tias tswvyim muab tau los siv kom yeejtsum tau kev zoo siab? Vim licas tau los vim licas tsis tau?

______________________________________________________________

______________________________________________________________

3. Hom kev sib cais raws pawg neeg twg nej tau pom nyob hauv lub neej?

______________________________________________________________

______________________________________________________________

4. Hom kev sib cais raws pojniam thiab txiv neej twg nej tau pom nyob hauv lub neej?

______________________________________________________________

______________________________________________________________

5. Hom nuj nqi dabtsi txawm tau zoo los ntawm ntau ntau hom kab li kev cai?

______________________________________________________________

______________________________________________________________

Name ______________________ Class ______________ Date ______________

# Unit Challenge Planner

The Unit 3 Challenge provides an opportunity to explore further the unit's six Big Ideas: The Secret of Life, The Search for Wisdom, The Violence of Change, The Search for Enlightenment, A Place in Society, and A Complex Heritage.

**Directions** From the topics listed in Section A, choose one that interests you. Once you have chosen a topic, choose a project in Section B that will help you present your ideas about the topic. Projects may be done alone, with a partner, or with a small group. Follow the steps in Section C to plan and complete your challenge project.

## Section A. Choose a Topic

1. Some of the earliest written records in the world are sacred texts that came from Southwest Asia, including texts from the religions of Judaism, Christianity, and Islam. Each text explains the purpose of life and provides guidelines for daily living, while offering stories of creation and the afterlife. Choose two unit selections that differ in beliefs and discuss how each presents life's purpose, guides human interactions, explains creation, and describes the afterlife.
2. Over the centuries, political and cultural upheaval in Southwest Asia has led to violent outbursts among people of different religions and nationalities. These conflicts have contributed to strained relations between nations and have damaged the lives of many people. Choose two unit selections and discuss how their authors have been affected. What literary elements do the authors use to convey their emotions?
3. Searching for enlightenment is part of each Hindu's spiritual journey toward fulfilling his or her *dharma.* Completing set tasks and going through a series of rebirths allows Hindus to eventually unite with the universal spirit. Many works of Hindu literature reflect the moral duties of those who have reached their *dharma.* Compare and contrast characters in two unit selections. How do they reflect Hindu religious beliefs? What must each character do to find enlightenment?
4. For generations, the caste system in India classified people by the social group into which they are born. The strict regulations determined a person's employment and possessions. The lower castes were often subjected to degradation, movement between classes was nearly impossible, and women were given few opportunities. Choose one unit selection that shows how the caste system affected people. What do you believe is the author's message?
5. The complexity of South Central Asia's heritage stems from its wide variety of religious beliefs and ethnic customs. Economic and social barriers have crumbled in recent years, but the region still struggles with overpopulation and conflicts between countries. Choose one or two unit selections that portray changes in modern life in the region. Are the changes mostly positive, mostly negative, or about the same? How are the characters affected by these changes?

Name ______________________ Class ______________ Date ______________

## Section B. Choose a Project

1. **Picture Book.** Work alone or with a partner whose topic is the same as yours to create a picture book containing a series of illustrations that tells the story without words. Write an introduction to your book that explains how your book addresses your topic. Using Topic 1, for example, create a series of sketches depicting the mental images that the words create for you.

2. **Artist's Conception.** Work alone, with a partner, or with a group to use visual media to create a written or an oral presentation. Use a computer, for example, to create an interactive presentation with text and visuals on the screen or outline the main points on the screen to accompany an oral presentation. Other possibilities include a book with illustrations or photos, a poster or three-dimensional representation with explanatory text, or a videotaped presentation. For example, using Topic 3, create a presentation on characters in Hindu literature. Describe how these characters reflect Hindu religious belief. Touch on the spiritual journeys these characters take to find enlightenment.

3. **Letter to the Editor.** Imagine that one of the unit selections was printed in your local or school newspaper. Working alone or with a partner, write a letter to the editor that expresses your opinion about a topic or issue suggested by the selection. Your letter should present strong evidence to support your argument as you try to persuade readers to agree with you. Using Topic 2, for example, address the hostilities in Southwest Asia. Include reasons why these conflicts have arisen and discuss how violence has affected the people living there.

4. **Daily Journal.** Work alone or with a partner whose topic is the same as yours to create a series of journal entries that address your topic. Using Topic 4, for example, write journal entries from the point of view of a person in a particular caste. Based on his or her social caste, write a chronicle of the person's daily life experiences.

5. **Be the Biographer.** Working alone or with a partner whose topic is the same as yours, write a brief biography about one of the unit authors. Using Topic 5, for example, you might write a biography about an author who has experienced firsthand the changes in south central Asia. Address in your biography the author's motivation for writing.

Name ______________________ Class ______________ Date ______________

## Section C. Make a Plan

1. Clarify any class requirements.

   ☐ Project due date ______________________

   ☐ Interim deadlines ______________________

   ☐ Research beyond the textbook

   **A.** sources required ____________ **C.** other ____________

   **B.** recommended ____________ **D.** none

   ☐ Source documentation

   **A.** required for all research ____________ **C.** other ____________

   **B.** required for quotations ____________ **D.** none

2. Choose your topic from Section A.

   ☐ Topic ______________________

3. Choose your project from Section B.

   ☐ Project ______________________

4. Decide whether you will be working alone or with others.

   ☐ alone ☐ partner ☐ group

5. If you will be working with others, meet with all the participants to decide on the authors and selections that you will focus on for the project.

   ☐ Authors ______________________

   ☐ Selections ______________________

6. At this meeting or for your own project, determine whether there are advanced preparations that you need to make early in the process. For example

   ☐ Reserve space for a performance.

   ☐ Invite people to the performance.

   ☐ Advertise the performance.

   ☐ Obtain materials for graphic representations, sets, costumes, or other items.

   ☐ Other ______________________

## Section C, cont.

7. If you will be working with others, agree on each person's responsibility before your next meeting on ______________________.

☐ Name ______________________
Responsibilities ______________________
______________________

☐ Name ______________________
Responsibilities ______________________
______________________

☐ Name ______________________
Responsibilities ______________________
______________________

☐ Name ______________________
Responsibilities ______________________
______________________

8. Do your research. If you will be using sources beyond your textbook, find the sources, take notes, and jot down ideas. If you will be using only the textbook, re-read the selections you have chosen and take notes that are relevant to your project.

   ☐ Research complete.

9. Document your sources. Make copies of outside sources and keep them in a project folder labeled "Sources."

   ☐ Source documentation complete.

10. Sort through your notes. You might write each idea on an index card. Add details and examples to support each idea. Be sure to record each direct quote exactly as it appeared in the source and note the source.

    ☐ Details and examples complete.

11. Arrange your index cards in the order in which you will present the ideas.

    ☐ Order of material complete.

12. Make a rough draft of your script, graphic representation, or letters. If you are working with a partner or group, edit each other's drafts.

    ☐ Rough draft complete.

13. How you refine and polish your project depends on the project you have chosen. If the end product includes written material, you should reread, revise, and edit your draft. If you will be performing, determine whether you will perform with or without scripts. In either case, allow time to rehearse. As you rehearse or read your written work aloud, listen critically. Do the ideas build logically? Does the language flow smoothly, or do you need to reshape some sentences? Make any improvements you think are needed.

    ☐ Project polished.

14. Share your work with others through a performance, display, reading, videotape, Web site, or other form of communication.

Name ______________________ Class ______________ Date ______________

# Academic Vocabulary Development

## Introduction

A wide vocabulary allows you to express ideas about literature more effectively. This unit's academic vocabulary words can help you analyze the selections so that you can move beyond such responses as "I enjoyed it" or "That was confusing."

### Unit 3 Academic Vocabulary

**via** *prep.* by way of, or by means of
**restore** *v.* to bring back to an original condition
**framework** *n.* the basic structure of something
**inspection** *n.* the act or process of examining something
**inhibition** *n.* an internal restraint on behavior
**alternative** *n.* a choice between two or more things
**outcome** *n.* result, or ending
**instance** *n.* occasion
**link** *n.* a connection between two or more persons, places, things, or ideas
**technology** *n.* the application of knowledge to practical tasks and problems

## ACTIVITY

**Directions** Use the boldface vocabulary words in your answers to these questions.

1. In *Gilgamesh,* the title character could have responded to Enkidu's death by vowing to enjoy his own remaining time on Earth as much as possible. But Gilgamesh chooses an **alternative.** He first tries to **restore** Enkidu to life and then tries to **restore** his own youth. The **outcome** of all these efforts is failure. In light of all this, what do you think Gilgamesh did after he returned to Uruk?

______________________________________________

______________________________________________

______________________________________________

______________________________________________

2. Based on *Gilgamesh,* what are some **technologies** that the people of Uruk used?

______________________________________________

______________________________________________

______________________________________________

______________________________________________

## Academic Vocabulary Development *(cont.)*

**3.** What important **link** can you identify between *Gilgamesh* and "The Flood"?

**4.** In "The Parable of the Prodigal Son," the father readily **restores** the prodigal son to a position of favor in his household. How do you feel about this? Is the father's action fair? Is it wise? Explain.

**5.** Identify and briefly explain some important **links** among Judaism, Christianity, and Islam.

**6.** Describe the **framework** of "The Thousand and One Nights."

**7.** It is often said that people learn more **via** experience than they do **via** words. How is "The Counsels of the Bird" an example of this?

## Academic Vocabulary Development *(cont.)*

**8.** Describe an **instance** in which you learned something **via** experience rather than **via** words.

______________________________________________

______________________________________________

______________________________________________

______________________________________________

**9.** "Regarding Rania" describes the queen of Jordan and contrasts her with other women in Arab nations. The article describes how laws and tradition limit the roles of women in these nations and how Rania works to end these limitations. Do you think that Rania must work to overcome her own personal **inhibitions,** as well as external restraints? Explain.

______________________________________________

______________________________________________

______________________________________________

______________________________________________

**10.** In "Rama and Ravana in Battle," Rama's **inspection** of Ravana's body leads him to question his killing of Ravana. Rama's confidence in his actions is **restored,** however, when Ravana's brother explains that Rama has reached a faulty conclusion about the manner of Ravana's death. What can you infer from this episode about the characters of Rama and of Ravana's brother?

______________________________________________

______________________________________________

______________________________________________

______________________________________________

# PART 1

# Southwest Asia: 3500 B.C.—Present

Name ______________________ Class ____________ Date ____________

# English Language Coach, Part 1

## Acronyms and Abbreviations

An **acronym** is a word formed from the first or first few letters of a series of words. Unlike abbreviations, periods are not used with acronyms. An example of an acronym is *scuba:* ***s***elf-***c***ontained ***u***nderwater ***b***reathing ***a***pparatus.

An **abbreviation** is a shortened form of a word or phrase. Social, civil, and military titles may be abbreviated before the person's name. Examples include **Dr.** (Doctor), **Sen.** (Senator), and **Prof.** (Professor). Titles and academic degrees that follow proper names are also abbreviated (**Jr.** for *Junior,* **M.D.** for *medical doctor*). Company names or parts of company names may be abbreviated (**PBS** for *Public Broadcasting System;* **Inc.** for *Incorporated*). Other words you may see abbreviated are names of states, parts of addresses, months, and units of measurement.

## ACTIVITY

**Directions** Match each of the following words or group of words with its abbreviation or acronym.

| | |
|---|---|
| **1.** inches | **A.** R.N. |
| **2.** Fahrenheit | **B.** Jan. |
| **3.** light amplification by stimulated emission of radiation | **C.** U.S. |
| **4.** Street | **D.** St. |
| **5.** January | **E.** radar |
| **6.** United States | **F.** in. |
| **7.** Company | **G.** FAQ |
| **8.** Registered Nurse | **H.** F |
| **9.** radio detecting and ranging | **I.** Co. |
| **10.** frequently asked question | **J.** laser |

Name ______________________ Class ______________ Date ______________

## Summary/Resumen *(p. 448)*

### The Search for Everlasting Life *and* The Return *from* Gilgamesh

Gilgamesh, the king of Uruk, is deeply saddened when his friend Enkidu dies. He decides to go in search of Utnapishtim, who was made immortal by the gods, hoping that he too can become immortal. On his way, he meets the scorpion people and Shiduri, the tavern keeper, who takes pity on him and reluctantly tells him how to find Utnapishtim. Rising to each astounding challenge along his journey, Gilgamesh finally meets Utnapishtim, who tells Gilgamesh that if he can stay awake for seven days, he might learn to prevail against death. But Gilgamesh falls asleep right away. Before Gilgamesh leaves for home, Utnapishtim tells him about a plant that is the secret of youth. Gilgamesh finds the plant, but a snake carries it away, leaving Gilgamesh distraught. However, when he arrives back at Uruk, Gilgamesh is overcome with pride and love for his city.

---

### La búsqueda de la vida eterna *y* El regreso *de* Gilgamesh

Gilgamesh, el rey de Uruk, se entristece mucho cuando muere su amigo Enkidu, por lo que parte en busca de Utnapishtim, a quién los dioses habían hecho inmortal, con la esperanza de que también él pueda convertirse en inmortal. En el camino se encuentra con los hombres-escorpión y con Shiduri, la tabernera, que se apiada de él y le dice, de mala gana, cómo encontrar a Utnapishtim. Superando cada uno de los desafíos extraordinarios que encuentra en el camino, Gilgamesh halla finalmente a Utnapishtim, quien le dice que si puede permanecer despierto durante siete días puede aprender a vencer a la muerte. Pero Gilgamesh se duerme de inmediato. Antes de que Gilgamesh regrese a su hogar, Utnapishtim le cuenta de una planta que encierra el secreto de la juventud. Gilgamesh encuentra la planta, pero una serpiente se la lleva, dejando angustiado a Gilgamesh. Sin embargo, cuando regresa a Uruk, Gilgamesh se siente abrumado por el amor y orgullo que siente por su ciudad.

Name ________________________________ Class ________________ Date ________________

# Tóm Tắt *(p. 448)*

## *trích từ* Thiên Sử Thi Gilgamesh, Cuộc Đi Tìm Sự Bất Tử và Trở Về

Gilgamesh, vị Vua của Uruk, vô cùng đau khổ khi bạn ngài là Enkidu chết, vì vậy ngài đi tìm Utnapishtim, người được các vị thần biến thành bất tử, với hy vọng rằng mình cũng có thể trở thành bất tử. Trên đường đi, ngài gặp những quái vật nửa người nửa bọ cạp và một người chủ quán rượu tên là Siduri. Siduri thấy thương hại ngài và miễn cưỡng nói cho ngài biết cách tìm Utnapishtim. Vua Gilgamesh phải đối mặt với nhiều thách thức kinh hoàng dọc hành trình, nhưng cuối cùng cũng gặp được Utnapishtim. Ông ta nói với Gilgamesh rằng nếu đức vua có thể thức bảy ngày liền thì có thể ngài sẽ học được cách đánh bại tử thần. Nhưng Gilgamesh ngủ gục ngay tức thì. Trước khi quay trở về nhà, Utnapishtim mách cho Gilgamesh biết về một loại cây bí mật dùng để làm phương thuốc trường sinh bất lão. Gilgamesh tìm được loại cây đó, nhưng một con rắn tha nó đi mất, khiến Gilgamesh điên cuồng tức giận. Tuy nhiên, khi quay trở lại Uruk, Gilgamesh ngập tràn trong sự tự hào và tình yêu dành cho thành phố của mình. Điều này cho thấy rằng hạnh phúc hay không phụ thuộc vào quan điểm sống.

Name ______________________ Class ______________ Date ______________

## Buod *(p. 448)*

### *mula sa* Gilgamesh Ang Paghahanap sa Walang-Hangganang Buhay at Ang Pagbalik

Lubós na nalungkot si Gilgamesh, ang Hari ng Uruk, nang namatáy ang kaibigan niyang si Enkidu, kaya hinanap niya si Utnapishtim, na siyang ginawang imortal o walang-kamatáyan ng mga diyos, dahil inaasahan niyang gagawin din siyang imortal ng mga ito. Sa kanyang pagbiyahe, nakilala niya ang mga taong scorpion at si Siduri, ang babaeng gumagawa ng alak, na naawa sa kanya at nag-alangan na magsabi sa kanya kung paano niya mahahanap si Utnapishtim. Nagtagumpay si Gilgamesh sa maraming nakagugulat na mga hámon na sumalubong sa kanya habang siya'y nagbibiyahe, at sa wakás ay natagpuan din niya si Utnapishtim, na nagsabi sa kanya na kung magawa niyang hindi matulog nang pitóng araw, maaari niyang matutunan kung paano mangibabaw sa kamatáyan. Pero kaagad nakatulog si Gilgamesh. Bago umalis si Gilgamesh pauwí, sinabi sa kanya ni Utnapishtim na may isang halaman na makapagbibigay sa kanya ng sikreto ng walang-katapusang pagkabata. Nahanap ni Gilgamesh ang halaman, pero kinuha ito ng isang ahas, kaya lubós na nabahala si Gilgamesh. Gayunman, nang makabalik na siya sa Uruk, lugod-na-lugod at punông-punô ng pagmamahal si Gilgamesh para sa kanyang siyudad, at ipinapakita nito na ang kaligayahan ng tao ay dalá ng kanyang perspektibo o paningin.

Name ______________________ Class ______________ Date ______________

# 摘要 *(p. 448)*

## 來自《Gilgamesh敘事詩》的《長生不老之尋與歸途》

Uruk的國王Gilgamesh在他的朋友Enkidu去世後感到非常憂傷；而去尋找被神變成永生不死的Utnapishtim，希望自己也能變成永生不死。他在路上遇到了天蠍宮星座的人以及一位酒館主人Shiduri；這個人很同情他，而勉強地告訴他要如何找到Utnapishtim。Gilgamesh在沿路上奮起應付所有令人驚奇的挑戰，而終於遇到了Utnapishtim；Utnapishtim告訴Gilgamesh如果他可以七天不睡覺，或許可以學會如何戰勝死亡。可是，Gilgamesh馬上就睡著了。在踏上回家的歸途之前，Utnapishtim告訴Gilgamesh一種隱藏年輕秘密的植物。Gilgamesh找到了這個植物；但是這個植物被蛇帶走，而讓Gilgamesh感到心煩意亂。可是當他回到Uruk的時候，Gilgamesh激動地對他的城市感到驕傲和熱愛，而瞭解到快樂完全來自於希望。

Name ______________________________ Class ________________ Date ________________

## Rezime Selekyson *(p. 448)*

### Lanmò Enkidu nan Istwa Epik Gilgamesh

Gilgamesh, Wa Uruk, tris anpil poutèt zanmi li Enkidu mouri, kidonk l al chèche Utnapishtim, dye yo te rann imòtèl, paske li swete li menm tou va tounen imòtèl. Pandan li sou wout, li kontre moun eskòpyon yo avèk Siduri, dam ki fè diven an, ki pran li an pitye epi ki ezite anvan yo di li kijan pou li jwenn Utnapishtim. Apre li simonte yon seri gwo defi, Gilgamesh finalman rankontre Utnapishtim, ki di Gilgamesh si li kapab rete reveye pandan sèt jou, li gen dwa aprann kijan pou li bat lanmò. Men dòmi pran Gilgamesh touswit. Anvan li pati al lakay li, Utnapishtim pale Gilgamesh de yon plant ka va revele ba li sekrè lajenès. Gilgamesh jwenn plant la, men yon sèpan pran li, sa ki fè Gilgamesh dezespere. Men, lè li tounen Uruk, Gilgamesh santi li anvayi avèk fyète ak lanmou pou vil sa a, sa ki revele bonè se yon kesyon pèspektiv.

Name ______________________ Class ______________ Date ______________

## Zuag Tswvyim *(p. 448)*

### *los ntawm* Gilgamesh: Kev Nrhiav Txoj Sia Tsis txawj Xaus thiab Kev Rov Los

Gilgamesh, tus Huabtais tom Uruk, tusiab heev thaum paub tias nws tus phoojywg Enkidu tuag, ces nws mus nrhiav Utnapishtim, uas cov vajtswv tsim los kom txhob txawj tuag, cia siab tias nws yuav tsis txawj tuag thiab. Thaum taug kev mus, nws ntsib cov neeg kab liv tshooj thiab Siduri, tus neeg zov tsev pw, uas pom nws ntxim hlub tabsis tsis txhua xav qhia nws nrhiav Utnapishtim. Nyuaj zuj zus raws kev, thaum kawg Gilgamesh thiaj ntsib Utnapishtim, uas qhia Gilgamesh tias yog nws txhob tsaug zog xya hnub, tej zaum nws yuav kawm zam kev tuag tau. Tabsis Gilgamesh tsaug zog tamsim ntawd. Ua ntej Gilgamesh mus tsev, Utnapishtim qhia nws txog ib tsob tshuaj uas yog qhov tseeb ntawm kev hluas. Gilgamesh nrhiav tau tsob tshuaj, tabsis ib tus nab kwv khiav lawm thiab tso Gilgamesh nyob vwm ntsuav cia. Li ntawd los, thaum rov txog Uruk, Gilgamesh zoo siab rau nws lub nroog, qhia sawvdaws tias kev zoo siab nyob ntawm yus kev xav.

Name ______________________ Class ____________ Date ____________

# Literary Element *(page 448)*

## Epic Hero

## The Search for Everlasting Life *and* The Return *from* Gilgamesh

Long ago, many stories were told as epics, or long narrative poems. These poems focused on the adventures of an **epic hero,** a courageous person who was traditionally male. The epic hero usually went on a lengthy, distant journey in search of something and often encountered supernatural beings on the journey.

Here are some general characteristics of epic heroes:

- They are noble and admirable, representing the ideals of their people.
- They are intelligent and highly skilled.
- They undergo many adventures.
- They have special powers or display great acts of courage.

## ACTIVITY

**Directions** Reread "The Search for Everlasting Life" and "The Return." Complete the chart to show how Gilgamesh embodies the characteristics of an epic hero.

| Characteristics of an Epic Hero | Gilgamesh's Actions |
|---|---|
| noble and admirable | **1.** |
| intelligent, highly skilled | **2.** |
| undergoes many adventures | **3.** |
| special powers, great acts of courage | **4.** |

Name ______________________ Class ______________ Date ______________

## Reading Strategy *(page 448)*

### Visualize

# The Search for Everlasting Life *and* The Return *from* Gilgamesh

To **visualize** means to create mental pictures of the events, characters, and setting of a story. The imagery and sensory details provided by the author help readers visualize. Sensory details appeal to the five senses and help readers "place" themselves in a story.

## ACTIVITY

**Directions** The web below contains descriptive passages from "The Search for Everlasting Life" and "The Return." For each descriptive passage, write the sense to which it appeals on the line after the passage.

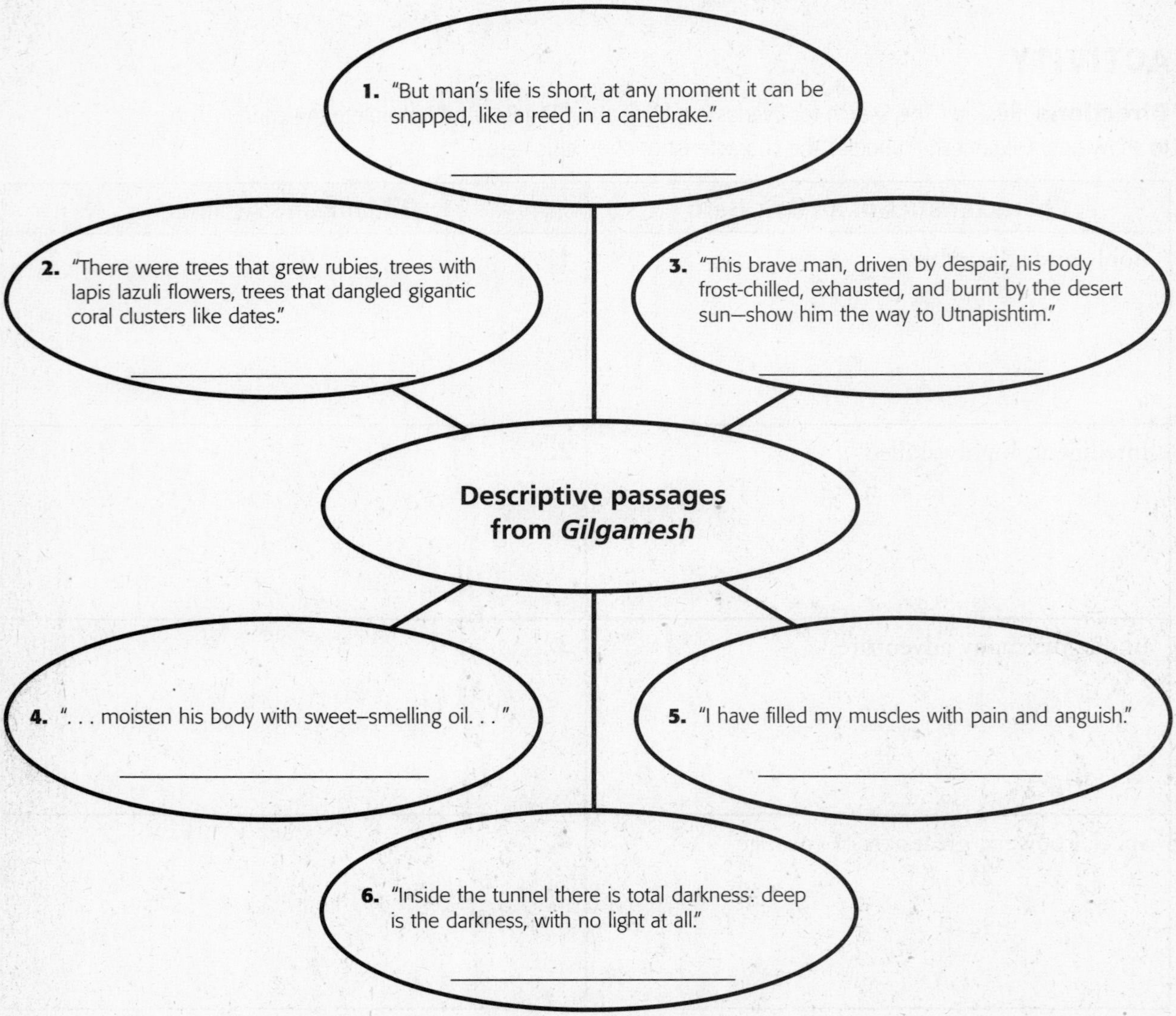

**Descriptive passages from *Gilgamesh***

1. "But man's life is short, at any moment it can be snapped, like a reed in a canebrake." ______________

2. "There were trees that grew rubies, trees with lapis lazuli flowers, trees that dangled gigantic coral clusters like dates." ______________

3. "This brave man, driven by despair, his body frost-chilled, exhausted, and burnt by the desert sun—show him the way to Utnapishtim." ______________

4. ". . . moisten his body with sweet–smelling oil. . ." ______________

5. "I have filled my muscles with pain and anguish." ______________

6. "Inside the tunnel there is total darkness: deep is the darkness, with no light at all." ______________

Name ______________________ Class ______________ Date ______________

## Selection Vocabulary Practice *(page 448)*

### The Search for Everlasting Life *and* The Return *from* Gilgamesh

**Vocabulary**

**ravaged** *adj.* devastated; ruined
**treacherous** *adj.* hazardous; dangerous
**prevail** *v.* to gain ascendancy through strength or superiority; to triumph
**antidote** *n.* something that relieves, prevents, or counteracts

### EXERCISE A Practice with Words in Context

Write the word from the vocabulary list that best completes each sentence.

1. All he wished for was a(n) __________ to his throbbing pain.
2. The storm left the town and coastline __________ beyond recognition.
3. The coach believed that with proper planning and execution, the team would __________.
4. Though she was hardly faint of heart, Carlina refused to traverse the __________ pass.

### EXERCISE B Applying Meanings

Determine whether the pairs of terms listed below are synonyms (words with nearly the same meaning) or antonyms (words with nearly opposite meanings). Write your answer on the line provided.

1. prevail – win ______________________
2. treacherous – perilous ______________________
3. antidote – remedy ______________________
4. ravaged – beautified ______________________

### EXERCISE C Analogies

Write a brief epic poem that focuses on the journey of a hero. Use all FOUR vocabulary words in your poem.

Name ______________________________ Class ______________ Date ______________

# Vocabulary Strategy *(page 448)*

## Multiple-Meaning Words

## The Search for Everlasting Life *and* The Return *from* Gilgamesh

> "Tell me, how is it that you, a mortal, overcame death and joined the assembly of the gods and were granted eternal life?"
>
> —"The Search for Everlasting Life" *from* Gilgamesh

**Connecting to Literature** This portion of the epic poem *Gilgamesh* contains an example of a multiple-meaning word: *assembly.* A **multiple-meaning word** is a word that has two or more meanings. The word *assembly* can mean "the putting together of parts to make a finished product," as in the phrase "some assembly required." The word *assembly* may also mean "a group of people gathered together for a common purpose." Readers use context clues to determine which meaning of the word is being used. It is clear from this sentence that the author is referring to a group.

### ACTIVITY

**Directions** Reread the selection. Find other multiple-meaning words. Write each word in the first column of the chart. Write the different meanings of each word in the second column. In the third column write the meaning of the word the way it is used in the selection.

| Multiple-Meaning Word | Meanings of Word | Meaning Used |
|---|---|---|
| pitched (p. 463) | • threw something<br>• set up a tent or area | set up a tent or area |
| | | |
| | | |
| | | |
| | | |
| | | |

Name ______________________ Class ____________ Date ____________

## Grammar Practice *(page 448)*

### Participles and Participial Phrases

# The Search for Everlasting Life *and* The Return *from* Gilgamesh

A **participle** is one type of verbal. Verbals are verb forms that function as nouns, adjectives, or adverbs. A present participle always ends in *-ing*. Past participles usually end in *-ed*.

The child watched the **spinning** top. (present participle)

We admired the freshly **planted** flowers. (past participle)

A **participial phrase** contains a participle and any modifiers needed to complete its meaning.

**Warmed by the fire,** we took off our jackets.

**Having misplaced my keys,** I could not get into my house.

## ACTIVITY

**Directions** Draw a line under the participle or participial phrase in each sentence.

1. He struggled to stay afloat on the tumbling sea.
2. Going for weeks without proper rest, he finally succumbed to sleep.
3. Prevented from seeing the king, she accepted an invitation from the queen.
4. The punishing cold left him shivering uncontrollably.
5. Listening closely, he carefully made his way through the dark forest.
6. What else could he do but sit and listen to the whispering wind blow?
7. Fearing the worst, he looked downward and trudged on.
8. Having lost his way, he searched frantically for the right path.
9. Disturbed by what he knew, the man tossed and turned in bed all night.
10. He realized a challenging conversation with his elders was coming.

Name ______________________ Class ____________ Date ____________

# Selection Quick Check *(page 448)*

## The Search for Everlasting Life *and* The Return *from* Gilgamesh

Use complete sentences to answer the following questions.

**1.** How does Gilgamesh respond to the death of Enkidu?

**2.** Why does Gilgamesh go in search of Utnapishtim?

**3.** What test does Utnapishtim challenge Gilgamesh to undergo?

**4.** What mystery of the gods does Utnapishtim reveal to Gilgamesh?

**5.** What role does a serpent play at the end of the selection?

Name ______________________ Class ____________ Date ____________

## Prueba Rápida *(pág. 448)*

### La búsqueda de la inmortalidad *y* El regreso *de* Gilgamesh

Contesta las siguientes preguntas con oraciones completas.

**1.** ¿Cómo respondió Gilgamesh a la muerte de Enkidu?

**2.** ¿Por qué fue Gilgamesh en busca de Utnapishtim?

**3.** ¿Qué desafío le planteó Utnapishtim a Gilgamesh?

**4.** ¿Qué misterio de los dioses le reveló Utnapishtim a Gilgamesh?

**5.** ¿Qué papel desempeña la serpiente al final de la lectura?

Name ______________________ Class ______________ Date ______________

# Grammar Workshop *(page 467)*

## Pronoun-Antecedent Agreement

A pronoun refers to a noun, a group of words acting as a noun, or another pronoun. An antecedent is the word to which a pronoun refers.

> As Gilgamesh spoke, he wept. (*Gilgamesh* is the antecedent for the pronoun *he.*)

Pronouns must agree with antecedents in number:

> The tunnel disappeared into its darkness. (*Its* and *tunnel* are singular.)
>
> The gem-trees cast their light throughout the fantastic garden. (*Their* and *gem-trees* are plural.)

Pronouns must agree with antecedents. in person:

> The woman who owned the tavern asked Gilgamesh who he was. (*He* and *Gilgamesh* are third person.)

Pronouns must have clear antecedents. If a pronoun does not have a clear antecedent, make the antecedent clear or use a noun rather than a pronoun:

> Enkidu died, and it made Gilgamesh weep. (*It* has no antecedent.)
>
> Enkidu died, and his death made Gilgamesh weep.

## ACTIVITIES

**Directions** On the line provided, write the pronoun that matches the underlined antecedent.

1. As the scorpion people guarded the tunnel, ______________ discussed Gilgamesh's options.
2. Gilgamesh and Enkidu had to finish ______________ tasks before resting.
3. During the journey, the man wept until ______________ no longer had tears.
4. Gilgamesh asked the woman if ______________ could show him the way to go.
5. When the gods assemble, ______________ decide when each man will die.
6. The Stone Men worked on a boat until Gilgamesh smashed ______________ to pieces.
7. The cedar forest finally finished ______________ spring growth.

**Directions** Rewrite each sentence to avoid the pronoun without an antecedent.

8. Gilgamesh cut off the stones, which made his body shoot up to the surface.

______________________________________________________________

9. They sailed for three days and nights, even though it would take ordinary men six weeks.

______________________________________________________________

Name ______________________ Class ______________ Date ______________

# Literary History *(p. 468)*

## Sacred Texts

Sacred texts, which are also called sacred scripture, Holy Writ, or revered texts, make up a major part of the world's literature. These sacred texts vary greatly in age and in length, but their common characteristic is that the texts are revered by their believers, who strive to live their lives based upon the principles outlined in the texts. Religious writings compiled centuries ago continue to play a vital role in the five major religions of the modern world: Christianity, Judaism, Islam, Hinduism, and Buddhism.

Many diverse forms of literature can be found within sacred texts, including hymns, prayers, chants, myths, stories, parables, epics, fables, historical and legal writings, lessons, moral anecdotes, dialogues, letters, and philosophical discussions. Sacred texts basically include every form of literature capable of expressing religious feeling or conviction.

One of these forms, the parable, can be frequently found in the Christian Bible, especially in the Gospels of Matthew, Mark, and Luke. Parables are simple stories that have both literal and metaphorical meanings and teach moral lessons. Jesus Christ used parables to reveal moral lessons in a simple yet effective manner. People follow Jesus's teachings in the parables as way to a more fulfilling life. One such parable is the Parable of the Farmer Scattering Seed:

> "Hearken; Behold, there went out a sower to sow:
> And it came to pass, as he sowed, some fell by the way side, and the fowls of the air came and devoured it up.
> And some fell on stony ground, where it had not much earth; and immediately it sprang up, because it had no depth of earth:
> But when the sun was up, it was scorched; and because it had no root, it withered away.
> And some fell among thorns, and the thorns grew up, and choked it, and it yielded no fruit.
> And other fell on good ground, and did yield fruit that sprang up and increased; and brought forth, some thirty, and some sixty, and some a hundred."
>
> —*from the* King James Version of the Bible

When Jesus's twelve disciples questioned him as to the meaning of this parable, this is how Jesus responded:

> "The sower soweth the word.
> And these are they by the way side, where the word is sown; but when they have heard, Satan cometh immediately, and taketh away the word that was sown in their hearts.

> And these are they likewise which are sown on stony ground; who, when they have heard the word, immediately receive it with gladness;
> And have no root in themselves, and so endure but for a time: afterward, when affliction or persecution ariseth for the word's sake, immediately they are offended.
> And these are they which are sown among thorns; such as hear the word,
> And the cares of this world, and the deceitfulness of riches, and the lusts of other things entering in, choke the word, and it becometh unfruitful.
> And these are they which are sown on good ground; such as hear the word, and receive it, and bring forth fruit, some thirtyfold, some sixty, and some a hundred."
>
> —*from the* King James Version of the Bible

The religion of the Jewish people is based on the Hebrew Bible, also known as the *Tanakh.* The Hebrew Bible inspires the worship of the Jewish people and plays an essential role in determining how the Jewish people live their lives. In Deuteronomy Chapter 5, Moses said:

> "Ye shall observe to do therefore as the LORD your God hath commanded you: ye shall not turn aside to the right hand or to the left. Ye shall walk in all the ways which the LORD your God hath commanded you, that ye may live, and that it may be well with you, and that ye may prolong your days in the land which ye shall possess."
>
> —*from the* Hebrew Bible

The commandments that Moses spoke of continue to guide the moral behavior of Jews and Christians today. In fact, millions of people today who do not think of themselves as religious live their lives with basic human values that stem from sacred literature.

The sacred texts of Islam, Hinduism, and Buddhism are also filled with stories, hymns, and poems that help to guide the lives of Muslims, Hindus, and Buddhists throughout the world.

## ACTIVITY

**Directions** Write a parable of your own. Remember that parables are short, simple stories that teach a moral lesson. They usually describe situations from daily life on the surface, but they actually have a much deeper meaning. Use a separate sheet of paper if you need more space.

________________________________________

________________________________________

________________________________________

________________________________________

Name ______________________ Class ______________ Date ______________

## Summary/Resumen *(p. 470)*

### Genesis 6–9: The Flood *from the* King James Version of the Bible

At a time of great wickedness in the world, God decides to destroy all his creations. He saves only the family of Noah, a righteous man. God commands Noah to build an ark and to take with him a male and female of every species. It rains for forty days and forty nights, flooding the earth. After the ark comes to rest on the top of a mountain, Noah releases birds, but they cannot find a resting place. Finally a dove returns with an olive leaf, indicating that the waters are receding. The next time the dove does not return. Noah and his family leave the ark. God establishes a covenant with Noah's descendants; He will never destroy the earth with a flood again. The rainbow is the symbol of that covenant.

---

### Génesis 6–9: El diluvio *de la* versión *King James* de la Biblia

En un momento en que hay mucha maldad en el mundo, Dios decide destruir todo lo que ha creado. Salva únicamente a la familia de Noé, un hombre justo. Dios ordena a Noé que construya un arca y que lleve con él un macho y una hembra de cada especie. La lluvia dura cuarenta días y cuarenta noches e inunda la Tierra. Cuando el arca encalla en la cima de una montaña, Noé libera a dos aves, pero no encuentran lugar donde posarse. Finalmente, una paloma regresa con una hoja de olivo, indicando que las aguas están retrocediendo. La vez siguiente, la paloma no regresa. Noé y su familia abandonan el arca y Dios hace una alianza con los descendientes de Noé: nunca más volverá a destruir la Tierra con una inundación. El arco iris es el símbolo de esa alianza.

Name ______________________ Class ____________ Date ____________

# Tóm Tắt *(p. 470)*

## Sáng Thế Ký 6–9: Đại Hồng Thủy *trích từ* phiên bản Kinh Thánh của Vua James

Vào thời kỳ nhiễu loạn trên trần gian, Chúa Trời quyết định tiêu hủy mọi sinh vật được Ngài tạo ra. Ngài chỉ chừa lại mạng sống của gia đình Nô-ê, một người đàn ông lương thiện. Chúa Trời ra lệnh cho Nô-ê đóng một con thuyền lớn và cho phép ông được mang theo mình một con đực và một con cái của tất cả các loài vật. Trời mưa 40 ngày đêm làm cả thế gian ngập lụt. Sau khi con thuyền đến nghỉ trên đỉnh một ngọn núi, Nô-ê thả chim bay đi nhưng chúng không thể tìm được một nơi làm tổ. Cuối cùng một con bồ câu quay trở lại với một chiếc lá ôliu cho thấy nước đang xuống. Lần sau ông thả con chim bồ câu, nó không quay lại nữa. Nô-ê và gia đình mình rời con thuyền lớn. Chúa Trời thỏa thuận với con cháu của Nô-ê; Ngài sẽ không bao giờ hủy diệt trái đất bằng lũ lụt nữa. Cầu vồng chính là biểu tượng của thỏa hiệp đó.

Name ______________________ Class ______________ Date ______________

## Buod *(p. 470)*

### Genesis 6–9: Ang Bahâ *mula sa* bersiyón ng Bibliya na King James

Nang grabe ang kasamaan sa mundo, nagpasiya ang Diyos na sirain ang lahat ng kanyang mga nilikha. Niligtas lamang niya ang pamilya ni Noah, isang tapat na lalaki. Inutusan ng Diyos si Noah na magtayô ng isang arka at magdala ng isang lalaki at babae ng bawat uri ng species. Umulan nang apatnapung araw at apatnapung gabi, at binahâ ang mundo. Nang ang arka ay tumigil sa tuktok ng isang bundok, pinalaya ni Noah ang mga ibon, pero wala silang mahanap na lugar na matutungtungan. Sa kahulihan ay may bumalik na isang kalapati nang may dalang dahon ng olive, na nagpapahayag na bumababâ na ang tubig. Sa sumunod na beses ay hindi na bumalik ang kalapati. Umalis sa arka si Noah at ang kanyang pamilya. Nagtatag ang Diyos ng isang tipan sa mga inapo ni Noah; hindi niya kailanman sisirain ang mundo muli gamit ang isang bahâ. Ang bahaghari ay simbolo ng covenant o tipan na iyon.

Name ______________________ Class ______________ Date ______________

## 摘要 *(p. 470)*

### 創世紀 6 ~ 9：洪水來自《英皇欽定本聖經》

在世界上充滿了邪惡的時候，上帝決定要摧毀所有祂所創造的事物。祂只留下了正直的諾亞這一家人。上帝命令諾亞打造一艘方舟，並在每一種生物中，帶一隻公的和一隻母的到方舟上。連續四十個日夜的大雨，淹沒了地球。在方舟停在一個山頂之後，諾亞把鳥放走了；可是它們找不到可以休息的地方。最後，一隻鴿子終於銜著橄欖葉回來，表示水正在退去。下一次，鴿子沒有再回來。諾亞和家人離開了方舟。上帝對諾亞的後裔許下諾言，祂再也不會用洪水摧毀地球了。彩虹就是這個諾言的象徵。

Name ______________________ Class ______________ Date ______________

## Rezime Selekyson *(p. 470)*

### Jenèz 6–9: Delij la *nan* vèsyon King James Labib

Yon lè te gen anpil mechanste nan lemonn, Bondye deside detwi tout kreyasyon li yo. Li sove sèlman fanmi Nowe, yon moun dwat. Bondye bay Nowe kòmannman pou li bati yon gwo bato epi pou li pran avèk li yon mal ak yon femèl nan chak espès. Lapli tonbe pandan karant jou ak karant nwit, inonde latè. Apre gwo bato a vin rete sou tèt yon mòn, Nowe lage zwazo yo, men yo pa kapab jwenn yon kote pou yo poze. Finalman yon toutrèl tounen avèk yon fèy olivye, sa ki endike dlo yo ap desann. Pwochen fwa a, toutrèl la pa tounen. Nowe ak fanmi li kite gwo bato a. Bondye pran yon angajman ak desandan Nowe yo; Li pap janm detwi latè a ak delij ankò. Lakansyèl se senbòl angajman sa a.

Name ______________________ Class ______________ Date ______________

## Zuag Tswvyim *(p. 470)*

### Genesis 6-9: Dej Nyab *los ntawm* Huabtais James feem Vaj Lus Kub

Thaum txog lub caij liam tshaj hauv ntiajteb, Vaj Tswv txiavtxim siab rhuav txhua tsav yam nws tau tsim. Nws tsuas tseg Naoh tsev neeg xwb, ib tus neeg ncaj. Vaj Tswv hais kom nws txua ib lub nkoj thiab coj txhua nkawm niam txiv tsiaj txhu nrog nws. Ntuj los nag tau plaub caug hnub thiab plaub caug hmo, nyab ntiaj teb tas. Thaum lub nkoj los khuam saum lub hau roob, Noah tso cov noog ya tawm, tabsis lawv nrhiav tsis tau chaw tsaws. Thawm kawg ib tus nquab ya rov los nrog ib daim nplooj ntoo olive, qhia tau tias cov dej tabtom nqig. Zaum tom qab tus nquab tsis los lawm. Noah thiab nws tsev neeg tawm saum nkoj los. Vaj Tswv cog lus rau Noah tsev neeg; Nws yuav tsis xyuas dej nyab ntiajteb ntxiv lawm. Cov sab hnub zaj haus dej yog tus cim pov thawj.

Name ______________________ Class ____________ Date ____________

# Literary Element *(page 470)*

## Theme

## Genesis 6–9: The Flood *from the* King James Version of the Bible

The central message of a literary work is called the **theme.** Writers share their views about society, culture, and events in their lives through themes. Understanding a writer's theme allows the reader to grasp an insight about the life the writer wishes to share.

### ACTIVITY

**Directions** Each sentence below is a possible theme for a story. Write one or two sentences explaining what the possible theme means. Then name at least one example of a story, TV episode, or film that demonstrates the theme.

1. **Theme:** Don't judge a book by its cover.

   **Explanation:** ______________________

   ______________________

   **Example(s):** ______________________

2. **Theme:** Slow and steady wins the race.

   **Explanation:** ______________________

   ______________________

   **Example(s):** ______________________

3. **Theme:** No one will believe a liar, even when he's telling the truth.

   **Explanation:** ______________________

   ______________________

   **Example(s):** ______________________

4. **Theme:** Brains often win over brawn.

   **Explanation:** ______________________

   ______________________

   **Example(s):** ______________________

Name ______________________ Class ______________ Date ______________

## Reading Strategy *(page 470)*

### Question

### Genesis 6–9: The Flood *from the* King James Version of the Bible

Asking yourself **questions** as you read will help you understand important aspects of a story's setting, characters, and plot. Questioning can also help you analyze how the author has developed the theme or overall message of the story. To generate questions as you read, think about the details provided by the author.

## ACTIVITY

**Directions** Complete the chart below as you reread the selection. List key details from the selection, the questions you asked based on these details, and your answers to the questions. Then think about how the details and questions relate to the Big Idea of The Secret of Life.

| Detail | Question | Answer | Connection to Big Idea: The Secret of Life |
|---|---|---|---|
| 1. | | | |
| 2. | | | |
| 3. | | | |
| 4. | | | |

Name ____________________ Class ____________ Date ____________

# Selection Vocabulary Practice *(page 470)*

## Genesis 6–9: The Flood *from the* King James Version of the Bible

**Vocabulary**

**corrupt** *adj.* morally unsound; evil
**covenant** *n.* an agreement; a pact
**abate** *v.* to lessen or decrease

### EXERCISE A Practice with Word Origins

Use a dictionary to find the etymology of each vocabulary word. Then write a sample sentence using the word correctly.

1. corrupt **etymology:** ____________________
   **sample sentence:** ____________________
2. covenant **etymology:** ____________________
   **sample sentence:** ____________________
3. abate **etymology:** ____________________
   **sample sentence:** ____________________

### EXERCISE B Applying Meanings

Do the following sentences correctly use one of the vocabulary words? Answer *yes* or *no* and then explain your answer.

1. The two girls had a covenant to travel together to Europe after graduating college.

____________________

2. After 14 inches of snow covered the ground, the snowfall finally began to abate.

____________________

3. The corrupt company owner handled his business matters justly.

____________________

### EXERCISE C Responding to the Selection

Write a dialogue that takes place between Noah and one of his sons on the ark. Use all THREE vocabulary words in the dialogue.

Name ______________________ Class ______________ Date ______________

# Vocabulary Strategy *(page 470)*

## Homonyms and Homophones

## Genesis 6–9: The Flood *from the* King James Version of the Bible

> "And God blessed Noah and his sons, and said unto them, 'Be fruitful, and multiply, and replenish the earth. And the fear of you and the dread of you shall be upon every beast of the earth, and upon every fowl of the air, upon all that moveth upon the earth, and upon all the fishes of the sea . . . "
>
> —"Genesis 6–9: The Flood" *from the* King James Version of the Bible

**Connecting to Literature** The rich language used in "The Flood" includes both homonyms and homophones. **Homonyms** are words that are spelled alike but have different meanings. For example, the words *right* (opposite of left) and *right* (correct) are homonyms. **Homophones** are words that sound alike but have different meanings and spellings. For example, the words *fowl* and *foul* are homophones. *Fowl* is a noun and means "chicken or bird." *Foul* is an adjective that means "disgusting."

## ACTIVITY

**Directions** Search for homophones in "Genesis 6–9: The Flood." Complete the chart below by writing the homophone from the text, a corresponding homophone, and the meanings of both homophones.

| Word from Text | Corresponding Homophone | Meanings of Words |
|---|---|---|
| **1.** rain | reign | rain: liquid precipitation<br>reign: to control or lead |
| **2.** | | |
| **3.** | | |
| **4.** | | |
| **5.** | | |

Name ______________________ Class ____________ Date ____________

# Grammar Practice *(page 470)*

## Gerunds and Gerund Phrases

## Genesis 6–9: The Flood *from the* King James Version of the Bible

A **gerund** is another type of verbal that ends in *–ing.* It is a verb form that is used as a noun. A gerund may function as a subject, an object of a verb, or the object of a preposition.

Nina made us laugh by **packing** for the trip two weeks in advance.

A **gerund phrase** includes a gerund and any complements and modifiers needed to complete its meaning.

The rules prohibited **eating anywhere in the library.**

## ACTIVITY

**Directions** Underline the gerunds or gerund phrases in each sentence as shown in the following example.

Rich is responsible for <u>bringing the equipment to practice</u>.

1. They prepared for the flooding by crafting a huge ship.
2. He soon set sail on a boat carrying many animals.
3. Sailing across an endless sea was hardly his idea of fun.
4. I enjoyed seeing all of the people and animals.
5. The animals' constant grunting unnerved some people on the ship.
6. He could only imagine returning home.
7. She did her best to keep up with all of the cleaning.
8. Someone on the ship recalled hearing noises outside the ship.
9. Consulting with others was the best way to figure out how to build the ship.
10. Were it not for his inspiring us, we probably wouldn't have completed the task.

Name ______________________ Class ______________ Date ______________

## Selection Quick Check *(page 470)*

### Genesis 6–9: The Flood *from the* King James Version of the Bible

Use complete sentences to answer the following questions.

**1.** What does God regret creating? Why?

**2.** What does God tell Noah to build?

**3.** Who and what does God command Noah to take with him?

**4.** What happens to the people and animals left behind?

**5.** What does the dove bring back to Noah on its second trip from the ark?

Name ______________________ Class ______________ Date ______________

## Prueba Rápida *(pág. 470)*

### Génesis 6–9: El diluvio *de la* versión *King James* de la Biblia

Contesta las siguientes preguntas con oraciones completas.

**1.** ¿De qué se arrepiente Dios de haber creado? ¿Por qué?

**2.** ¿Qué le manda construir Dios a Noé?

**3.** Dios le manda a Noé que lleve con él, ¿a quiénes y a qué?

**4.** ¿Qué pasa con las personas y los animales que no entraron en el arca?

**5.** ¿Qué le trajo la paloma a Noé en su segundo vuelo desde el arca?

Name ______________________ Class ______________ Date ______________

## Summary/Resumen *(p. 477)*

### The Book of Ruth *from the* King James Version of the Bible

At a time of famine in Judah, Naomi goes to Moab with her husband and sons to find food. Her sons marry Moabite women, but first Naomi and then her daughters-in-law are widowed. Hearing that conditions have improved in Judah, Naomi decides to return there and her daughter-in-law, Ruth, insists on going with her. Once there, Naomi tells Ruth to glean in the fields of Boaz, a kinsman of her late husband, Elimelech. Boaz treats Ruth kindly and they eventually marry and have a son, from whose line the future king David will descend.

---

### El libro de Rut *de la* versión *King James* de la Biblia

Durante un período de hambruna en Judá, Noemí se dirige a Moab con su marido y sus hijos para buscar alimento. Sus hijos contraen matrimonio con mujeres moabitas, pero primero Noemí y luego sus nueras quedan viudas. Al escuchar que las condiciones han mejorado en Judá, Noemí decide regresar y su nuera Rut insiste en acompañarla. Una vez de regreso, Noemí le indica a Rut que recoja espigas en los campos de Boaz, un pariente de su difunto marido, Elimelec. Boaz trata a Rut con bondad y con el tiempo contraen matrimonio y tienen un hijo, de cuya línea descenderá el futuro rey David.

Name ________________ Class ________ Date ________

# Tóm Tắt *(p. 477)*

## Sách Ru-tô *trích từ* phiên bản Kinh Thánh của Vua James

Vào thời điểm diễn ra nạn đói ở Giu-đa, Na-ô-mi đến Mô-áp cùng chồng và các con trai để tìm lương thực. Các con trai của bà kết hôn với những người phụ nữ Mô-áp, nhưng thoạt tiên là Na-ô-mi rồi lần lượt đến các cô con dâu đều trở thành góa phụ. Biết được tin điều kiện sống ở Giu-đa đã cải thiện, Na-ô-mi quyết định quay trở lại đó và cô con dâu Ru-tô khăng khăng đi theo bà. Khi ở đó, Na-ô-mi bảo Ru-tô đi mót lúa trên các cánh đồng của Bô-ô, một người bà con của người chồng quá cố của bà là E-li-mê-léc. Bô-ô đối xử thật tử tế với Ru-tô và cuối cùng họ lấy nhau và sinh được một cậu con trai, tạo ra dòng dõi vị vua tương lai Đa-vít. Na-ô-mi vui sướng khi nhìn thấy Ru-tô có cuộc hôn nhân hạnh phúc với Bô-ô.

Name ______________________________ Class ________________ Date ________________

## Buod *(p. 477)*

### Ang Aklat ni Ruth *mula sa* bersiyón ng Bibliya na King James

Noong panahon ng taggutom sa Judah, nagpunta si Naomi sa Moab kasama ng kanyang asawa at mga anak upang maghanap ng pagkain. Pinakasalan ng kanyang mga anak na lalaki ang mga Moabite na babae, pero una munang nabiyuda si Naomi at pagkatapos ang kanyang mga manugang na babae. Nang nabalitaan na bumuti ang mga kondisyon sa Judah, nagpasiya si Naomi na bumalik doon at ang kanyang manugang na babaeng si Ruth ay nagpumilit na sumama sa kanya. Pagdating doon, sinabi ni Naomi kay Ruth na kunin ang palay na naiwan ng mga nag-aani sa bukid ng Boaz, isang kamag-anak ng kanyang yumaong asawang si Elimelech. Mabait ang pagtrato ni Boaz kay Ruth at sa kahulihan ay naging mag-asawa sila at nagkaroon ng anak na lalaki, kung saan nanggaling ang panghinaharap na haring David. Tuwang-tuwa si Naomi na makitang si Ruth ay masayang kasal kay Boaz.

Name ______________________ Class ______________ Date ______________

# 摘要 *(p. 477)*

## 路得記來自《英皇欽定本聖經》

在 Judah 發生饑荒的時候，Naomi 和她的丈夫與兒子到 Moab 尋找食物。她的兒子們娶了 Moabite 的女人為妻子；但 Naomi 變成了寡婦，而後她的媳婦們也變成寡婦。在聽到 Judah 的狀況已經變好之後，Naomi 決定要回去；而她的媳婦 Ruth 則堅持要與她一起去。到了那裡之後，Naomi 要 Ruth 去 Boaz 的田裡拾落穗；Boaz 是她逝去丈夫 Elimelech 的親戚。Boaz 對 Ruth 很親切，並最終娶她為妻並生了一個兒子，從而延續了未來大衛王的血脈。Naomi 很高興看到 Ruth 能幸福地嫁給 Boaz。

Name ______________________ Class ______________ Date ______________

## Rezime Selekyson *(p. 477)*

### Liv Rit la nan Tanakh *nan* vèsyon King James Labib

Pandan yon tan grangou nan Jide, Nawomi al Mowab avèk mari li ak pitit gason li yo pou jwenn manje. Pitit li yo marye ak fanm mowabit yo, men Nawomi an premye epi apre sa bèlfi li yo vin vèv. Lè li tande kondisyon yo amelyore nan Jide, Nawomi deside retounen la epi bèlfi li, Rit, ensiste pou li ale avèk li. Lè yo rive, Nawomi di Rit pou li keyi nan chan Boaz, yon fanmi ansyen mari li a, Elimelèk. Boaz trete Rit ak bonte epi yo fini pa marye epi gen yon pitit gason, ki se zansèt fiti wa David. Nawomi kontan anpil lè li wè Rit byen marye ak Boaz.

## Zuag Tswvyim *(p. 477)*

### Ruth Phau Ntawv *los ntawm* Huabtais James feem Vaj Lus Kub

Txog lub caij tshaib plab nyob Judah, Naomi mus rau Moab nrog nws tus txiv thiab cov tub mus nrhiav zaub mov. Nws cov tub yuav cov pojniam Moabite, tabsis Naomi xub ua poj ntsuam ces dhau ntawd yog nws cov nyab. Thaum hnov tias lub neej hauv Judah hloov lawm, Naomi txiav txim siab rov tuaj dua thiab nws tus nyab, Ruth, pheej liam nrog nws tuaj thiab. Thaum txog tod, Naomi hais kom Ruth mus nram Boaz cov liaj, uas yog ib yim neeg ntawm nws tus qub txiv Elimelech. Boaz hlub Ruth heev thiab nkawd cia li sib yuav ces muaj ib tus tub, uas yog caj ces los ntawm tus huabtais pemsuab King David. Naomi zoo siab tau pom Ruth ua neej zoo nrog Boaz.

Name ______________________ Class ____________ Date ____________

# Literary Element *(page 477)*

## Parallelism

## The Book of Ruth *from the* King James Version of the Bible

**Parallelism** is the use of repeated grammatical structure. Writers use parallelism to help words flow smoothly, call attention to important ideas, balance different ideas, and set up a cadence or rhythm. **Repetition** is closely related to parallelism. Repetition is the recurring use of the same words, phrases, or sentences.

## ACTIVITY

**Directions** Identify examples of parallelism in the selection.

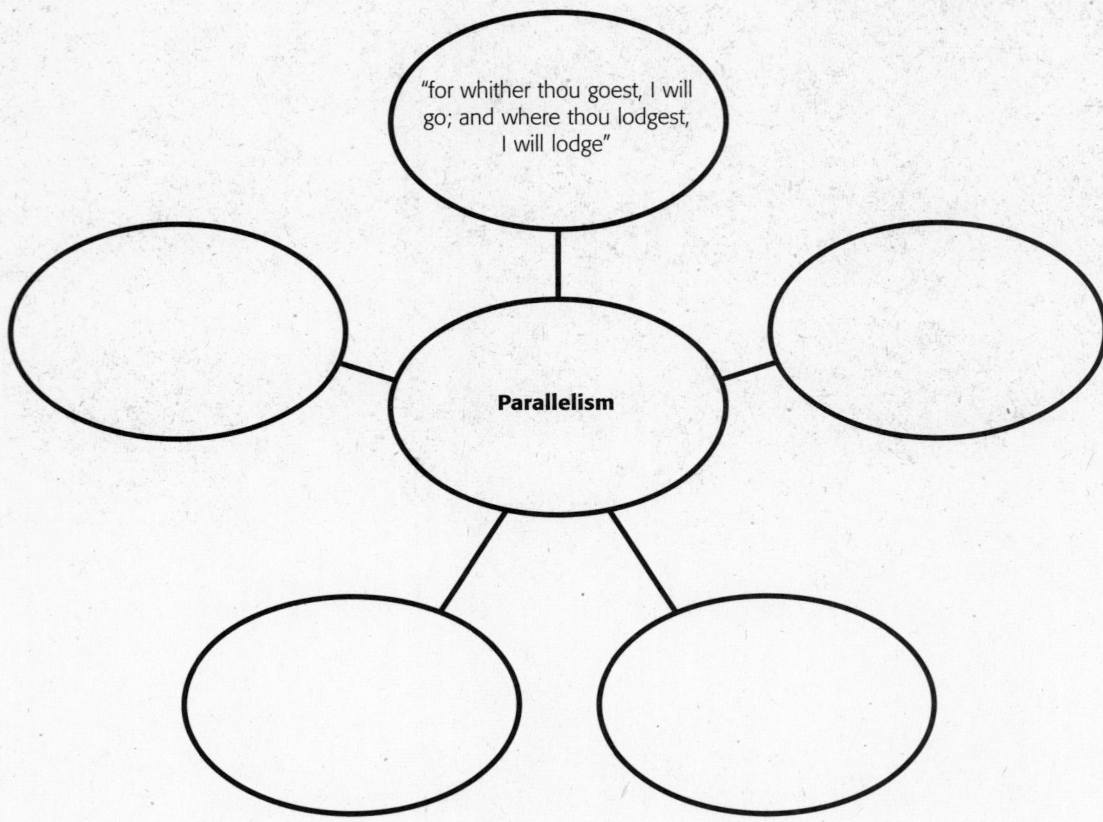
"for whither thou goest, I will go; and where thou lodgest, I will lodge"
Parallelism

Name ______________________ Class ____________ Date ____________

## Reading Strategy *(page 477)*

### Respond to Characters

### The Book of Ruth *from the* King James Version of the Bible

Readers **respond to the characters** in stories by reacting to what they like, dislike, or find surprising about the characters. Readers' responses are shaped by a character's words, thoughts, and actions. To better understand and respond to characters in a story, consider them to be people in real life. Then think about the things they say and do, and how you would likely respond to them.

## ACTIVITY

**Directions** For each character listed in the chart, write some of the character's words, thoughts, and actions that interest you. Think about and write your responses to these. You may respond with opinions, questions, encouragement, advice, and/or warnings.

| Character | Character's Words, Thoughts, or Actions | Response |
|---|---|---|
| Naomi | | |
| Ruth | | |
| Boaz | | |

Name ______________________ Class ____________ Date ____________

## Selection Vocabulary Practice *(page 477)*

### The Book of Ruth *from the* King James Version of the Bible

**Vocabulary**

**sojourn** *v.* to stay or reside temporarily
**glean** *v.* to gather what's left by reapers; to gather slowly bit by bit; to discover or find out slowly
**winnow** *v.* to remove by exposing to air currents; to free from lighter particles; to sift; to separate
**redeem** *v.* to buy back, as with property

### EXERCISE A Practice with Context Clues

Write the word from the vocabulary list that best completes each sentence.

**1.** First, we will gather the wheat; then, we will ____________________ it.

**2.** The poor people would ____________________ every last kernel from each row.

**3.** How do you expect to ____________________ the property if you have never before owned it?

**4.** I will ____________________ here for a few days, then I will likely move on to Bethany and other parts east.

### EXERCISE B Applying Meanings

Underline the correct ending for each open-ended sentence below.

**1.** When people **glean**, they usually have to

**a.** wade through water. **b.** bend down. **c.** roll over.

**2.** If a man decides to **sojourn** a bit, he will most likely

**a.** walk away quickly. **b.** stay a while. **c.** move in permanently.

**3.** When you **winnow** something, the result is

**a.** one large pile. **b.** a new substance. **c.** two separate piles.

**4.** A woman who wishes to **redeem** an area of land must

**a.** sell it. **b.** inherit it. **c.** pay for it.

### EXERCISE C Responding to the Selection

On the back of this page, write a letter that Ruth might have written to her sister Orpah after she wed Boaz. Use at least THREE of the vocabulary words in the letter.

Name ______________________ Class ______________ Date ______________

## Vocabulary Strategy *(page 477)*

### Latin Word Origins

### The Book of Ruth *from the* King James Version of the Bible

> "Now it came to pass in the days when the judges ruled, that there was a famine in the land."
>
> —"The Book of Ruth" *from the* King James Version of the Bible

**Connecting to Literature** As you read, you will encounter words that come from other languages. Many words in the English language originate in **Latin.** For instance, in the above quote, the word *famine* comes from the Latin root *fames,* which means "hunger."

Knowledge of common word parts, such as **prefixes, suffixes,** and **roots,** can help you understand the meanings of unfamiliar words. Prefixes and suffixes are added to base words or root words. Prefixes are added at the beginning of a word; suffixes are placed at the end. Most roots cannot stand alone. They must have prefixes, suffixes, or both added to them.

## ACTIVITY

**Directions** Each of the words below was used in "The Book of Ruth." Use a dictionary to find the Latin root or word part of each word. Then write a definition for each word.

| Word | Root | Definition |
|---|---|---|
| **1.** testified | | |
| **2.** afflicted | | |
| **3.** redeem | | |
| **4.** confirm | | |
| **5.** nativity | | |
| **6.** morsel | | |

Name ______________________ Class ______________ Date ______________

# Grammar Practice *(page 477)*

## Infinitives and Infinitive Phrases

## The Book of Ruth *from the* King James Version of the Bible

An **infinitive** is another type of verbal. It is a verb that is usually preceded by the word *to*. An infinitive functions as a noun, adjective, or adverb. The word *to* may also begin a prepositional phrase. However, when *to* precedes a verb, it is not a preposition but instead signals an infinitive.

We were content **to wait.**

I am excited **to visit** my grandfather tomorrow.

An **infinitive phrase** includes the infinitive and any complements and modifiers.

**To lose the championship** would be devastating for the team.

## ACTIVITY

**Directions** Underline the infinitive or infinitive phrase in each sentence.

1. The young woman did her best to find a new home.
2. Of all the people in the village, Uma and her children were the last to leave.
3. He decided it was in his best interest to sell the cows.
4. She knew in her heart what it meant to be loyal to her child.
5. Her days of wandering left her with an intense desire to eat.
6. To forgive those who had continually wronged her was her goal.
7. She sometimes failed to notice that she was surrounded by goodness.
8. When she was asked to gather firewood, she did so immediately.
9. To traverse the river safely, she used a large tree branch.
10. She was elated to find that, amazingly, her life had changed for the best.

Name ______________________ Class ______________ Date ______________

## Selection Quick Check *(page 477)*

### The Book of Ruth *from the* King James Version of the Bible

Use complete sentences to answer the following questions.

**1.** What causes Elimelech and his wife Naomi to leave Bethlehem and go to Moab?

**2.** Why is Naomi left without her husband and two sons?

**3.** How does Ruth respond to Naomi's request that she return to her own mother?

**4.** Why does Boaz treat Naomi so kindly when he first meets her?

**5.** What act of loyalty does Naomi perform that impresses Boaz?

Name ______________________ Class ____________ Date ____________

## Prueba Rápida *(pág. 477)*

### El libro de Rut *de la* versión *King James* de la Biblia

Contesta las siguientes preguntas con oraciones completas.

**1.** ¿Cuál es la causa por la que Elimelech y su esposa Noemí parten de Belén y se dirigen hacia a Moab?

**2.** ¿Por qué Noemí se queda sin esposo y sin sus dos hijos?

**3.** ¿Cómo responde Rut al pedido de Noemí de volver con su propia madre?

**4.** ¿Por qué Booz trata muy amablemente a Noemí cuando se encuentra con ella por primera vez?

**5.** ¿Cuál es el acto de lealtad que hace Noemí y que impresiona a Booz?

## Summary/Resumen *(p. 486)*

### The Parable of the Prodigal Son *from the* King James Version of the Bible

This parable is about forgiveness and the importance of family ties. The younger of two sons asks his father for his inheritance. The father immediately gives it to him, and the son travels to a distant land and soon fritters away all his wealth. Then a famine occurs, and the son is starving. He decides to go to his father, confess his sin, and beg the father to make him one of a servant so at least he can eat. However, the father is overjoyed to see the son alive and well. Instead of punishing him, the father clothes him and celebrates his return with a great feast. The older son, who has been working for his father since his brother left, is angry at his father for not punishing his brother. The father responds that the older son has always been with him, whereas the younger son was "dead" in his father's eyes, and his return should make the entire family glad.

---

### La parábola del hijo pródigo *de la* versión *King James* de la Biblia

Esta parábola trata sobre el perdón y la importancia de los lazos familiares. El menor de dos hijos le pide al padre su herencia. El padre se la da de inmediato y el hijo viaja a una tierra distante y pronto la derrocha por completo. Llega un período de hambruna y el hijo no tiene qué comer. Decide regresar junto a su padre, confesarle su pecado y rogarle que lo haga uno de sus sirvientes para al menos tener algo que comer. Sin embargo, el padre está feliz de ver a su hijo vivo y saludable. En lugar de castigarlo, lo viste y celebra su regreso con una gran fiesta. El hijo mayor, que ha estado trabajando para el padre desde que partió su hermano, se enoja con su padre por no haberlo castigado. El padre le responde que él, el hijo mayor, siempre ha estado a su lado, mientras que el menor se había ido y había "muerto" para los ojos de su padre, por lo que su regreso debe alegrar a toda la familia.

# Tóm Tắt *(p. 486)*

## Dụ Ngôn về Đứa Con Hoang Toàng, *trích từ* phiên bản Kinh Thánh của Vua James

Câu truyện dụ ngôn này nói về sự tha thứ và tầm quan trọng của các mối quan hệ trong gia đình. Cậu con út trong hai người con trai đòi cha phát sớm phần thừa kế của mình. Người cha đưa cho anh ta ngay lập tức, và anh con trai du hành đến một vùng đất xa xôi và tiêu xài hết phần tiền của mình. Rồi nạn đói xảy ra và người con trai bị đói. Anh ta quyết định về gặp cha, thú nhận tội lỗi của mình và cầu xin cha cho anh ta làm một người hầu của ôngđể ít nhất anh ta cũng có cái để ăn. Tuy nhiên, người cha quá sung sướng khi thấy con trai vẫn còn sống sót khỏe mạnh nên thay vì trừng phạt con, người cha cho anh ta quần áo và chào mừng sự trở về của anh ta bằng một bữa tiệc linh đình. Người con cả làm việc cho người cha kể từ khi em mình bỏ đi thấy giận cha vì hành động tha thứ đó. Người cha trả lời rằng người con trai cả luôn ở bên ông trong khi cậu út bỏ đi xa, và trong mắt người cha anh ta "đã chết", cho nên sự trở về này lẽ ra phải khiến cho cả gia đình cùng cảm thấy vui mừng.

## Buod *(p. 486)*

### Ang Parábolá ng Mapág-aksayáng Anak, *mula sa* bersiyón ng Bibliya na King James

Ang parabula na ito ay tungkol sa pagpapatawad at sa kahalagahan ng pagsasamahan ng pamilya. Hiniling ng mas nakakabata sa dalawang anak na lalaki ang kanyang mana mula sa kanyang ama. Kaagad ibinigay ito sa kanya ng ama, at ang anak ay naglakbay sa malalayong lugar at winaldas niya lahat ng kanyang minana. Pagkatapos ay nagkaroon ng malaking kagutuman at wala nang makain ang anak. Nagpasiya siyang magbalik sa kanyang ama, ipinagtapat niya rito ang kanyang kasalanan, at nagmakaawa siya sa kanyang ama na tanggapin siya bilang isang katulong para makakain man lang siya. Gayunman, lubós ang kaligayahan ng ama nang makita niyang buháy at nasa mabuting kalagayan ang kanyang anak. Sa halip na parusahan siya, binihisan siya ng ama at ipinagdiwang nito ang pagbalik ng anak sa pamamagitan ng paghanda ng isang malaking piyesta. Ang nakatatandang anak, na siyang naiwang nagtratrabaho para sa kanilang ama simula nang umalis ang bunsô, ay nagalit dahil hindi niya nagustuhan ang malugod na mapagbigay na pagbati ng ama sa bunsô. Sinagot ng ama sa panganay na lagi siyang kapiling ng ama, pero ang bunsô ay nawalá, o "namatáy na" sa mga mata ng kanyang ama, kaya dapat maligaya ang buong pamilya sa kanyang pagbalik.

# 摘要 *(p. 486)*

## 來自《新約全書》的《揮霍兒子的寓言》來自《英皇欽定本聖經》

這是一個關於寬恕和家庭力量之重要性的寓言。有一位父親的兩個兒子中的小兒子向他要求繼承財產。父親立刻就給了他，而兒子則去了遠方把財產都花光了。後來出現了一個饑荒，使得這個兒子開始挨餓。他決定回到父親身邊，承認自己的罪惡，並乞求父親讓他成為父親的僕人，讓他最少不必挨餓。但是，父親看到他兒子安好地活著而感到狂喜。父親不但沒有懲罰他，還給他衣服穿，並舉辦盛宴來慶祝兒子的歸來。在弟弟離去之後一直在為父親工作的哥哥，對於父親的寬恕行為感到憤怒。父親表示大兒子一直和他在一起，而小兒子則離開了，在父親的眼中如同是「死了」；所以弟弟的歸來應該讓整個家庭都感到高興。

Name ______________________ Class ______________ Date ______________

## Rezime Selekyson *(p. 486)*

### Paraböl Pitit Gason Pwodig la" *nan* vèsyon King James Labib

Parabòl sa a osijè padon avèk enpòtans fanmi genyen. Pi piti de frè mande papa li pou li ba li pati eritaj pa li a. Papa a ba li l touswit epi pitit gason an vwayaje al sou yon tè byen lwen epi li depanse tout lajan an. Kounye a vin gen yon grangou epi pitit la nan grangou. Li deside tounen al jwenn papa, konfese peche li, epi li mande papa a pran l kòm sèvitè pou omwen li kapab manje. Men, papa a te kontan anpil lè li wè pitit li an vi epi anfòm. Olye pou li pini pitit la, papa a abiye li epi fè yon gwo fèt pou selebre retou li. Pi gran gason an, ki t ap travay pou papa a pandan toutan lòt la te ale a, fache anvè papa a poutèt papa a padone li twò rapid. Papa a reponn pi gran gason an te toujou avèk li, alòske li te panse lòt la te mouri, kidonk fòk tout fanmi an ta kontan li tounen.

Name ____________________ Class ____________ Date ____________

## Zuag Tswvyim *(p. 486)*

### Zaj Lus Qhia ntawm tus Tub Yuamkev, *los ntawm* Huabtais James feem Vaj Lus Kub

Zaj kwvhuam nov hais txog kev zam txim thiab qhov tseemceeb ntawm yus tsev neeg caj ces. Tus tub ntxawg ntawm ob tug tub nug leej txiv txog nws puav pheej. Leej txiv muab kiag rau nws, ces nws pib ncig tebchaws thiab siv nyiaj tas nrho. Thaum kev tshaib plab tshwmsim ces tus tub tshaib plab. Nws rov mus cuag nws txiv, lees lub txim txhaum, thiab kom nws txiv tso nws ua ib tus qhev tom tsev tsuav tau mov noj. Li ntawd los, leej txiv zoo siab pom tus tub ciaj sia thiab zoo neej. Dua qhov rau txim, leej txiv muab ris tsho rau nws hnav thiab ua koobtsheej tos nws rov los tsev. Tus tub hlob uas ib txwm ua hauj lwm txij thaum tus kwv mus lawd, chim heev rau leej txiv txog zam lub txim. Leej txiv teb tias tus tub hlob ib txwm nrog nws nyob, thaum tus tub ntxawg lawm, "tuag" hauv leej txiv qhov muag, ces nws kev rov los yuav tsum ua rau txhua leej hauv tsev zoo siab.

# Literary Element *(page 486)*

## Parable

## The Parable of the Prodigal Son *from the* King James Version of the Bible

Many stories in the Bible are parables. **Parables** are short, simple stories that teach morals or religious lessons. Parables are metaphorical, but they also include details and scenarios from everyday life. As you read a parable, ask yourself questions about the content, such as "What moral lesson is this story teaching?" or "What lesson about life can I learn from this story?"

## ACTIVITY

**Directions** Read the summaries of the parables in the chart below. Then explain what you think the lesson of each parable may be.

| Parable Summary | Lesson of Parable |
|---|---|
| A man owns an auto repair shop. One day a wealthy man with an expensive car comes to the shop in order to have his car repaired. The shop owner realizes that the wealthy man knows little about cars. The owner uses cheap parts for the repair so he can make a larger profit. A week later, the parts fail, causing the wealthy man's car to crash. The wealthy man sues the shop owner, who loses in court and is put out of business. | **1.** |
| A woman consistently helps her children execute simple daily tasks. As the children become young adults, she still takes care of basic tasks for them. For example, she packs their suitcases for them before they go on vacations. One day the youngest daughter, who is 28, gets sick. The mother is visiting a friend overseas, so she cannot help her daughter. The daughter doesn't know how to take care of herself, and as a result becomes even more sick and has to be rushed to a hospital. | **2.** |

Name ______________________ Class ______________ Date ______________

# Reading Strategy *(page 486)*

## Make Inferences About Theme

## The Parable of the Prodigal Son *from the* King James Version of the Bible

The **theme** is the overall message of a literary work. Sometimes the author directly states the theme. At other times, the theme is not directly stated, so the reader must make an inference, or educated guess, to determine what the theme is. Readers make inferences by combining their own knowledge, ideas, and opinions with important events or details from the literary work.

## ACTIVITY

**Directions** Complete the graphic organizer below. First, review the story "The Parable of the Prodigal Son." Use the information in the story along with your own knowledge, ideas, and opinions in order to make an inference about the story's theme. Describe the theme in the top box of the organizer. In the lower boxes, list information from the story and your own knowledge that you used to make your inference.

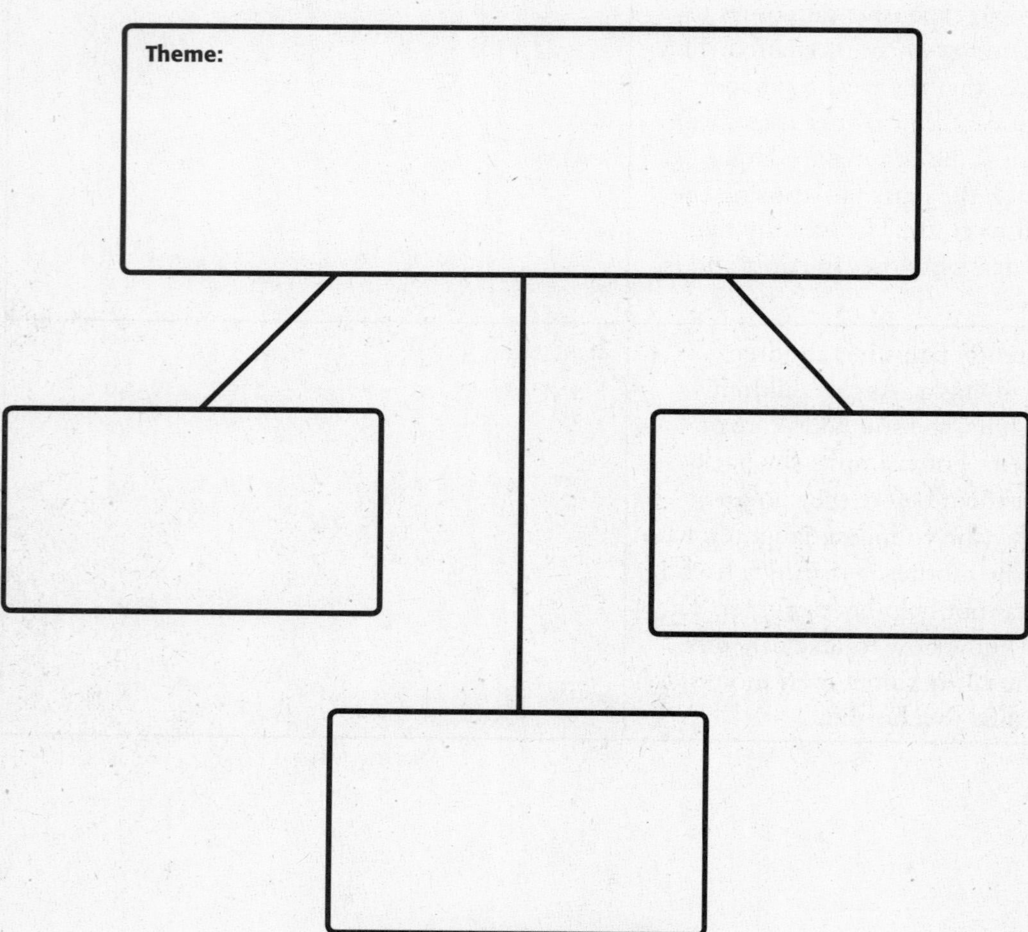

Name ______________________________ Class ______________ Date ______________

## Grammar Practice *(page 486)*

### Main and Subordinate Clauses

# The Parable of the Prodigal Son *from the* King James Version of the Bible

A **main clause** is a group of words that contain a complete subject and a complete predicate. Also known as an independent clause, a main clause can stand alone as a complete sentence.

Example: A light gray wall served as background for Lisel's paintings.

A **subordinate clause** also contains a subject and a predicate but cannot stand alone. Because it depends on a main clause to make sense, a subordinate clause is also known as a **dependent clause**. Usually, a **subordinating conjunction** introduces a subordinate clause, although it may begin with a relative pronoun (such as who, whose, whom, or what) or a relative adverb (such as when, where, or why). Sometimes, the connecting word also serves as the subject of the clause.

Examples: The clown **who left his red nose in the dressing room** should report to Lost and Found.

Lisel's paintings stood out vividly **when they were displayed against a neutral background.**

| SUBORDINATING CONJUNCTIONS | |
|---|---|
| **Time** | after, as, soon as, before, since, until, when, whenever, while |
| **Place** | where, wherever |
| **Manner** | as, as if, as though |
| **Cause** | as, because, inasmuch as, since, so that |
| **Concession** | although, even though, though |
| **Condition** | if, than, unless |

## ACTIVITY

**Directions** Write SUB in the blank before each sentence that contains a subordinate clause. Underline the subordinate clause.

1. ______ When the father saw the prodigal son, he ran toward him.
2. ______ Although the son loved his father, he wanted to leave home for a life of adventure.
3. ______ The brother resented his father's mercy to the prodigal son.
4. ______ The prodigal son spent his entire inheritance on riotous living.
5. ______ After the famine swept the land, the prodigal son realized his mistake.

Name ______________________ Class ______________ Date ______________

## Selection Quick Check *(page 486)*

### The Parable of the Prodigal Son *from the* King James Version of the Bible

Use complete sentences to answer the following questions.

**1.** How did the prodigal son spend the money he received from his father?

**2.** What is the prodigal son's financial situation after his money runs out?

**3.** How does the father respond when the prodigal son returns home?

**4.** Do you think the father's response to his son's return is correct? Why or why not?

**5.** Do you think there are aspects of this story that occur in the modern world? Why or why not?

Name ______________________ Class ______________ Date ______________

## Prueba Rápida *(pág. 486)*

### La parábola del hijo pródigo *de la* versión *King James* de la Biblia

Contesta las siguientes preguntas con oraciones completas.

**1.** ¿De qué manera gastó el hijo pródigo el dinero que recibió de su padre?

______________________________________________

______________________________________________

______________________________________________

**2.** ¿Cuál es la situación financiera del hijo pródigo una vez que se quedó sin dinero?

______________________________________________

______________________________________________

______________________________________________

**3.** ¿Cómo responde el padre cuando el hijo pródigo regresa a su casa?

______________________________________________

______________________________________________

______________________________________________

**4.** ¿Crees que la respuesta del padre respecto al regreso de su hijo es correcta? Explica por qué.

______________________________________________

______________________________________________

______________________________________________

**5.** ¿Crees que hay aspectos de este cuento que ocurren en el mundo moderno? Explica por qué.

______________________________________________

______________________________________________

______________________________________________

Name ______________________ Class ____________ Date ____________

## Summary/Resumen *(p. 491)*

### The Exoridum *and* Daylight *from the* Qur'an

In "The Exordium," the text praises Allah, the "Lord of the Universe," and professes loyalty and worship. The text also asks for guidance along the path of a righteous life. In "Daylight," the text explains that the Lord has not forsaken the reader. Allah has provided the shelter, guidance, and riches the reader has obtained in life. The text then urges the reader to proclaim the goodness of the Lord and look after the less fortunate.

---

### El exordio *y* La luz del día *del* Corán

En "El exordio", el texto alaba a Alá, el "Señor del Universo" y le profesa su lealtad y adoración. Le pide asimismo que le brinde guía en el camino de una vida virtuosa. En "La luz del día" el texto explica que el Señor no ha abandonado al lector. Alá ha brindado el refugio, la guía y las riquezas que tú has logrado en tu vida. El texto urge entonces al lector a proclamar la bondad del Señor y a cuidar a los menos afortunados.

Name ______________________ Class ____________ Date ____________

# Tóm Tắt *(p. 491)*

## Đoạn Mào Đầu và Ánh Sáng Ban Ngày *trích từ* Kinh Coran

Nhân vật trong "Đoạn Mào Đầu" ngợi ca Thánh Ala, "Chúa Tạo Hóa" và nói rằng mọi người thờ thánh Ala và nguyện cầu ngài giúp đỡ. Nhân vật cầu xin thánh Ala dẫn đường chỉ lối cho mọi người, giúp họ tìm ra đúng đường lối của thánh Ala vạch ra, chứ không phải đường lối khiến thánh Ala nổi giận hay khiến mọi người xa cách thánh Ala. Nhân vật trong bài "Ánh Sáng Ban Ngày" dẫn giải rằng Chúa Tạo Hóa không bỏ bạn và ngài không căm ghét bạn. Nhân vật tuyên bố rằng "Cuộc sống sắp tới dành giữ cho bạn một phần thưởng trị giá hơn phần thưởng mà cuộc sống hiện tại dành cho bạn". Nhân vật cũng cho rằng nơi trú ngụ, những chỉ dẫn và những của cải mà bạn đạt được trong cuộc sống là nhờ có thánh Ala ban phát. Do đó nhân vật khuyên chúng ta không nên hắt hủi người khác cho dù họ là ai hay nghèo đến mức nào. Thay vào đó, hãy nói về sự hào hiệp của Chúa Tạo Hóa khi chăm sóc những ai kém may mắn hơn bạn.

Name ______________________ Class ______________ Date ______________

## **Buod** *(p. 491)*

### Ang Exoridum at Ang Liwanag ng Araw *mula sa* Qur'an

Sa "Ang Exordium," pinupuri ng nagsasalitá si Allah, ang "Hari ng lahat ng Nilikhâ," at sinabi niyang sinasambâ ng mga tao si Allah, at nagdarasal ang mga ito sa kanya para humingi ng tulong. Hiniling ng nagsasalitá na patnubayan ni Allah ang mga tao, para matulungan silang mahanap ang landás na nagugustuhan ni Allah, at hindi ang landás na ikagagalit ni Allah, o ang landás na magpapalayô sa mga tao kay Allah. Sa "Liwanag ng Araw," ipinaliwanag ng nagsasalitá na hindi ka iniwanan ng Panginoon, at hindi ka rin niya kinamumuhían. Ayon sa nagsasalitá, "mas mayaman ang gantimpala na makukuha mo sa susunod na buhay kaysa dito sa kasalukuyang buhay." Sinabi rin ng nagsasalitá na galing kay Allah ang anumang silong, patnubay, at kayamanan na natanggap mo sa iyong buhay. Kaya pinapayuhan tayo ng nagsasalitá na huwag talikuran ang mga ibang tao, kahit na sinuman, o gaano man kahirap ang mga ito. Sa halip nito, pag-usapan mo ang kabaitan ng Panginoon habang inaalagaan mo ang mga taong hindi kasing suwerte mo.

# 摘要 *(p. 491)*

## 古蘭經的開端與黎明

在 The Exordium 中，敘述者讚美「造物主」阿拉，而表示人們崇拜阿拉並祈求祂的幫助。敘述者祈求阿拉指引人們，協助他們找到阿拉所喜歡的道路；而不是會觸怒阿拉，或是遠離阿拉的道路。在 Daylight 中，敘述者解釋了主並沒有離棄你也沒有恨你。敘述者宣稱「來生的報酬比今生更豐富」。敘述者並把人生中所有的住所、指引、與財富歸功於阿拉。因此，敘述者建議我們，不論對方是誰或是有多麼貧窮，都不要拋棄他人。我們反而應該在照顧那些沒有你幸福的人的同時，讚揚主的恩典。

Name ______________________________ Class ________________ Date ________________

## Rezime Selekyson *(p. 491)*

### Egzòd ak Limyè Lajounen nan Koran an

Nan "The Exordium," oratè a chante lwanj Allah, "Seyè Kreyasyon an;" li di moun chante glwa Allah epi lapriyè pou li ede yo. Oratè a sipliye Allah pou li gide pèp la, pou ede li viv yon jan Allah renmen, pa yon jan ki pou fache Allah oswa yon jan ki fè pèp la vire do bay Allah. Nan "Daylight," oratè a eksplike Allah pa kite ou epi li pa rayi ou. Oratè a deklare "Lavi k ap vini an gen pi bèl richès pou ou pase lavi w ap mennen kounye a." Oratè a di tou se Allah ki bay nenpòt ki refij, konsèy, ak richès ou jwenn nan lavi. Se konsa moun k ap pale a konseye nou pou nou pa rejte lòt moun, kèlkeswa kimoun yo ye, oswa kèlkeswa jan yo pòv. Olye sa, pale sou fason Allah bon pandan w ap okipe moun ki pa gen chans menm jan avèk ou.

## Zuag Tswvyim *(p. 491)*

### Zaj Lus Pib thiab Sab Hnub *los ntawm* phau Qur'an

Hauv "Zaj Lus Pib," tus hais zaj lus muab meejmom rau Allah, tus "Vajtswv ntawm kev Tsim," hais tias tibneeg hawm Allah thiab thov nws kom pab. Tus hais zaj lus thov kom Allah coj tibneeg, pab tibneeg nrhiav kev zoo rau Allah, tsis yog kev phem ua rau Allah chim lossis cov kev coj tibneeg tawm ntawm Allah. Hauv "Sab Hnub," tus hais zaj lus piav tias vajtswv tsis tau ncaim nej thiab tsis ntxub nej. Nws khaiv tias "lub neej tom ntej muaj nuj nqi dua lub neej nov." Tus hais zaj lus ua Allah tsaug txog tej chaw nyob, kev qhia, nyiaj txiag uas nejtau hauv lub neej. Tus hais zaj lus qhia kom peb txhob thuam lwm tus, txawm leej twg los xij, pluag los xij. Dua ntawd, peb yuav tsum hais lus txog lawv qhov zoo rau vajtswv thaum peb pab tej neeg peem lossis txomnyem tshaj peb.

Name ______________________ Class ______________ Date ______________

# Literary Element *(page 491)*

## Antithesis

## The Exoridum *and* Daylight *from the* Qur'an

**Antithesis** is the balanced contrast of two ideas or phrases. It is often used to emphasize a point or an argument by showing differences between two aspects of the same concept. "Daylight," the excerpt from the Qur'an on page 494, includes the following example of antithesis: *Did He not find you poor and enrich you?* These words emphasize a quality of God's mercy by contrasting the state of a person who goes from poverty to enrichment.

## ACTIVITY

**Directions** Read the statements in the first column of the chart below. In the next column, identify which statements are examples of antithesis and which are not by underlining the appropriate words in the parentheses. Then, give reasons for your responses.

| | |
|---|---|
| **"I have a dream . . . that they will not be judged by the color of their skin but by the content of their character."**<br>—*Martin Luther King Jr.* | **(<u>is</u> / is not) an example of antithesis because** it contrasts physical appearance with character to make a point about what matters most in a person. |
| **1. "All the joy the world contains<br>Has come through wishing happiness for others.<br>All the misery the world contains<br>Has come through wanting pleasure for oneself.**<br>—*Shantideva* | **(is / is not) an example of antithesis because** |
| **2. "Freedom is the right to tell people what they do not want to hear."**<br>—*George Orwell* | **(is / is not) an example of antithesis because** |
| **3. "Reckless words pierce like a sword, but the tongue of the wise brings healing."**<br>—Proverbs 12:18 *from the* Bible | **(is / is not) an example of antithesis because** |

Name ______________________ Class ______________ Date ______________

# Reading Strategy *(page 491)*

## Interpret Imagery

## The Exoridum *and* Daylight *from the* Qur'an

**Imagery** refers to the "word pictures" the writer creates in literary works. Imagery helps you visualize and experience the details and descriptions the writer provides. **Interpreting imagery** can help you better understand a poem. To interpret imagery, identify the images or "word pictures" in the poem, and then think about how these images help you visualize the writer's insights and observations.

## ACTIVITY

**Directions** Reread "The Exordium" and "Daylight." In the right column of the table below, write your interpretation of the images listed.

| Image | Interpretation |
|---|---|
| The straight path | **1.** |
| The orphan | **2.** |
| The beggar | **3.** |

Name ______________________ Class ______________ Date ______________

# Selection Vocabulary Practice *(page 491)*

## The Exoridum *and* Daylight *from the* Qur'an

**Vocabulary**

**incur** *v.* to bring upon oneself
**abhor** *v.* to detest
**chide** *v.* to scold

### EXERCISE A Practice with Synonyms and Antonyms

Draw a line to connect each vocabulary word with its antonym, or word with nearly the opposite meaning.

**1.** incur — love, respect

**2.** chide — praise, soothe

**3.** abhor — inflict, harm

Draw a line to connect each vocabulary word with its synonym, or word with nearly the same meaning.

**4.** abhor — acquire, receive

**5.** incur — reprimand, rebuke

**6.** chide — despise, hate

### EXERCISE B Applying Meanings

Write the vocabulary word that could replace the word or phrase in bold type in each sentence.

**1.** It was one thing to hear him point out our mistakes, but it was quite another to hear him **admonish** us so angrily. __________

**2.** To say that I am **thoroughly repulsed by** all of her actions lately is a huge understatement. __________

**3.** Why should I have compassion for your dilemma when it's obvious that you **invite** it yourself? __________

### EXERCISE C Responding to the Selection

On the back of this page, write a poem about the importance of peace. Use ALL of the vocabulary words in the poem.

# Vocabulary Strategy *(page 491)*

## Denotation and Connotation

## The Exoridum *and* Daylight *from the* Qur'an

"Did He not find you an orphan and give you shelter?"

—"Daylight" *from the* Qur'an

**Connecting to Literature** The poem "Daylight" uses words whose denotations and connotations help the reader understand the poem's theme or message. The **denotation** of a word is its literal meaning. The **connotation** of a word is its implied meaning. The poem "Daylight" uses the word *orphan.* The literal meaning of *orphan* is "a child whose parents are dead or whose parents have abandoned him or her." However, the connotation of *orphan* is "one who is alone." The use of the word *orphan* helps the poem strongly suggest that people who do not accept God in their lives will ultimately be alone in the world. This connotation helps inspire the reader to embrace the poem's message.

## ACTIVITY

**Directions** Complete the chart below in order to think about the words used in the poems "Daylight" and "The Exordium." Use a dictionary to find the denotation, or literal meaning, for each word. Write the denotation in the second column. Then think about what ideas, images, or feelings are associated with each word. Describe each word's connotation in the third column.

| Word | Denotation | Connotation |
|---|---|---|
| error | a mistake | behaving inappropriately; living in an unrighteous manner |
| straight | | |
| shelter | | |
| poor | | |
| prize | | |

Name ______________________ Class ______________ Date ______________

# Grammar Practice *(page 491)*

## Simple and Compound Sentences

## The Exoridum *and* Daylight *from the* Qur'an

A **simple sentence** has one complete subject and one complete predicate. The subject, the predicate, or both may be compound.

| SUBJECT | PREDICATE |
|---|---|
| Long strands of ivy | curled around the window ledge. |
| Ivy and juniper | filled the flower boxes. |
| Plants | breathe air and absorb sunlight. |

Two or more simple sentences, which are connected by punctuation or a conjunction, comprise a **compound sentence**. Main clauses can be joined to build a compound sentence by using a comma followed by a conjunction, such as *or*, *and*, or *but*. A semicolon may also be used to join two main clauses without a conjunction. A semicolon is also used before a conjunctive adverb, such as *moreover* or *however*.

Spring arrived late this year, **but** Mona's garden was as beautiful as ever.

Spring arrived late this year**;** Mona's garden was as beautiful as ever.

Spring arrived late this year**; however,** Mona's garden was as beautiful as ever.

## ACTIVITY

**Directions** Write in the blank whether the sentence is *simple* or *compound.*

__________ **1.** Trust the goodness and grace of the Almighty, and you will always have peace in your heart.

__________ **2.** Who would not want to walk the path of righteousness?

__________ **3.** His ways have been good for me; I am better than I ever have been in my life.

__________ **4.** Would you rather suffer for the rest of your days or bask in the goodness of life?

__________ **5.** I am strong; I am wise.

__________ **6.** Be content in the way you have chosen to walk upon this earth.

__________ **7.** We can strive to be our best; however, sometimes we can't reach our goals on our own.

__________ **8.** Keep faith at the forefront of your mind, and you will act justly.

__________ **9.** My words and deeds have given me the confidence to go on.

Name ______________________ Class ____________ Date ____________

## Selection Quick Check *(page 491)*

### The Exoridum *and* Daylight *from the* Qur'an

Use complete sentences to answer the following questions.

**1.** Whom does the speaker address in "The Exordium"?

**2.** Where does the speaker in "The Exordium" ask to be guided?

**3.** According to the speaker of "Daylight," what does the "life to come" hold?

**4.** In "Daylight," what does the speaker urge followers to proclaim?

Name ______________________ Class ______________ Date ______________

## Prueba Rápida *(pág. 491)*

### El exordio *y* La luz del día *del* Corán

Contesta las siguientes preguntas con oraciones completas.

**1.** ¿A quién se dirige el hablante de el exordio?

______________________________________________

______________________________________________

______________________________________________

**2.** ¿Adónde pide el hablante del exordio que sea llevado?

______________________________________________

______________________________________________

______________________________________________

**3.** Según el hablante de luz del día, ¿que ofrece "la otra vida"?

______________________________________________

______________________________________________

______________________________________________

**4.** En luz del día, ¿qué pide el hablante que proclamen sus seguidores?

______________________________________________

______________________________________________

______________________________________________

Name ______________________ Class ____________ Date ____________

## Summary/Resumen *(p. 496)*

### The Second Voyage of Sindbad the Sailor *from* The Thousand and One Nights

Sindbad the mariner sets out on a second voyage, only to find himself left behind after a stopover on a strange island. Exploring the island, he finds a huge roc's egg and ties himself to the giant mother bird's leg. The bird lifts him from the island, setting him down near a deep valley covered with diamonds. Sindbad takes some of the diamonds for himself and saves himself again by tying himself to an animal. He returns home a wealthy man and shares his riches.

---

### El segundo viaje de Sindbad el marino *de* Las mil y una noches

Sindbad el marino se lanza a un segundo viaje, sólo para encontrarse abandonado después de una parada en una extraña isla. Explorando la isla, encuentra un huevo enorme de ave Roc y se amarra a la pata de la gigante ave madre. El ave lo saca de la isla, depositándolo cerca de un profundo valle cubierto de diamantes. Sindbad toma algunos de los diamantes para sí y vuelve a salvarse amarrándose a un animal. Regresa a su hogar como un hombre rico y comparte sus riquezas.

# Tóm Tắt *(p. 496)*

## Chuyến Đi Biển Thứ Hai của Thủy Thủ Xin-bát *trích từ* Nghìn Lẻ Một Đêm

Thủy thủ Xin-bát thực hiện chuyến vượt biển thứ hai để rồi thấy mình bị bỏ quên ở một hòn đảo lạ sau khi con tàu dừng nghỉ tại đó. Trong khi khám phá hòn đảo, chàng tìm thấy một quả trứng chim khổng lồ và tự buộc mình vào chân con chim mẹ khổng lồ. Con chim đưa chàng ra khỏi hòn đảo và thả chàng xuống gần một vực sâu toàn kim cương. Xin-bát lấy một ít kim cương cho mình và tự cứu mình bằng cách lại tự buộc mình vào một con vật. Chàng quay trở về quê nhà, trở thành một người giàu có và chia sẻ của cải của mình.

# Buod *(p. 496)*

## Ang Pangalawang Biyahe ni Sindbad, ang Magdaragat *mula sa* Isang Libo't Isang Gabi

Umalis si Sindbad, ang Magdaragat, para sa kanyang pangalawang pagbiyahe, pero naiwan siya pagkatapos tumigil sa isang kakaibang isla. Tiningnan niya ang isla, at nakakita siya ng itlog ng malaking roc; tinali niya ang kanyang sarili sa binti ng higanteng inang ibon. Tinangay siya ng ibon mula sa isla, at inilapag siya nito malapit sa malalim na lambak na may takip ng mga diyamante. Kumuha si Sindbad ng ilang mga diyamante para sa kanyang sarili at niligtas niya muli ang kanyang sarili sa pamamagitan ng pagtali sa kanyang sarili sa isang hayop. Umuwi siya nang mayaman at ipinamahagi niya ang kanyang mga kayamanan.

Name ______________________ Class ______________ Date ______________

# 摘要 *(p. 496)*

## 來自《一千零一夜》的《辛巴達第二次航海記》

辛巴達和水手們開始了第二次的航程；在一個奇怪的島嶼中途停留之後，辛巴達發現自己被一個人留在島上。他在島上探索，而發現了一個巨鳥的蛋；於是他把自己綁在巨鳥媽媽的腳上。這隻鳥帶著他飛離了這個島嶼，在一個覆蓋著鑽石的深谷附近把他放下。辛巴達為自己拿了一些鑽石；然後把自己綁在一個動物上，又解救了一次自己的性命。他回家後成了一個富人，並分享他的財富。

Name ______________________ Class ______________ Date ______________

## Rezime Selekyson *(p. 496)*

### Dezyèm Vwayaj Maren ki te rele Sindbad la *nan* Mileyen Nwit

Maren ki rele Sindbad la fè yon dezyèm vwayaj, epi li vin rete dèyè apre yon eskal sou yon zile etranj. Pandan l ap eksplore zile la, li jwenn yon ze wòk enòm, epi li mare tèt li nan pye manman zwazo jeyan an. Zwazo a leve li sòti sou zil la, epi lage li bò yon vale fon ki kouvri ak dyaman. Sindbad pran kèk nan dyaman yo pou tèt pa li epi li mare kò li sou yon bèt pou sove ankò. Li retounen lakay li rich epi li pataje richès li yo.

Name ______________________ Class ____________ Date ______________

## Zuag Tswvyim *(p. 496)*

### Kev Ncig ntawm tus Nquam Nkoj Sindbad *los ntawm* Ib Txhiab Ib Hmo

Tus kws hiavtswv Sindbad npaj nws txoj kev ncig zaum ob, uas coj nws mus khuam rau tim ib lub pobtxwv txawv txawv. Nrhiav ncig lub pobtxwv, nws pom ib lub qe zeb loj loj ces cia li muab nws khi rau niam noog txhais taw. Tus niam noog ya nws ntawm lub pob txwv tawm, txoj nws mus tso rau ib lub kwj ha tob npog pov haum ntsuab. Sindbad nqa ib cov pov haum thiab rov khi nws tus kheej rau ib tus tsiaj. Nws rov los txog tsev ua ib tus neeg nplua nuj thiab faib nws tej txiaj rau sawv daws.

# Literary Element *(page 496)*

## Point of View

## The Second Voyage of Sindbad the Sailor *from* The Thousand and One Nights

**Point of view** is the perspective from which a story is told. Points of view include first person, third-person limited, and third-person omniscient. "The Second Voyage of Sindbad the Sailor" is told from the first-person point of view. The narrator, Sindbad, is a character in the story and uses pronouns such as *I* and *my.* Readers experience events through Sindbad's eyes; they cannot know more than he does. How would Sindbad's story be different if it were told from a different point of view? In the third-person limited point of view, for instance, the narrator stands outside the story and uses pronouns such as *he, she, they,* and *their* to tell the story.

## ACTIVITY

**Directions** Rewrite the following scene from "The Second Voyage of Sindbad the Sailor" from the third-person limited point of view. Then compare the first-person to third-person point of view. Explain how the story changes with the change in point of view.

> "Overwhelmed with horror, and oblivious of hunger and fatigue, I roamed the valley all day searching with infinite caution for a shelter where I might pass the night. At dusk I came upon a narrow-mouthed cave, into which I crawled, blocking its entrance from within by a great stone. I thought to myself: 'Here I shall be safe tonight. When tomorrow comes, let Destiny do its worst.'"

Name ____________ Class ____________ Date ____________

# Reading Strategy *(page 496)*

## Identify Problem and Solution

## The Second Voyage of Sindbad the Sailor *from* The Thousand and One Nights

When you identify **problems and solutions** in a literary work, you consider a character's problems and then evaluate his or her solutions. Many plots, including the plot of "The Second Voyage of Sindbad the Sailor," revolve around a dilemma the main character faces. Sindbad encounters his first serious problem when he falls asleep on the shore and his ship and crew sail off without him. How does he attempt to solve this problem and the ones that follow? How often is he successful?

## ACTIVITY

**Directions** List a problem Sindbad faces in the first box in each pair. Then explain how he solves or fails to solve the problem in the second box.

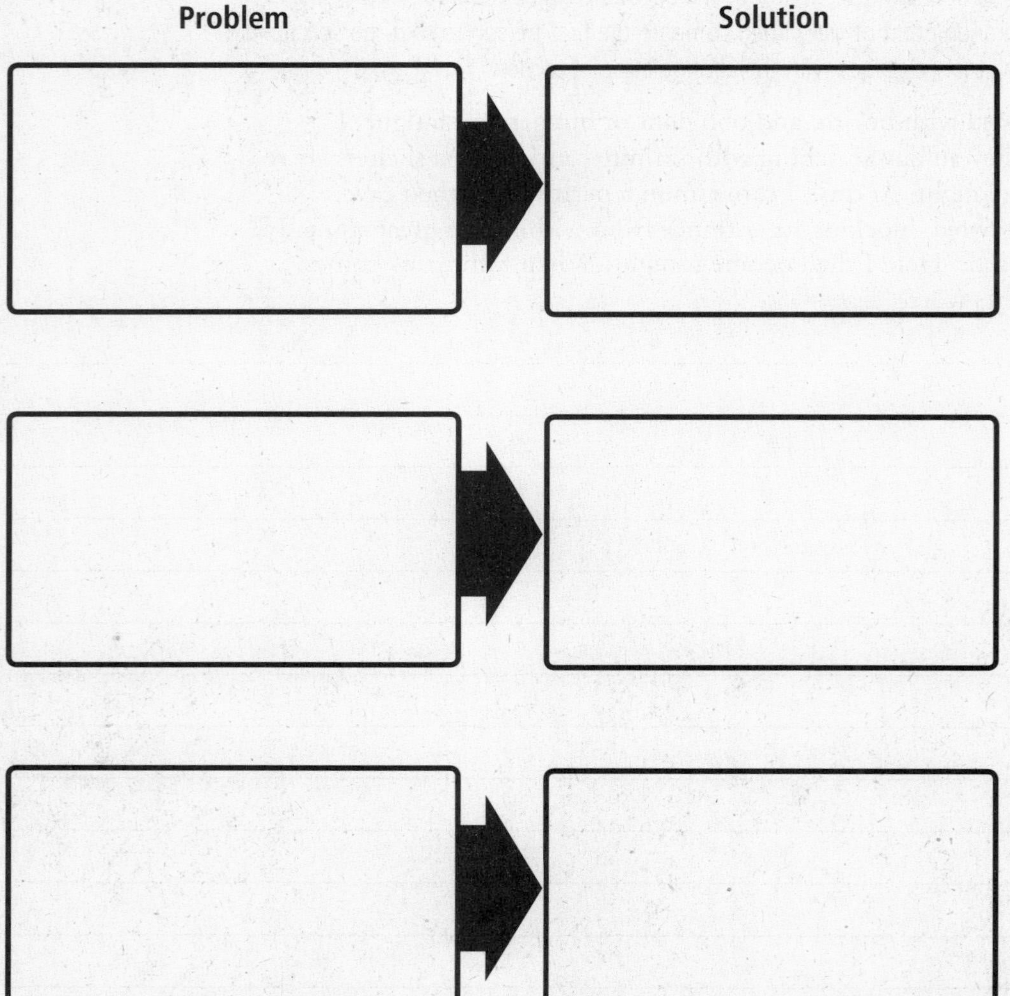

Name ____________________ Class ____________ Date ____________

## Selection Vocabulary Practice *(page 496)*

### The Second Voyage of Sindbad the Sailor *from* The Thousand and One Nights

**Vocabulary**

**thicket** *n.* a dense growth of shrubs, underbrush, or small trees
**fruitless** *adj.* unproductive; useless; sure to end in failure
**confound** *v.* to confuse or bewilder
**tumult** *n.* commotion or noisy confusion

### EXERCISE A Practice with Classifying

Write the vocabulary word that best completes each group of related words.

1. meadow, forest, hedges, ____________
2. fool, perplex, distress, ____________
3. fuss, riot, melee, ____________
4. doomed, worthless, failed, ____________

### EXERCISE B Applying Meanings

Write complete sentences using the correct vocabulary word to answer each question.

1. Mia is looking for a contact lens she dropped somewhere at the beach. How would you describe the likely outcome of her search?

____________

2. Keegan scratched his hand picking raspberries. Where was he?

____________

3. What followed the automobile collision at the market?

____________

4. What did the magician do to the little boy?

____________

### EXERCISE C Responding to the Selection

Write a letter to Sindbad asking which of his adventures thrilled him the most. Use at least THREE vocabulary words in your letter.

Name ______________________ Class ____________ Date ____________

# Vocabulary Strategy *(page 496)*

## Dictionary Use

## The Second Voyage of Sindbad the Sailor *from* The Thousand and One Nights

> "Looking around, I found myself on a precipitous hillside overlooking an exceedingly deep and vast valley."
>
> —"The Second Voyage of Sindbad the Sailor" *from* The Thousand and One Nights

**Connecting to Literature** In this quote Sindbad has just unfastened himself from the roc and watched the bird fly off with a serpent in its claws. Now, as he sets off to explore his new surroundings, he explains where he finds himself. To understand what the hillside is like, you must understand what *precipitous* means. You can turn to a dictionary for help.

Look for guide words at the top of each page of the dictionary. These show you the first and last words defined on the page and help you locate entries quickly.

A dictionary entry explains far more about an entry word than its definition. Here is what one dictionary includes in the entry for *precipitous.*

Entry word is broken into syllables.

The pronunciation is indicated.

The etymology gives the history of the word.

**pre•cip•i•tous** (pri sip'i təs) *adj.* [F *précipiteux,* fr MF, fr. L *precipitium* precipice] **a.** very steep, perpendicular, or overhanging in rise or fall <a ~ slope> **b.** having precipitous sides <a ~ gorge> **c.** having a very steep ascent <a ~ street> ***syn*** see STEEP **pre•cip•i•tous•ly** *adv.* **pre•cip•i•tous•ness** *n.*

The part of speech is shown.

Example phrases demonstrate usage.

## ACTIVITY

**Directions** Use the dictionary entry to answer the questions.

1. What part of speech is *precipitous?* ____________________
2. What other forms of *precipitous* are included? What part of speech is each?

   ________________________________________
3. From what language did *precipitous* first come? ____________________
4. What is a synonym of *precipitous?* ____________________
5. Which definition most closely matches the meaning of *precipitous* used in the quoted lines from "The Second Voyage of Sindbad the Sailor"? ____________

Name ______________________________ Class ______________ Date ______________

# Grammar Practice *(page 496)*

## Complex and Compound-Complex Sentences

## The Second Voyage of Sindbad the Sailor *from* The Thousand and One Nights

A **complex sentence** contains a main clause and one or more subordinate clauses.

| MAIN CLAUSE | SUBORDINATE CLAUSE |
|---|---|
| Sindbad was terrified | when he realized he was stranded. |

Notice that the main clause *Sindbad was terrified* can stand alone as a sentence, but the subordinate clause *when he realized he was stranded* cannot.

A **compound-complex sentence** has more than one main clause and one or more subordinate clauses.

SUBORDINATE CLAUSE — MAIN CLAUSE — MAIN CLAUSE

When the roc flew away with Sindbad, Sindbad's mouth went dry, and his heart thumped.

## ACTIVITY

**Directions** Draw one line under each main clause and two lines under each subordinate clause. Write *C* in the blank if the sentence is complex, and write *CC* if the sentence is compound-complex.

1. The moment Sindbad awoke and became aware of his situation, he threw himself on the sand and sobbed. ___________
2. Despite his terror, Sindbad immediately began searching the island for signs of life. ___________
3. When he discovered the roc, Sindbad made a plan, and he executed it perfectly. ___________
4. The roc dropped Sindbad in a more inhospitable place, so, ironically, he was worse off than before. ___________
5. A vulture saved the day for Sindbad, which amazed him and probably amazes readers, too. ___________
6. The karkadan was reported to have a horn that looked like a man, although that seems unlikely to modern-day readers. ___________
7. After he sold thousands of diamonds, Sindbad's thoughts turned toward home, and he started making plans. ___________
8. When he got back home, people treated Sindbad as a hero, and everyone wanted to be his friend. ___________

## Selection Quick Check *(page 496)*

### The Second Voyage of Sindbad the Sailor *from* The Thousand and One Nights

Use complete sentences to answer the following questions.

**1.** What kind of life does Sindbad lead in Baghdad?

**2.** For what does Sindbad feel an irresistible longing?

**3.** How does Sindbad become stranded on the island?

**4.** What covers the ground of the valley where Sindbad next lands?

**5.** What gigantic beast does Sindbad see on the densely wooded island?

Name ______________________ Class ______________ Date ______________

## Prueba Rápida *(pág. 496)*

### El segundo viaje de Sindbad el marino *de* Las mil y una noches

Contesta las siguientes preguntas con oraciones completas.

**1.** ¿Qué tipo de vida llevaba Sindbad en Bagdad?

**2.** ¿Cuál es el deseo irresistible de Sindbad?

**3.** ¿Por qué Sindbad queda abandonado en una isla?

**4.** ¿Qué cubre el valle donde Sindbad desembarca la siguiente vez?

**5.** ¿Qué bestia gigantesca ve Sindbad en la isla cubierta de un espeso bosque?

## Summary/Resumen *(p. 505)*

### *from the* Rubáiyát OMAR KHAYYÁM

The speaker welcomes the spring morning and casts off the "Winter Garment of Repentance." The speaker urges people to enjoy their freedom and live life to the fullest. He says that after studying philosophy and religion he learned only the fleeting nature of life, where people are "helpless Pieces of the Game" played by God. The speaker drinks wine without regret and wishes that the world were remade "nearer to the Heart's Desire!"

---

### *de los* Rubaiyat

El hablante da la bienvenida a la mañana de primavera y se despoja de la "Vestidura de Penitencia Invernal". El hablante urge a la gente a que disfruten de su libertad y a que vivan la vida a plenitud. Afirma que, después de estudiar filosofía y religión, sólo aprendió la naturaleza fugaz de la vida, en la que las personas son "piezas desvalidas de un juego" que Dios juega. El hablante bebe vino sin arrepentirse y desea que el mundo fuese creado de nuevo "más parecido a los deseos del corazón".

# Tóm Tắt *(p. 505)*

## *trích từ* Rubáiyát OMAR KHAYYÁM

Dường như nhân vật trong đoạn trích này đang đưa ra lời khuyên về việc làm thế nào để sống tốt trong một thế giới đầy những thách thức không thể chinh phục được. Thậm chí mặt trời buổi sáng cũng được mô tả như một thách thức—mặt trời ló dạng vào buổi sáng thì được gọi là "Người Đi Săn Của Phương Đông" chuyên bắt mọi vật "bằng Thòng Lọng Bình Minh". Mọi người đều phạm lỗi lầm, vì thế ta không nên dằn vặt mình trong hối tiếc. Thay vì đó, mọi người nên tận hưởng sự tự do của mình và sống trong những giây phút tự do đó. Nhân vật cảm thấy rằng chúng ta đơn thuần chỉ là những trò tiêu khiển của một vị thần được miêu tả là "Chủ Cuộc Chơi", người coi cuộc sống của chúng ta như một ván cờ. Nhân vật không thấy tiếc thứ rượu chàng/nàng đã uống, và cảm thấy rằng thế giới nên được tái tạo lại "gần hơn với Khát Vọng của Trái Tim!"

Name ______________________ Class ______________ Date ______________

## Buod *(p. 505)*

### *mula sa* Ang Rubáiyát OMAR KHAYYÁM

Tila nagbibigay ng payô ang nagsasalitá tungkol sa kung paano mabuhay nang mabuti sa isang mundong punô ng mga imposibleng hámon. Kahit ang araw sa umaga ay inilalarawan bilang parang isang hámon din—bilang "ang Mangangaso ng Silangan," na siyang nanghuhuli ng mga bagay "sa isang Silo ng Ilaw" kapag sumikat ito sa umaga. Ang mga tao ay nagkakamalî, at hindi nila dapat pahirapan ang kanilang mga sarili sa pagsisisi. Sa halip nito, dapat magsaya sila sa kanilang kalayaan at mabuhay sila sa kasalukuyan. Sa palagay ng nagsasalitá, tayo ay mga laruan lamang ng isang diyos na inilalarawan bilang "Maestro ng Palabás" na siyang tumitingin sa ating mga buhay na parang isang larô ng dama. Hindi pinagsisisihan ng nagsasalitá ang alak na kanyang ininom, at sa palagay niya ay dapat ilikhâ muli ang mundo "na mas nalalapít sa Ninanais ng Pusô!"

# 摘要 *(p. 505)*

## 來自《魯拜詩集》 OMAR KHAYYÁM

敘述者似乎是在對如何活在這個充滿不可能挑戰的世界提出他的建議。即使是清早的太陽也被敘述者形容為一種挑戰，如同是「東方的獵人」在太陽升起的早上「用陽光的絞索」捕捉東西。人都會犯錯，而不應該後悔地活在痛苦中。人們應該享受自己的自由而活在當下。敘述者認為我們只不過是神的玩物；這個神才是「表演的主人」，而把我們的生命看成是一盤棋。敘述者並不後悔自己所喝的酒，而覺得應該重造這個世界，以「更接近心裡的慾望！」

Name ________________________ Class ______________ Date ______________

## Rezime Selekyson *(p. 505)*

### *nan* Rubáiyát OMAR KHAYYÁM

Oraté a sanble l ap bay konsèy sou jan pou moun viv byen nan yon monn ki plen ak defi. Li menm dekri solèy lematen an tankou yon defi—tankou "Chasè Lès la," ki kenbe bagay "nan yon Kòd Limyè" lè li leve lematen. Moun fè erè; yo pa ta dwe bay tèt yo pwoblèm avèk regrè. Olye de sa, moun ta dwe jwi libète yo epi viv lavi yo. Oratè a santi nou se poupe nan men yon Bondye li di ki se "Mèt Espektak la" ki wè lavi nou tankou yon jwèt pou jwe. Oratè a pa regrèt diven li bwè a, epi li santi fòk yo ta rebati lemonn "pi pre Dezi Kè a!"

## Zuag Tswvyim *(p. 505)*

### *los ntawm* Rubáiyát OMAR KHAYYÁM

Tus hais zaj lus txais zaj lus qhia txog kev ua neej zoo licas hauv ib lub ntiajteb uas muaj kev khaiv ntau yam. Txawm sab hnub sawv ntxov xwb twb zoo li ib hom cuamtshuam—li "tus Kws Raws Nqaij Sab Hnub Tuaj," uas txhom tau tej yam "hauv sab hnub laim" thaum hnub tawm sawv ntxov. Tibneeg ua yuamkev thiab yuav tsum txhob rau txim rau tus kheej tias khuvxim. Dua ntawd, lawv yuav tsum nyiam kev ywjsiab thiab nyob nrog lub sijhawm ntawd. Tus hais zaj lus xav tias peb yog tej yam khoom uasi uas ib tus vajtswv teev cia ua "tus thawj seev cev" uas ntsia lub neej li uasi nrog checkers. Nws tsis khuvxim cov cawv nws tau haus, thiab paub tias lub ntiajteb yuav raug tsim dua kom "ze Qhov lub Siab Xav Tau Dua!"

Name ______________________ Class ______________ Date ______________

# Literary Element *(page 505)*

## Rhyme Scheme

### *from the* Rubáiyát OMAR KHAYYÁM

A **rhyme scheme** is a pattern of rhyming lines in a poem. The rhyme scheme of the *Rubáiyát*, with a single exception, can be described as *aaba*. This designation tells us that in each stanza, or ruba'i, the words at the end of the first, second, and fourth lines rhyme.

## ACTIVITIES

**Directions** On the lines below, write a poem of four-line stanzas that follows the *aaba* rhyme scheme of the *Rubáiyát*. In your poem react to the wisdom of Khayyám's advice to live for the moment.

**Directions** Is it easier to write rhymed poetry that follows a particular rhyme scheme or unrhymed poetry? Give specific reasons for your opinion.

Name ______________________ Class ____________ Date ____________

# Reading Strategy *(page 505)*

## Clarify Meaning

### *from the* Rubáiyát OMAR KHAYYÁM

To **clarify the meaning** of difficult passages in the *Rubáiyát,* reread them slowly and carefully. Look for clues to the meaning of the work that you may have missed when you first read the passages. Follow the syntax, or arrangement of the lines, to track complete thoughts. You may find it helpful in clarifying meaning to rephrase inverted word order in a more typical form.

## ACTIVITY

**Directions** Clarify the meaning of each of the following passages from the *Rubáiyát* by reading it carefully, paying particular attention to word order. Explain the meaning of the passage in the second column.

| Passage from the *Rubáiyát* | Explanation/Interpretation |
|---|---|
| "Awake! For Morning in the Bowl of Night/Has flung the Stone that puts the Stars to Flight" | **1.** |
| "The Bird of Time has but a little way/ To fly—and Lo! The Bird is on the Wing." | **2.** |
| "We are no other than a moving row/ Of Magic Shadow-shapes that come and go" | **3.** |
| "Hither and thither moves, and checks, and slays,/And one by one back in the Closet lays." | **4.** |
| "Would not we shatter it to bits—and then/ Re-mold it nearer to the Heart's Desire!" | **5.** |

Name ______________________________ Class ______________ Date ______________

# Vocabulary Strategy *(page 505)*

## Homonyms and Homophones

### *from the* Rubáiyát OMAR KHAYYÁM

"With them the Seed of Wisdom did I sow, . . .
We are no other than a moving row . . . "

—*Omar Khayyám, from the* Rubáiyát

**Connecting to Literature** In these lines from the *Rubáiyát,* Omar Khayyám uses the word *row,* meaning "a number of items arranged in a straight line." *Row* also means "to propel a boat using oars." Words like *row* that sound and are spelled alike but have different meanings are called **homonyms**. The first line above includes the word *I*. The words *I* and *eye* are **homophones**, words that sound alike but are spelled differently and have different meanings. Context clues can help readers determine the appropriate meaning of homonyms and homophones. Here are other examples:

| Homonyms | Homophones | Homophones |
|---|---|---|
| pump: shoe, machine | scent/sent/cent | ate/eight |
| bear: animal, carry | their/there/they're | one/won |
| chuck: throw, beef | some/sum | wear/where/ware |

## ACTIVITY

**Directions** Use context clues to choose the correct homonym meaning or homophone in each sentence below. Write the correct word or words on the lines. Use a dictionary if you need help.

**1.** In the *Rubáiyát*, the sky is called the Bowl of (Knight/Night). ___________

**2.** A bird on the wing stands for (thyme/time). ___________

**3.** The speaker explains that people are a moving row (line/to use oars) of shadows. ___________

**4.** The speaker believes that people are (know/no) more than shadows. ___________

**5.** "Doctor and Saint" helped the speaker (sow/sew) wisdom. ___________

**6.** The speaker wonders what vintners (by/bye/buy). ___________

Name ______________________ Class ____________ Date ____________

## Selection Quick Check *(page 505)*

### *from the* Rubáiyát OMAR KHAYYÁM

Use complete sentences to answer the following questions.

**1.** In stanza I, what is caught "in a Noose of Light"?

**2.** What advice does the speaker give in stanza XII?

**3.** To what does the speaker give the human quality of speech in stanza XIII?

**4.** What knowledge does the speaker gain in stanza XXVIII?

**5.** In stanza XCIX, what does the speaker wish that he and his love could do?

# Prueba Rápida *(pág. 505)*

## *de los* Rubaiyat OMAR KHAYYÁM

Contesta las siguientes preguntas con oraciones completas.

**1.** En la estrofa I, ¿qué queda atrapado "en un nudo de luz"?

**2.** ¿Qué consejo da el hablante en la estrofa XII?

**3.** ¿A qué cosa le da el hablante de la estrofa XIII la capacidad humana de hablar?

**4.** ¿Qué conocimiento adquiere el hablante en la estrofa XXVIII?

**5.** En la estrofa XCIX, ¿qué desea el hablante que él y su amante pudieran hacer?

Name ______________________ Class ______________ Date ______________

## Summary/Resumen *(p. 511)*

### The Counsels of the Bird *from* The Masnavi RUMI

A captured bird bargains for its release by promising its captor three good pieces of advice, to be delivered from increasingly distant places. The bird guarantees that its advice will make the man happy. In his first counsel, the bird tells the man not to believe anyone's foolish assertions. Flying farther away, the bird then counsels the man not to grieve for what is past. In giving its third counsel, the bird declares that it is useless to waste advice on an ignoramus.

---

### Los consejos del pájaro *de* El Masnavi

Un pájaro capturado negocia su liberación prometiendo a su captor tres buenos consejos, que le serán entregados desde lugares cada vez más distantes. El pájaro le garantiza que sus consejos lo harán feliz. En su primer consejo, el pájaro dice al hombre que no crea las afirmaciones insensatas de nadie. Volando más lejos, el pájaro aconseja al hombre no lamentarse por lo que ya pasó. Y, en su tercer consejo, el pájaro declara que es inútil desperdiciar consejos en un ignorante.

Name ______________________ Class __________ Date __________

# Tóm Tắt *(p. 511)*

## Những Lời Khuyên của Con Chim *trích từ* Tập Thơ Masnavi RUMI

Một con chim bị bắt thương lượng để được thả. Nó hứa cho người bắt được nó ba lời khuyên từ ba khoảng cách dần xa anh ta. Con chim quả quyết rằng những lời khuyên của nó sẽ mang lại hạnh phúc cho anh ta. Ở lời khuyên thứ nhất, con chim nói với người đàn ông không nên tin vào những lời quả quyết ngu ngốc của bất cứ ai. Bay xa thêm tí nữa, con chim khuyên người đàn ông không nên nuối tiếc quá khứ. Khi đưa ra lời khuyên thứ ba, con chim tuyên bố rằng phí phạm lời khuyên cho một kẻ ngu dốt là điều vô ích.

## Buod *(p. 511)*

### Ang mga Conseho ng mga Ibon *mula sa* Ang Masnavi RUMI

Upang siya'y palayain, nangako ang isang hinuling ibon sa kanyang manghuhuli ng tatlong magandang payô, na ipapadala mula sa mga palayô nang palayô na lugar. Ginarantiya ng ibon na magiging masaya ang lalaki sa kanyang payô. Sa kanyang unang payô, sinabi ng ibon sa lalaki na huwag paniwalaan ang kalokohang pagsasabi ng sinuman. Lumipad ang ibon nang mas malayô, at sinabi nito sa lalaki na huwag magdalamhati tungkol sa nakaraan. Nang ibinigay nito ang pangatlong payô, sinabi ng ibon na walang kabuluhan ang mag-aksaya ng payô sa isang taong ignorante.

Name ______________________ Class ______________ Date ______________

# 摘要 *(p. 511)*

## 來自 Masnavi 的《鳥兒的建議》 RUMI

有一隻被捉住的鳥，向捕獲它的人協議釋放它；而答應要從愈來愈遠的地方，提供三個好的建議給這個人。這隻鳥保證它的建議會讓這個人快樂。在它的第一個建議中，這隻鳥告訴這個人不要相信任何人愚蠢的宣稱。在飛遠了一點之後，這隻鳥建議這個人不要為過去的事情悲傷。在提出第三個建議的時候，這隻鳥表示浪費建議給無知的人毫無用處。

Name ______________________ Class ____________ Date ____________

## Rezime Selekyson *(p. 511)*

### Konsèy Zwazo a *nan The Masnavi* RUMI

Yon zwazo yo kaptire ap machande liberasyon li ak pwomès pou li bay ravisè li twa bon konsèy, diferan kote ki ofi-amezi lwen. Zwazo a garanti konsèy li ap fè misye kontan. Nan premye konsèy li, zwazo a di misye pou li pa kwè afimasyon estipid pèsòn. Zwazo a vole pi lwen, epi li konseye misye pou li pa kriye sou sa ki pase. Lè l ap bay twazyèm konsèy la, zwazo a deklare sa pa sèvi anyen gaspiye konsèy sou yon inyoran.

Name ______________________ Class ______________ Date ______________

## Zuag Tswvyim *(p. 511)*

### Tus Noog cov Lus Qhia *los ntawm* The Masnavi RUMI

Ib tus noog raug txhom nrog nws tus tswv khom lus hais tias yog tso nws mus, nws yuav muab peb zaj lus qhia zoo pub rau thaum nws ya deb zuj zus. Tus noog lees tau tias cov lus ntawd yuav ua rau tus neeg zoo siab. Hauv nws thawj zaj lus qhia, tus noog hais rau tus neeg kom txhob ntseeg ib leej twg tej lus vwm. Ya mus deb zog, tus noog hais rau tus neeg tias txhob tusiab rau yav dhau los. Thaum txog zaj lus qhia peb, tus noog hais tias tsis muaj nuj nqi dabtsi los nkim sijhawm rau ib tus neeg ruam lawm.

Name ______________________ Class ____________ Date ____________

# Literary Element *(page 511)*

## Maxim

## The Counsels of the Bird *from* The Masnavi RUMI

A **maxim** is a concisely expressed general truth, fundamental principle, or rule of conduct. "The early bird gets the worm" is a maxim. Benjamin Franklin was a well-known and prolific writer of maxims. Nearly everyone knows Franklin's maxims such as "Early to bed and early to rise makes a man healthy, wealthy, and wise" and "A penny saved is a penny earned." The best maxims, like Franklin's, are brief, insightful, and memorable.

## ACTIVITY

**Directions** In the first column write the three maxims from "The Counsels of the Bird." In the second column, explain what each means. In the third column, write your own version of the maxim. Be sure your maxim expresses the same general truth as the one from "The Counsels of the Bird."

| Maxim | Interpretation | My Version |
|---|---|---|
| 1. | | |
| 2. | | |
| 3. | | |

Name ______________________ Class ______________ Date ______________

## Reading Strategy *(page 511)*

### Make Generalizations About Characters

### The Counsels of the Bird *from* The Masnavi RUMI

**Making generalizations about characters** in works of fiction can help you understand the characters better. This understanding can help you figure out what the author hopes you learn from the characters. To make generalizations about characters, draw conclusions based on evidence in the text.

## ACTIVITY

**Directions** Look for details that reveal important traits of the man and of the bird. For each character, write three such details in the left-hand column below. In the right-hand column, write a generalization you can make about each character based on these details.

| Details About the Man | Generalization Drawn from Details |
|---|---|
| | |
| | |
| | |
| **Details About the Bird** | **Generalization Drawn from Details** |
| | |
| | |
| | |

Name ______________________ Class ______________ Date ______________

# Selection Vocabulary Practice *(page 511)*

## The Counsels of the Bird *from* The Masnavi RUMI

**Vocabulary**

**deem** *v.* to regard in a certain way
**assertion** *n.* a forceful or confident statement of fact or belief
**prosperity** *n.* the state of being successful

### EXERCISE A Practice with Words in Context

Write the word from the word list that belongs in the blank in each sentence.

**1.** The bird in the poem displays his intelligence with every __________.

**2.** Eventually the bird does not __________ the man worthy of help.

**3.** The bird teases the man with dreams of __________.

### EXERCISE B Applying Meanings

Write the vocabulary word that could replace the word in bold type in each sentence.

**1.** The bird comes to **judge** the man a fool. __________

**2.** To the bird, true **wealth** is determined by freedom. __________

**3.** No **claim** the man could make would change the bird's mind. __________

### EXERCISE C Responding to the Selection

What do you suppose the bird's third counsel would have been? Write the good advice you imagine the bird would have given the man. Use at least TWO of the vocabulary words in your maxim.

Name ______________________ Class ______________ Date ______________

# Vocabulary Strategy *(page 511)*

## Latin Word Origins

## The Counsels of the Bird *from* The Masnavi RUMI

"And likewise sacrificed many camels"

—*Rumi,* "The Counsels of the Bird" *from* The Masnavi

**Connecting to Literature** Thousands of words have entered the English language from Latin. The word *sacrificed* in the passage above is one of them. Consult a dictionary to find information on word origins. When we look up *sacrifice* in the dictionary, we learn that *sacrifice* comes from the Latin *sacr-* or *sacer,* "sacred" and *facere* "to make." How does knowing the origin help illuminate the meaning of *sacrifice?* The chart shows some other words from "The Counsels of the Bird" that originated in Latin.

| Word | Latin Word/Meaning | Definition |
|---|---|---|
| counsel | consulere; to consult | advice |
| grieve | gravis; heavy, grave | feel or show grief over |
| vex | vexare; agitate, harry | bring trouble or distress to |

## ACTIVITY

**Directions** Use a dictionary to fill in the chart with four words from "The Counsels of the Bird" that have Latin origins. As in the examples above, write each word, the Latin word or words and meaning, and the dictionary definition.

| Word | Latin Word/Meaning | Definition |
|---|---|---|
| 1. | | |
| 2. | | |
| 3. | | |
| 4. | | |

Name ______________________ Class ______________ Date ______________

## Grammar Practice *(page 511)*

### Adjective Clauses

### The Counsels of the Bird *from* The Masnavi RUMI

When a subordinate clause modifies a noun or a pronoun, it is called an **adjective clause**. Often an adjective clause is introduced by a relative pronoun.

Rumi's poetry, **which has remained popular for eight centuries**, continues to fill literature anthologies. (modifies the noun *poetry*)

Have you found someone **who will read Rumi's poetry** to the class? (modifies the pronoun *someone*)

| RELATIVE PRONOUNS | | |
|---|---|---|
| that | whom | whomever |
| which | whose | what |
| who | whoever | whatever |

## ACTIVITY

**Directions** Draw one line under each adjective clause and two lines under each word that introduces an adjective clause.

1. In "The Counsels of the Bird," a man who captures a bird learns a lesson.
2. The bird, whose fear of the man isn't evident, offers him advice.
3. Has there ever been a bird whose gift of gab was greater?
4. Can you imagine anyone who would trust the advice of a bird?
5. The advice that the bird gives is excellent though.
6. The bird, who must have made a plan, tests the effect of his counsel.
7. He tempts the man with a story about a pearl, which can't possibly be true.
8. The man, whose greed overcomes his common sense, falls for the story.
9. The second counsel that the man ignores is to let bygones be bygones.
10. The bird has the final word in the story, which is how it should be.

Name ______________________ Class ______________ Date ______________

## Selection Quick Check *(page 511)*

### The Counsels of the Bird *from* The Masnavi RUMI

Use complete sentences to answer the following questions.

**1.** What does the word *counsels* refer to in the title?

______________________________________________

______________________________________________

______________________________________________

**2.** Why does the bird say the man will not be satisfied by the bird's flesh?

______________________________________________

______________________________________________

______________________________________________

**3.** How does the bird claim the man will feel after receiving the counsels?

______________________________________________

______________________________________________

______________________________________________

**4.** What does the bird claim to have hidden inside his body?

______________________________________________

______________________________________________

______________________________________________

**5.** Who is the "sleepy ignoramus" in the poem?

______________________________________________

______________________________________________

______________________________________________

Name ______________________ Class ______________ Date ______________

## Prueba Rápida *(pág. 511)*

### Los consejos del pájaro *de* El Masnavi RUMI

Contesta las siguientes preguntas con oraciones completas.

**1.** ¿A qué se refiere la palabra *consejos* en el título?

______________________________________________

______________________________________________

______________________________________________

**2.** ¿Por qué el pájaro le dice al hombre que la carne del pájaro no le gustará?

______________________________________________

______________________________________________

______________________________________________

**3.** ¿Según el pájaro, ¿cómo se sentirá el hombre después de recibir sus consejos?

______________________________________________

______________________________________________

______________________________________________

**4.** ¿Qué dice el pájaro que lleva escondido en el cuerpo?

______________________________________________

______________________________________________

______________________________________________

**5.** ¿Quién es el ignorante con sueño en el poema?

______________________________________________

______________________________________________

______________________________________________

## Summary/Resumen *(p. 516)*

### Elegy for a Woman of No Importance NĀZIK AL-MALĀ'IKAH

The death of a woman is met without grief or mourning by her neighbors. Her coffin passes through the street with only the faintest notice. The next day the neighborhood goes about its business as it would on any other day. The woman is completely forgotten.

---

### Elegía a una mujer sin importancia

A la muerte de una mujer, ninguno de sus vecinos se siente triste o la llora. Su féretro pasa por la calle sin que casi nadie lo note. Al día siguiente, el vecindario sigue su vida como cualquier otro día. La mujer ha sido olvidada por completo.

# Tóm Tắt *(p. 516)*

## Khúc Bi Thương Dành Cho Một Người Phụ Nữ Không Quan Trọng NĀZIK AL-MALĀ'IKAH

Khi một người phụ nữ nào đó qua đời, không ai cảm thấy buồn, không ai nhắc đến cô và không ai than khóc tiếc thương cô. Không ai đến đưa tang cô; người ta chỉ có cảm giác thoáng qua rằng quan tài của cô vừa đi ngang phố. Chả ở đâu người ta nói về cái chết của cô, nhưng tin về cái chết của cô ở đâu cũng có, và rồi bị người đời phớt lờ. Thiên nhiên buồn bã quan sát cảnh không một tiếng khóc than. Tuy nhiên sáng hôm sau, thậm chí thiên nhiên dường như cũng lãng quên cô bởi vì mọi thứ lại diễn ra như trước. Một con mèo đói bụng, những người bán hàng rong rao to để mời khách, các cậu bé trai chơi đùa, và nước chảy qua những rãnh nước quanh nhà. Những mùi hương thoảng qua trong gió rồi bay đến mái nhà nơi người phụ nữ đã bị quên lãng và ký ức về cô cũng đơn côi.

Name ______________________ Class ______________ Date ______________

## Buod *(p. 516)*

### Malungkot na Tulá para sa Isang Babaeng Walang Kahalagahan NĀZIK AL-MALĀ'IKAH

Kapag namatáy ang isang babae, walang nalulungkot, walang nag-uusap tungkol sa kanya, at walang nagluluksâ para sa kanya. Walang dumadaló sa kanyang libíng; mararamdaman mo lamang na dumaan ang kanyang ataól sa kalye. Walang balita ng kanyang pagkamatay kahit saanman, pero ito ay nagkalat din sa lahat ng lugar, at ito ay hindi pinapansin. Malungkot na pinanonood ng Kalikasan ang kakulangan ng pagluluksâ na nagaganap. Gayunman, kinabukasan, tila nalimutan na rin ito ng kalikasan dahil lahat ay patuloy pa rin tulad ng dati. Ginugutom ang isang pusa, nagtatawag ang mga tindero ng mga tao para bumili ng kanilang mga ibinebenta, naglalarô ang mga batang lalaki, at umaagos ang tubig sa mga kanal. Dumaraan ang mga amoy sa hangin, at dinadalá ang mga ito sa mga bubungán, kung saan nalimutan ná ang babae at mag-isa na lamang ang kanyang alaala.

Name ______________________ Class ______________ Date ______________

# 摘要 *(p. 516)*

## 對一位無足輕重婦女的哀歌 NĀZIK AL-MALĀ'IKAH

當某位婦女去世的時候，沒有人感到悲傷、沒有人談論她、也沒有人哀悼她。沒有人參加她的葬禮；你只能感覺到她的棺材路過了街上。她去世的消息根本不存在，卻也到處都存在，而最終被人忽略。大自然憂傷地看著這個缺乏悲傷的狀況。但是第二天早上，一切作息都如同往常，似乎大自然也遺忘了她。一隻貓的肚子餓了、生意人叫賣他們的貨物、小男孩玩耍、而積水流過了水溝。風中的味道吹到了屋頂；在那裡，這位婦女被遺忘了，而她的記憶僅留存在孤獨中。

Name ______________________ Class ______________ Date ______________

## Rezime Selekyson *(p. 516)*

### Eleji Pou yon Fanm san Enpòtans NĀZIK AL-MALĀ'IKAH

Lè yon sèten fi mouri, pèsòn pa tris, pèsòn pa pale de li, pèsòn pa kriye pou li. Pèsòn pa ale nan antèman li; se apèn si ou santi sèkèy li pase nan lari a. Yo pa anonse lanmò li ankenn kote e poutan li tout kote; yo inyore sa. Lanati gade avèk tristès paske yo pa kriye pou fi sa a. Men, lelandemen, menm lanati sanble li bliye sa paske tout bagay kontinye kòm si anyen pat rive. Yon chat grangou, machann yo rele moun vin achte, timoun ap jwe, epi dlo koule nan rigòl. Gen sant van an pote sou tèt kay, kote yo bliye fi a epi yo kite souvni li poukont li.

Name ______________________ Class ______________ Date ______________

## Zuag Tswvyim *(p. 516)*

### Zaj Nkauj Tuag rau ib tus Pojniam tsis Tseemceeb

NĀZIK AL-MALĀ'IKAH

Thaum ib tus pojniam tuag, tsis muaj neeg tusiab, tham txog nws, thiab khuvxim txog nws. Tsis muaj neeg mus nws lub ntees; nej tsuas xav tau tias nws lub hleb raug thauj ceev ceev dhua kev. Cov xov txog nws txoj kev tuag tsis nyob qhov twg tabsis thoob txhua chaw, thiab tsis muaj neeg paub. Ntiaj nras tusiab ntsuav tias tsis muaj tus quaj li. Taig kis hnub, ntiaj nras twb ho nov qab nws lawm thiab vim txhua yam rov mus li qub. Ib tus miv tshaib plab, neeg muag zaub qw zom zaws kom neeg los yuav khoom, menyuam uasi, thiab dej ntws raws ciav. Pa hluav taws ya saum cua thiab ntswj dhau rw tsev, qhov chaw tus pojniam tuag twb raug nov qab thiab nws kev nco twm zeej lawm.

Name ______________________ Class ______________ Date ______________

# Literary Element *(page 516)*

## Personification

## Elegy for a Woman of No Importance NĀZIK AL-MALĀ'IKAH

One poetic device, which the poet uses elegantly in "Elegy for a Woman of No Importance," is **personification**, in which nonhuman beings, objects, or ideas are given human attributes. The poet's use of personification contributes greatly to the melancholy mood of the poem.

## ACTIVITY

**Directions** Complete the chart following the example given. In the first column, write an item from "Elegy for a Woman of No Importance" that is personified. In the second column, write the phrase from the poem in which that item appears. In the last column, explain how the example demonstrates personification. An example is provided.

| Item Personified | Phrase from Poem | Explanation |
|---|---|---|
| doors | "doors heard no retelling of her death" | Doors are given the human quality of hearing. |
| 1. | | |
| 2. | | |
| 3. | | |
| 4. | | |

Name ______________________ Class ______________ Date ______________

# Reading Strategy *(page 516)*

## Analyze Tone

## Elegy for a Woman of No Importance NĀZIK AL-MALĀ'IKAH

**Tone** is an author's attitude toward the subject or audience. For example, an author's tone might be angry, joyous, disdainful, or amused. To analyze tone, consider elements such as word choice, imagery, and figures of speech.

## ACTIVITY

**Directions** Fill in the graphic organizer to analyze the tone of "Elegy for a Woman of No Importance." In the top box, write a word or phrase that best describes the tone of the poem. In the other boxes, give three examples or quotations from the poem that support your interpretation of the tone.

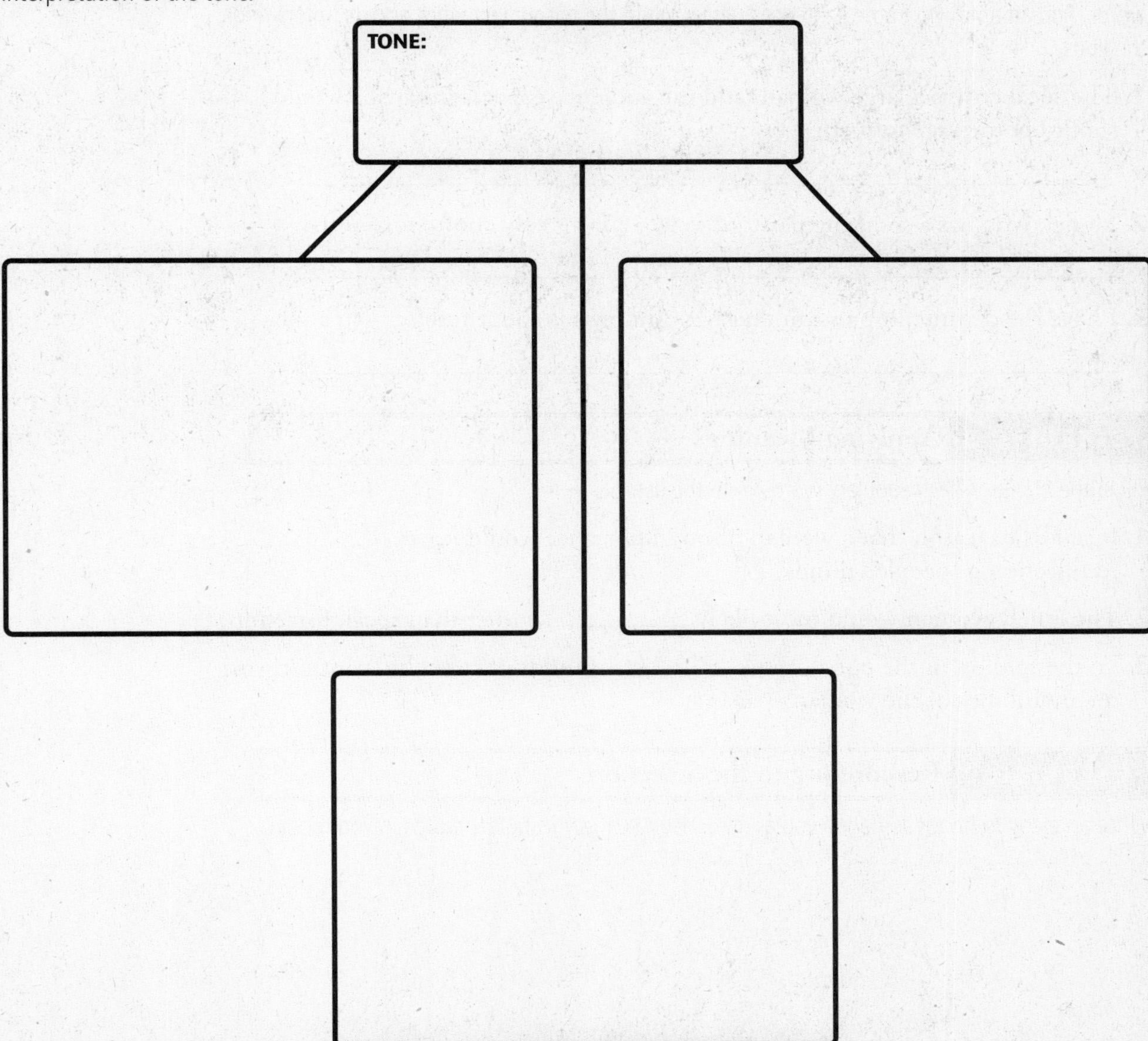

Name ______________________ Class ____________ Date ____________

# Selection Vocabulary Practice *(page 516)*

## Elegy for a Woman of No Importance NĀZIK AL-MALĀ'IKAH

**Vocabulary**

**vague** *adj.* unclear; without form; indistinct
**murmur** *v.* to say something in an indistinct voice; to say something quietly and cautiously
**shrill** *adj.* high pitched

### EXERCISE A Practice with Antonyms

Antonyms are words with opposite or nearly opposite meanings. For each of the vocabulary words, find an antonym in the sentences below. Write the vocabulary word and its antonym on the lines.

**1.** The speaker was a large woman, and the audience expected that she would shout her message to them.

______________________ ______________________

**2.** Lionel, who has a soothing baritone voice, was an easy choice for soloist.

______________________ ______________________

**3.** I have the definite impression that Mr. Andrews is about to offer you a job.

______________________ ______________________

### EXERCISE B Applying Meanings

Fill in the blanks with vocabulary words from the list.

**1.** It stands to reason that a woman of no importance would leave a __________ recollection in people's minds.

**2.** The lonely woman would most likely __________ rather than speak forcefully.

**3.** To the speaker in the poem, the __________ sounds of street life contrast with the invisibility of the woman's passing.

### EXERCISE C Responding to the Selection

Write an elegy to honor someone you admire. Use ALL the vocabulary words in your poem.

Name ______________________ Class ______________ Date ______________

# Vocabulary Strategy *(page 516)*

## Denotation and Connotation

## Elegy for a Woman of No Importance NĀZIK AL-MALĀ'IKAH

"the shrill cries of vendors in the bitter streets"

—*Nāzik al-Malā'ikah,* "Elegy for a Woman of No Importance"

**Connecting to Literature** All the words in a poem are important—not only for their sounds but for their meanings. You can be sure that the poet considered the **denotation**, or literal meaning, and the **connotation**, or implied meaning, of every word in "Elegy for a Woman of No Importance." She could have used *squeaky cries* instead of *shrill cries* or *mean streets* instead of *bitter streets.* But the connotations of those words were not the ones she wanted for her poem.

## ACTIVITY

**Directions** Analyze the denotation and connotation of five words from the poem. Write the words in the first column. For each word, write the denotation, the dictionary definition, in the second column. In the third column, describe the word's connotation, the ideas, images, or feelings you associate with the word.

| Word | Denotation | Connotation |
|---|---|---|
| 1. | | |
| 2. | | |
| 3. | | |
| 4. | | |
| 5. | | |

Name ____________________ Class ____________ Date ____________

## Selection Quick Check *(page 516)*

### Elegy for a Woman of No Importance NĀZIK AL-MALĀ'IKAH

Use complete sentences to answer the following questions.

**1.** According to the title of the poem, who has died?

______________________________________________

______________________________________________

______________________________________________

**2.** According to line 9, how does the moon respond to the woman's death?

______________________________________________

______________________________________________

______________________________________________

**3.** In lines 11–14, what sounds occur in the morning?

______________________________________________

______________________________________________

______________________________________________

Name ______________________ Class ______________ Date ______________

# Prueba Rápida *(pág. 516)*

## Elegía a una mujer sin importancia NĀZIK AL-MALĀ'IKAH

Contesta las siguientes preguntas con oraciones completas.

**1.** Según el título del poema, ¿quién murió?

______________________________________________

______________________________________________

______________________________________________

**2.** De acuerdo con los versos 7 a 10, ¿cómo reaccionó la luna ante la muerte de la mujer?

______________________________________________

______________________________________________

______________________________________________

**3.** En los versos 11 a 14, ¿qué sonidos ocurren en la mañana?

______________________________________________

______________________________________________

______________________________________________

Name ______________________ Class ______________ Date ______________

## Summary/Resumen *(p. 520)*

### The Sound of Birds at Noon DAHLIA RAVIKOVITCH

The poet writes about her admiration for birds and for their chirping that is "free of malice." She describes how the birds follow their instincts and fill their place in nature. Over time the poet begins to hear a note of "compassion" in the chirping.

---

### El sonido de los pájaros al mediodía

La poeta escribe sobre su admiración por los pájaros y por su gorjeo "libre de malicia". Ella describe cómo los pájaros siguen sus instintos y ocupan un lugar propio en la naturaleza. Con el tiempo, la poeta comienza a escuchar una nota de "compasión" en su gorjeo.

Name ______________________ Class ____________ Date ____________

# Tóm Tắt *(p. 520)*

## Âm Thanh của Loài Chim Lúc Ban Trưa DAHLIA RAVIKOVITCH

Người thuật truyện say mê loài chim và dường như đang nói rằng dù tiếng hót của loài chim nghe lúc nào cũng hay, nhưng nghe càng hay hơn khi chúng ta về già. Loài chim hành xử mà không có cảm xúc, thậm chí ngay cả khi chúng đang làm phương hại đến một loài vật khác, ví dụ như lúc chúng ăn một con giun. Nói chung thì loài chim cất tiếng hót bởi vì chúng cảm thấy vui vẻ chứ không bao giờ là do chúng cảm thấy buồn phiền. Loài chim tốt tính, nhưng chúng không nghĩ gì đến loài người khi líu lo cất vang lời ca. Theo người thuật truyện, loài chim "có một cuộc sống của riêng chúng, /chúng bay mà không hề suy nghĩ". Loài chim luôn thanh nhã cho dù đó là những loài chim quý hiếm hay những chú chim mà bạn nhìn thấy hàng ngày. Người thuật truyện cảm thấy rằng loài chim có thể là loài vật được sinh ra trên thiên đường, vì thế cũng chính là những kẻ làm chủ trái đất. Loài chim cứ sống mà dường như không quan tâm đến mối quan hệ của chúng với con người. Tuy nhiên, nếu chúng ta lắng nghe qua nhiều năm tháng, tiếng hót của loài chim dường như bắt đầu cho thấy chúng cũng quan tâm và yêu loài người.

Name ______________________ Class ______________ Date ______________

## Buod *(p. 520)*

### Ang Tunog ng mga Ibon sa Tanghali DAHLIA RAVIKOVITCH

Hinahangaan ng nagsasalitá ang mga ibon, at tila sinasabi niya na bagama't palaging maganda ang tunig ng mga awit ng mga ibon, lalong gumaganda ang tunog nito sa atin habang tayo ay tumatandâ. Ang mga ibon ay kumikilos nang walang emosyón, kahit na mayroon silang pinipinsala na ibang hayop, tulad ng kapag kumakain sila ng isang uod. Ang mga ibon ay umaawit kapag maganda ang kanilang pakiramdam, at hindi kailanman kapag nakakaramdam sila ng karahasan. Bagama't hindi masamâ ang ugali ng mga ibon, umaawit sila ng kanilang mga awit hindi para sa mga tao. Ayon sa nagsasalaysay, ang mga ibon ay "mayroong sariling buhay,/ lumilipad sila nang hindi nag-iisip." Palaging kaaya-aya ang mga ibon, maging 'di-pangkaraniwang ibon man sila o mga ibong nakikita mo sa araw-araw. Sa palagay ng nagsasalaysay, maaaring ang mga ibon ay mga hayop ng langit, at samakatwid, sila ang mga naghahari sa lahat ng nasa mundo. Tila nagpapatuloy mabuhay ang mga ibon nang talagang walang pakialam kahit anuman sa mga tao. Gayunman, kapag pinakikinggan natin sila habang lumilipas ang panahon, parang nagsisimulang magpakita ng pagmamahal at pagmamalasakit para sa mga tao ang pag-awit ng mga ibon.

Name ______________________ Class ______________ Date ______________

# 摘要 *(p. 520)*

## 中午的鳥叫聲 DAHLIA RAVIKOVITCH

敘述者很欣賞鳥兒，而似乎是在說雖然鳥叫聲隨時都很好聽，但我們年紀愈大愈覺得好聽。即使鳥兒在傷害其他的生物（例如是吃蟲子），它們的行為並沒有感情。通常來說，鳥兒會發出叫聲是因為它們感覺舒適，而絕不是因為它們感到暴躁。雖然鳥兒並不會不和善，但它們的叫聲與人類無關。根據敘述者的看法，鳥兒「有它們自己的生命，它們會不加思索地飛翔」。不論是稀有或常見的鳥，它們永遠都是優美的。敘述者認為鳥兒可能是來自天國的產物，因而是地球上一切的統治者。鳥兒自在地生活，似乎完全沒有想到自己與人類之間的關聯。但是，隨著我們一直不斷地聆聽，鳥兒的歌聲似乎開始顯露出對於人類的愛與關懷。

Name ______________________ Class ______________ Date ______________

## Rezime Selekyson *(p. 520)*

### Son Zwazo yo Amidi DAHLIA RAVIKOVITCH

Naratè a admire zwazo epi sanble l ap di malgre chante zwazo yo sonnen byen, yo sonnen pi byen toujou lè nou kòmanse ap pran laj. Zwazo yo aji san emosyon pa anvayi yo, menm lè y ap fè yon lòt bèt soufri, tankou lè y ap manje yon vè tè. Se yon règ; zwazo chante lè yo santi yo byen, yo pa janm chante paske yo santi mechanste nan kè yo. Menm si zwazo se pa bèt ki mechan, zwazo yo chante san yo pa panse a lèzòm. Selon sa naratè a di, zwazo "gen pwòp lavi pa yo, /yo vole san yo pa reflechi." Zwazo toujou gen gras, se zwazo ra oswa zwazo ou wè toulejou. Naratè a panse zwazo gen dwa kreyati paradi epi konsa yo se mèt tout sa ki sou latè a. Zwazo yo sanble yo viv san yo pa okipe lèzòm ditou. Men, lè nou koute yo pandan lane ap pase, chante zwazo yo sanble kòmanse ap montre lanmou ak tandrès pou lèzòm.

## Zuag Tswvyim *(p. 520)*

### Lub Suab Noog Tav Su DAHLIA RAVIKOVITCH

Tus hais zaj lus nyiam ntsia noog thiab zoo li xav hais tias thaum suab noog nrov zoo mloog, lawv haj yam nrov kho siab thaum peb laus zuj zus. Noog lam quaj tsis mob siab, txawm lawv ua raug lwm tus lub plawv mob, tib yam li noj cua nab. Raws txoj cai, noog quaj vim lawv zoo siab, tsis yog vim lawv npau taws. Thaum suab noog tsis txawj phem, lawv cov nkauj quaj tawm tsis yog tsim rau tibneeg. Raws li tus hais zaj lus, noog " muaj lawv lub neej rau lawv tus kheej,/lawv ya tsis tas xav." Noog ib txwm zoo nkauj, txawm yog tej hom noog txawv lossis hom nej niaj hnub pom. Tus hais zaj lus xav tias noog tej zaum yog tsiaj vajtswv tsim thiab, thaum kawg, noog zoo li yog cov tswj txhua yam hauv ntiaj teb. Lawv ua neej nyob tsis tas yuav txhawjxeeb txog tib neeg li. Txawm li los, thaum peb mloog lawv ntau xyoo dhau mus, cov suab noog zoo li pib qhia kev hlub thiab pom tib-neeg lub neej.

Name _______________ Class _______________ Date _______________

# Literary Element *(page 520)*

## Enjambment

## The Sound of Birds at Noon DAHLIA RAVIKOVITCH

**Enjambment** is the continuation of a sentence in a poem from one line to the next, as in this example from "The Sound of Birds at Noon":

> This chirping / is not in the least malicious.

Poets use enjambment for various reasons including creating a conversational flow, maintaining rhyme or rhythm, or emphasizing words or concepts.

## ACTIVITY

**Directions** Write four other examples of enjambment from "The Sound of Birds at Noon." Then describe the effect Ravikovitch creates through this device or why she may have used enjambment for these lines.

| Example of Enjambment | Effect/Reason |
|---|---|
| 1. | |
| 2. | |
| 3. | |
| 4. | |

Name ______________________ Class ______________ Date ______________

# Reading Strategy *(page 520)*

## Recognize Author's Purpose

## The Sound of Birds at Noon DAHLIA RAVIKOVITCH

Authors may have several overall purposes for writing: to persuade, to inform, to entertain, or to describe. To **recognize an author's purpose,** look for ideas expressed in the details of the text. If an author's main purpose is to persuade, for example, the author will likely include reasons that readers should believe something or take a particular action.

## ACTIVITY

**Directions** In the top box, write Ravikovitch's main purpose for writing "The Sound of Birds at Noon." In the other boxes, write details from the poem that support that purpose.

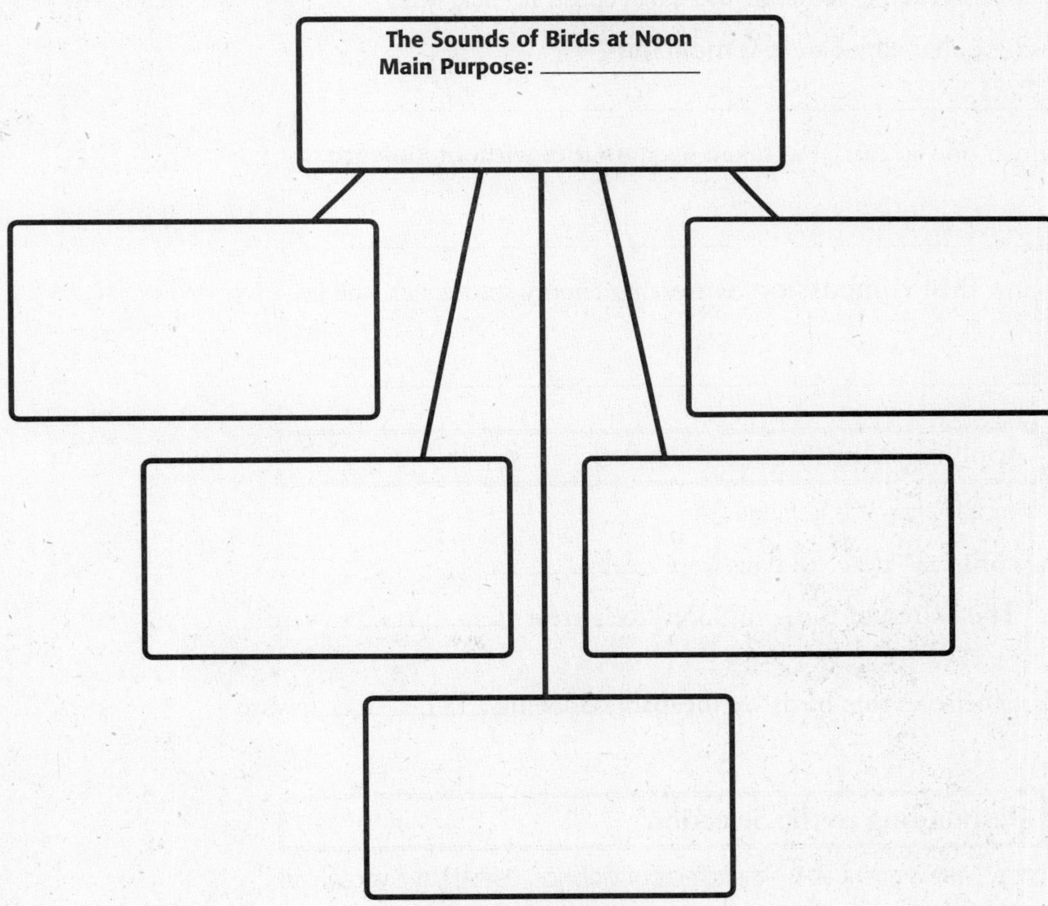

Name ______________________ Class ______________ Date ______________

## Selection Vocabulary Practice *(page 520)*

### The Sound of Birds at Noon DAHLIA RAVIKOVITCH

**Vocabulary**

**malicious** *adj.* marked by a desire to cause pain, injury, or distress to another
**rare** *adj.* distinctive or seldom seen
**compassion** *n.* sympathetic awareness of another's distress

### EXERCISE A Practice with Synonyms

Synonyms are words with the same or nearly the same meaning. On the lines below each sentence, write two synonyms for the vocabulary word that appears in bold type.

1. Some people believe that all violence is **malicious**.

   ______________________ ______________________

2. Examples in which one country has taken over another without violence are **rare.**

   ______________________ ______________________

3. Army medics show their **compassion** by treating enemy soldiers as well as their own.

   ______________________ ______________________

### EXERCISE B Applying Meanings

Fill in the blanks with vocabulary words from the list.

1. In the early years of Israel, peaceful days were __________.
2. The speaker in "The Sound of Birds at Noon" feels great __________ toward birds.
3. The speaker likely believes that birds are incapable of being __________ toward human beings.

### EXERCISE C Responding to the Selection

On the back of this page, write a poem about the effects of violence. Use ALL the vocabulary words in your poem.

Name ______________________ Class ____________ Date ____________

# Vocabulary Strategy *(page 520)*

## Multiple-Meaning Words

## The Sound of Birds at Noon DAHLIA RAVIKOVITCH

"Some are rare, some common, / but every wing is grace."
—*Dahlia Ravikovitch,* "The Sound of Birds at Noon"

**Connecting to Literature** If you did not know that the word *grace* in the quotation above had meanings other than "a short prayer at a meal," you could not understand the passage. In the quotation, *grace* actually means "a virtue coming from God." Many words have more than one, or multiple, meanings. You can find the related definitions of a **multiple-meaning word** listed in a dictionary entry. Use context to figure out which meaning applies. Multiple-meaning words are different from homographs, words that are spelled alike but differ in meaning or pronunciation. Homographs have separate dictionary entries.

Here are other multiple-meaning words from "The Sound of Birds at Noon."

| Word | Meanings | Example Sentences |
|---|---|---|
| peck | • strike with a beak or pointed tool<br>• to nag<br>• to eat reluctantly | • The woodpecker **pecked** at a tree.<br>• Why does he always **peck** at his wife?<br>• She is thin because she **pecks** at food. |
| heaven | • the expanse of space that seems to be over Earth like a dome<br>• a condition of utmost happiness | • The **heavens** are threatening today.<br>• I was in **heaven** when I won the scholarship. |

## ACTIVITY

**Directions** Circle the correct definition for the multiple-meaning word in each sentence.

**1.** Dahlia Ravikovitch lived through a time of violent **change** in the Middle East.

**a.** money in small denominations **b.** fresh set of clothes **c.** act or process of changing

**2.** At an early **age,** she lost her father to a hit-and-run driver.

**a.** an historic period **b.** the length of one's existence **c.** a long time

**3.** Ravikovitch's poetry often **addresses** conflicts within and outside the state of Israel.

**a.** directs the attention of oneself to **b.** communicates directly to **c.** marks directions for delivery to someplace

**4.** Her poetry **weds** the personal and the political in a particularly moving way.

**a.** takes for wife or husband **b.** places in close association **c.** links by custom

Name ______________________ Class ______________ Date ______________

## Selection Quick Check *(page 520)*

### The Sound of Birds at Noon DAHLIA RAVIKOVITCH

Use complete sentences to answer the following questions.

**1.** What does the speaker describe as "not in the least malicious"?

______________________________________________

______________________________________________

______________________________________________

**2.** In lines 8–9, what quality do the rare and the common birds share?

______________________________________________

______________________________________________

______________________________________________

**3.** What conclusion does the speaker draw in the last three lines of the poem?

______________________________________________

______________________________________________

______________________________________________

Name ______________________ Class ____________ Date ____________

## Prueba Rápida *(pág. 520)*

### El sonido de los pájaros al mediodía DAHLIA RAVIKOVITCH

Contesta las siguientes preguntas con oraciones completas.

**1.** ¿Qué describe el hablante como "no tiene ni pizca de malicia"?

______________________________________________

______________________________________________

______________________________________________

**2.** En los versos 8 y 9, ¿qué cualidad rara comparten los pájaros?

______________________________________________

______________________________________________

______________________________________________

**3.** ¿Qué conclusión saca el hablante en las últimas tres líneas del poema?

______________________________________________

______________________________________________

______________________________________________

Name ______________________ Class ______________ Date ______________

## Summary/Resumen *(p. 524)*

### The Diameter of the Bomb YEHUDA AMICHAI

This poem is about the far-reaching consequences of the destruction brought about by a terrorist's bomb. It describes ever-widening circles that encompass the size of the bomb, then the area of the blast. The next circle expands to include the nearby graveyard where a woman, killed by the blast, is buried. A larger circle includes a distant city where a loved one mourns the loss of the woman. And the last circle stretches beyond heaven to include the future generations that were lost because of the bomb.

---

### El diámetro de la bomba

Este poema trata sobre las consecuencias a largo plazo de la destrucción que produce un atentado terrorista con una bomba. Describe círculos que se amplían incesantemente, comenzando con el tamaño de la bomba y luego el área de la explosión. El círculo siguiente se expande para incluir el cementerio cercano, donde entierran a una mujer muerta por la explosión. Un círculo aún mayor incluye una ciudad lejana donde el amado de la mujer llora su muerte. Y el último círculo se extiende más allá del cielo para abarcar a las futuras generaciones que se perdieron a causa de la bomba.

# Tóm Tắt *(p. 524)*

## Đường Kính Một Quả Bom YEHUDA AMICHAI

Bài thơ này nói về những hậu quả sâu rộng của sự tàn phá do các hành động khủng bố gây ra. Bài thơ mở ra với cảnh tượng thành phố sau một vụ đánh bom làm bốn người thiệt mạng và mười một người bị thương. Quả bom có chiều rộng ba mươi centimét, nhưng nó đã tàn phá một khu vực rộng đến bảy mét. Một người phụ nữ bị thiệt mạng trong vụ đánh bom sinh ra ở một thành phố cách đó một trăm kilomét. Do đó, người ta than khóc cho cô rồi đem chôn cô ở một nơi xa chỗ xảy ra vụ đánh bom, có nghĩa là quả bom đó thực sự đã gây ảnh hưởng rộng lớn hơn phạm vi bảy mét. Một người đàn ông sống ở tận bên kia biển đã đem lòng yêu cô và giờ đây khóc thương cô, chứng tỏ vụ đánh bom gây ảnh hưởng khắp nhân gian. Đó là còn chưa tính đến những em bé mồ côi gào khóc cho cha mẹ chúng đã bị thiệt mạng trong những vụ khủng bố trên khắp thế giới. Tiếng than khóc của các em vang xa đến mức "Chúa Trên Trời và còn xa hơn nưa" đều nghe tiếng chúng. Rõ ràng, quả bom đã ảnh hưởng đến vạn vật và muôn người.

Name ______________________ Class ______________ Date ______________

# Buod *(p. 524)*

## Ang Diyametro ng Bomba YEHUDA AMICHAI

Ang tuláng ito ay tungkol sa malawak na inaabot ng mga konsekwensiya ng paninira na dalá ng mga aksiyón ng mga terorista. Nagsisimula ang tulá sa mga sandali matapos maganap ang pagbomba ng isang siyudad, kung saan apat na tao ang namatáy at labing-isang tao ang napinsala. Tatlumpung sentimetro ang lapad ng bomba, pero ang nasira nitong lugar ay pitóng metro ang lapad. Ang isang babaeng napatáy ng bomba ay isinilang sa isang siyudad na mahigit isang-daang kilometro ang layô. Dahil dito, ang babaeng ito ay ipinagluksâ at inilibing nang malayô sa lugar na pinutukan ng bomba, at ibig sabihin ay mas malawak sa pitóng metro ang naging epekto ng bomba. Ipinagluluksâ rin ang babae ng isang lalaking nagmahal sa kanya na nakatirá sa kabilang-dagat, kaya ang talagang epekto ng bomba ay kumalat na sa buong mundo. Hindi man kabilang dito ang katunayan na ang mga batang naulila sa buong mundo ay nagsisiiyakan para sa kanilang mga magulang na namatáy sa mga pag-atake ng mga terorista sa buong mundo. Sa kalaliman ng kanilang mga iyak ay narinig sila pati na "ng Diyos at bukod pa rito". Samakatwid, naaapektohan ng bomba ang lahat ng bagay at lahat ng tao.

Name ____________________ Class ____________ Date ____________

# 摘要 *(p. 524)*

## 炸彈的直徑 YEHUDA AMICHAI

這首詩敘述恐怖活動所帶來之毀滅的深遠影響。這首詩開始的部分描述了一個城市受到炸彈襲擊後的情況，四個人被炸死，而十一個人被炸傷。這個炸彈的寬度只有三十公分，但卻摧毀了一個七公尺寬的區域。一位被炸死的婦人，出生於超過一百公里之外的一個城市。所以，她在炸彈攻擊現場的很遠距離之外受到哀悼而被埋葬；這意味著這個炸彈的傷害遠超過七公尺。一位愛著這位婦人的男子住在海的另一方，而從遠方哀悼著她；這使得炸彈的影響遍及全世界。這些事實都尚未考慮到死於全世界各地恐怖攻擊之父母，所遺留下來的哭泣的孤兒。他們的哭聲是如此地哀痛，讓「神和更遙遠者」都能聽到。所以，這個炸彈事實上影響到了每一件事情和每一個人。

Name ______________________ Class ______________ Date ______________

## Rezime Selekyson *(p. 524)*

### Dyamèt Bonm nan YEHUDA AMICHAI

Powèm sa a konsène gwo konsekans zak teworis. Powèm nan kòmanse avèk bonbadman yon vil kote kat moun mouri epi onz ladan yo blese. Bonm nan te gen yon lajè trant santimèt, men li detwi yon zòn ki te yon lajè sèt mèt. Yon fi bonm nan touye te fèt nan yon vil ki te a yon distans depase san kilomèt. Kòm konsekans, yo kriye pou li epi yo antere li yon kote ki byen lwen bonm nan, sa ki vle di bonm nan te gen yon enpak ki depase sèt mèt. Yon nèg ki te renmen fi sa a epi ki rete lòt bò lanmè ap kriye pou li, sa ki fè bonm nan gen yon enpak mondyal. Fè sa a pa menm pran an konsiderasyon tout timoun ki san manman ak san papa kounye a, k ap kriye pou manman ak papa yo atak teworis touye nan lemonn. Yo si tèlman kriye "Bondye ak syèl la " tande yo. Kidonk enpak yon bonm afekte tout bagay ak tout moun.

## Zuag Tswvyim *(p. 524)*

### Txoj Kab Tav ntawm lub Foobpob YEHUDA AMICHAI

Zaj pajhuam nov hais txog kev tshwmsim deb ntawm kev puas ntsoog uas yog tes dejnum ntawm cov neeg terrorist. Zaj pajhuam pib tomqab ib lub foobpob tawg hauv ib lub nroog uas ua rau plaub tus neeg tuag thiab kaum ib tus raug mob. Lub foobpob dav li peb caug centimeter dav, tabsis nws rhuav ib cheeb tsam li xya meter dav. Ib tus pojniam yug hauv ib lub nroog uas nyob ib puas kilometer deb ntawd chaw foobpob tawg. Thaum kawg nws raug quaj nco thiab coj mus faus rau ib lub chaw deb ntawm thaj chaw foobpob tawg, uas qhia tau tias kev puas ntsoog deb tshaj li xya meter dav. Ib tus neeg uas nyiam tus pojniam ntawd nyob sab hiavtxwv sab tim ub, niaj hnub quaj tus pojniam, ua rau kev puas ntsoog thoob ntiaj teb. Qhov nov twb tsis xam cov menyuam ntsuag niaj hnub quaj rau lawv niam thiab txiv uas raug tua los ntawm cov neeg terrorist hauv ntiajteb. Lawv tej suab quaj tob kawg tias "vajtswv thiab dhau tod" hnov lawv. Thaum kawg, kev tshwmsim ntawm cov foobpob ua rau txhua tus muaj feemcuam tas nrho.

Name ______________________ Class ______________ Date ______________

# Literary Element *(page 524)*

## Diction

## The Diameter of the Bomb YEHUDA AMICHAI

**Diction**, a writer's choice and arrangement of words, is one of the most important elements of a writer's style. Diction is critical to Yehuda Amichai and to all poets. They choose words carefully with a particular purpose and specific mood in mind.

## ACTIVITY

**Directions** Reread "The Diameter of the Bomb." In the first column, write examples of phrases from the poem that intrigue you. In the second column, analyze the diction. How would you describe the diction? What effect does the diction create?

| Phrase from Poem | Description/Analysis |
| --- | --- |
| 1. | |
| 2. | |
| 3. | |
| 4. | |

Name ______________________ Class ____________ Date ____________

# Reading Strategy *(page 524)*

## Analyze Cause-and-Effect Relationships

## The Diameter of the Bomb YEHUDA AMICHAI

A **cause-and-effect relationship** exists when an event (a cause) occurs that makes something else happen (an effect). When you **analyze cause-and-effect relationships** in literature you come to realize that events are linked by a chain of causes and their effects. To identify a cause, ask yourself why something happens, and to identify an effect, ask yourself what happens as a result. Look for words and phrases such as *because, therefore, so, as a result,* and *consequently* that often signal cause-and-effect relationships.

## ACTIVITY

**Directions** The poem "The Diameter of the Bomb" is concerned with the effect of a bomb blast. List three causes and effects from the poem. Write the cause in the first column below and the effect in the box after the arrow.

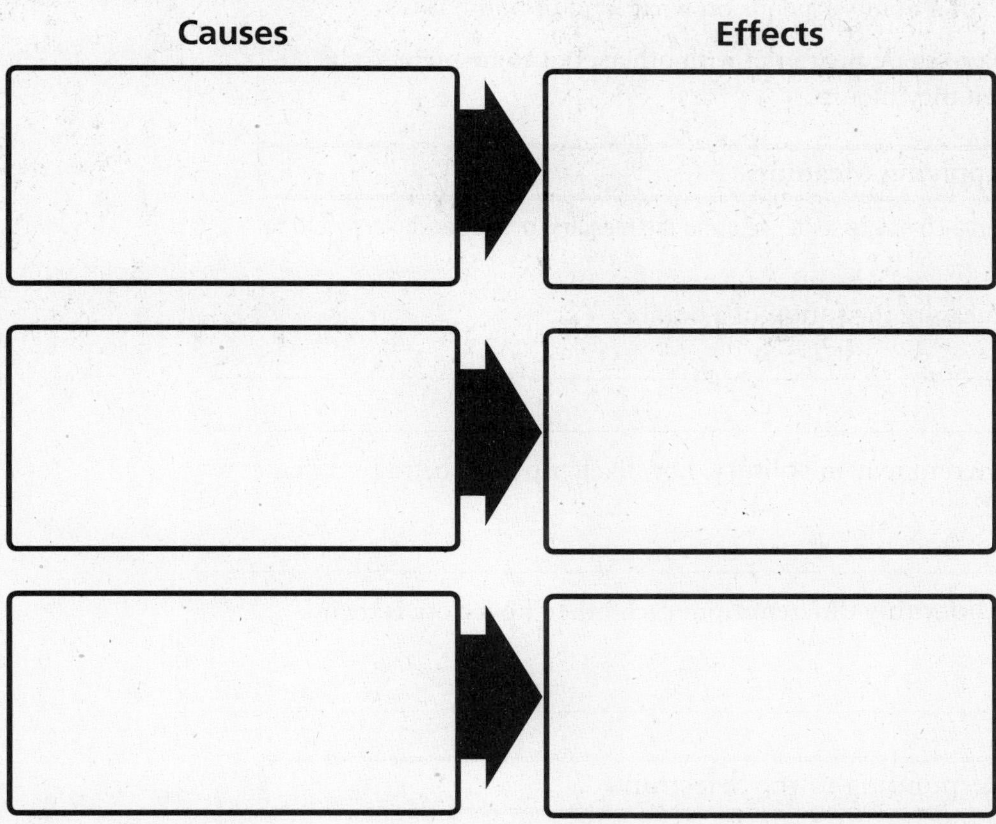

Name ______________________ Class ______________ Date ______________

# Selection Vocabulary Practice *(page 524)*

## The Diameter of the Bomb YEHUDA AMICHAI

**Vocabulary**

**range** *n.* the full extent over which something moves or is seen, heard, effective, etc.; scope
**considerably** *adv.* greatly; by a large amount
**solitary** *adj.* characterized by loneliness or lack of companions; lonely

### EXERCISE A Practice with Words in Context

Write the word from the vocabulary list that best completes each sentence.

**1.** The effect of the bomb is __________ greater than it seems at first.

**2.** The __________ of a bomb depends on what kind of bomb it is.

**3.** Many people look to share their grief with others, but some prefer to be __________ when they mourn.

### EXERCISE B Applying Meanings

Answer each question in a complete sentence using the meaning of the vocabulary word to explain your answer.

**1.** How could you measure the **range** of a bomb?

______________________________________________

______________________________________________

**2.** If someone preferred to remain **solitary,** how likely would it be to find that person in a crowd?

______________________________________________

**3.** If twins look **considerably** different from each other, how close is their resemblance?

______________________________________________

### EXERCISE C Responding to the Selection

On the back of this page, write a short essay describing your emotional response to "The Diameter of the Bomb." Use ALL the vocabulary words in your essay.

# Vocabulary Strategy *(page 524)*

## Greek and Latin Word Origins

## The Diameter of the Bomb YEHUDA AMICHAI

"The diameter of the bomb was thirty centimeters"
—*Yehuda Amichai,* "The Diameter of the Bomb"

**Connecting to Literature** Many English words have Greek and Latin origins. Consider the word *diameter* in the quotation above. *Diameter* comes from the Greek *dia-*, a prefix that means "through" or "across" and *metron*, meaning "measure." Knowing the word's origin helps us understand the meaning of *diameter*, "the length of a straight line through the center of a circle or sphere." Understanding the origin of the prefix *dia-* can help you figure out words such as *dialogue* and *dialect*. Knowing the origin of *meter* can help you understand words that contain this root. The chart shows a sample of common Greek and Latin roots.

| Root | Meaning | Example Words |
|---|---|---|
| fig (L) | form | figure, figment, effigy |
| geo (G) | earth | geography, geology |
| ped (L) | foot | pedal, biped, pedestal |
| therm (G) | heat | thermometer, thermal, thermostat |

## ACTIVITY

**Directions** Use a dictionary for this exercise. Fill in the chart using the words in the first column from "The Diameter of the Bomb" that have Greek or Latin origins.

| Word | Origin/Meaning | Definition |
|---|---|---|
| bomb | | |
| hospital | | |
| circle | | |
| solitary | | |

Name ____________________ Class ____________ Date ____________

# Selection Quick Check *(page 524)*

## The Diameter of the Bomb YEHUDA AMICHAI

Use complete sentences to answer the following questions.

**1.** Of what significance is the measurement of thirty centimeters in the poem?

______________________________________________

______________________________________________

______________________________________________

**2.** What objects are located "in a larger circle/of pain and time"?

______________________________________________

______________________________________________

______________________________________________

**3.** At the end of the poem, what does the speaker say he won't mention, but then does?

______________________________________________

______________________________________________

______________________________________________

# Prueba Rápida *(pág. 524)*

## El diámetro de la bomba YEHUDA AMICHAI

Contesta las siguientes preguntas con oraciones completas.

**1.** ¿Cuál es la importancia de la medida de treinta centímetros en el poema?

______________________________________________

______________________________________________

______________________________________________

**2.** ¿Qué objetos se encuentran "en un círculo mayor/de dolor y tiempo"?

______________________________________________

______________________________________________

______________________________________________

**3.** Al final del poema, ¿qué dice el hablante que no mencionará, pero después menciona?

______________________________________________

______________________________________________

______________________________________________

Name ______________________ Class ____________ Date ____________

## Summary/Resumen *(p. 528)*

### Butterflies FAWZIYYA ABU KHALID

The speaker in this poem has been abandoned by a loved one. Rather than despair, the speaker will follow "a flight of butterflies in my heart" that the loved one had placed there.

---

### Mariposas

El hablante de este poema ha sido abandonado por la persona amada. En lugar de desesperarse, el hablante seguirá a "un enjambre de mariposas en mi corazón" que la persona amada sembró en el mismo.

# Tóm Tắt *(p. 528)*

## Bướm FAWZIYYA ABU KHALID

Nhân vật trong bài thơ này dường như đang phải đối mặt với những chấn động tình cảm khi bị người yêu bỏ rơi. Nhân vật nói rằng việc mình bị bỏ rơi không phải là nguyên nhân gây ra nỗi thống khổ bởi vì tình nhân của mình là một người tuyệt vời đến mức anh/cô ta "đã thả/ một đàn bướm trong tim tôi". Nhân vật dường như đang nói rằng người tình nhân đã bỏ đi đã dạy nhân vật cách sống và cách nhận biết điều gì mới thật là quan trọng trong cuộc sống. Vì vậy, nhân vật biết cách tiếp bước trên đường đời mà người yêu đã dạy cho mình. Bài thơ diễn giải rằng ta không cần phải nắm giữ một vật gì đó để có thể thực sự cảm nhận nó, thay vì đó có thể cảm nhận vẻ đẹp và sự yêu kiều của nó chỉ bằng cách nhớ nó.

Name ______________________ Class ______________ Date ______________

## Buod *(p. 528)*

### Mga Parú-Paró FAWZIYYA ABU KHALID

Tila tinatalakay ng nagsasalitá sa tuláng ito ang mga epektong nararamdaman pagkatapos siyang iwanan ng kanyang minamahal. Sinabi ng nagsasalitá na ang pag-iwan sa kanya ng kanyang minamahal ay hindi isang dahilan para malungkot, dahil ang minamahal ay isang kahanga-hangang tao na "nakapagtanim/ng mga parúparóng nagsisiliparan sa aking pusô." Parang sinasabi ng nagsasalitá na ang umalis na minamahal ay nakapagturô sa nagsasalitá kung paano mabuhay at kung ano ang mahalaga sa buhay. Samakatwid, nalalaman ng nagsasalitá kung paano sundin ang landás sa buhay na itinurô sa kanya ng kanyang minamahal. Ipinaliliwanag ng tulá na hindi kinakailangang angkinin ng mga tao ang isang bagay para talagang maranasan ito. Maaaring maranasan ng mga tao ang kagandahan at kariktan nito sa pamamagitan ng pag-aalala lamang dito.

# 摘要 *(p. 528)*

## 蝴蝶 FAWZIYYA ABU KHALID

這首詩的敘述者似乎是正在接受被愛人拋棄後的震驚。敘述者表示這個拋棄並不是悲傷的原因，因為敘述者的愛人是一個如此美好的人「在我的心中播下了一群蝴蝶」。敘述者似乎是在說離去的愛人，教導了敘述者如何生活，以及人生中重要的事物。因此，敘述者知道要遵循愛人所教導的人生道路。這首詩解釋，人未必要實際持有什麼，才能真正地得到其體驗。人可以僅從回憶中體驗到事物的美麗與可愛之處。

Name ______________________ Class ______________ Date ______________

## Rezime Selekyson *(p. 528)*

### Papiyon FAWZIYYA ABU KHALID

Oratè nan powèm sa a sanble ap pale de chòk sa ba li lè yon moun li renmen abandone li. Oratè a di abandon an pa lakòz doulè paske moun li renmen an se tèlman yon moun estrawòdinè li "plante/yon ekip papiyon nan kè mwen." Oratè a sanble l ap di moun li renmen epi ki ale a aprann li kijan pou li viv epi kisa ki enpòtan nan lavi. Kidonk Oratè a konnen nan lavi sa a fòk li swiv wout moun li renmen an montre li a. Powèm nan eksplike moun pa oblije fèmen yon bagay a kle pou jwi li. Moun kapab jwi bote ak atrè li gras a memwa yo sèlman.

# Zuag Tswvyim *(p. 528)*

## Npauj Npaim FAWZIYYA ABU KHALID

Zoo li tus hais zaj pajhuam nov teev txog kev tusiab tomqab raug ib tus hlub tso cia. Nws hais tias raug tso cia tsis yog ib yam xwmtxheej rau yus quaj vim tus hlub yog ib tus neeg zoo uas tau "cog/ib lwm npauj npaim rau kuv lub siab." Zoo li tus hais zaj lus xav hais tias tus hlub dim lawd tau qhia nws txog tias yuav nyob licas thiab yam dabtsi tseemceeb hauv lub neej. Li ntawd, nws paub lawm tias yuav taug txoj kev hauv lub neej tus hlub tau qhia licas. Zaj pajhuam qhia tias tibneeg tsis tas yuav khaws txhua tsav yam cia rau nruab siab kom coj los ntsibtsum. Tibneeg ntsibtsum tau nws qhov kev zoo nkauj thiab kev hlub yog lawv nco qab ntsoov.

Name ________________________________ Class ______________ Date ______________

# Literary Element *(page 528)*

## Simile

## Butterflies FAWZIYYA ABU KHALID

A **simile** is a figure of speech that compares two unlike beings or things, usually using the word *like* or *as.* In "Butterflies," Abu Khalid uses the word *like* to compare the speaker's reaction to a lover's departure to a bedouin's tracking a mare. Though the situations differ, the poet establishes a surprising connection between them. The best similes, like this one, are fresh and engaging.

## ACTIVITY

**Directions** Complete the similes below. Then choose one of them and include it in a short poem that you write on the lines below.

**1.** A sleeping elephant is like ______________________________.

**2.** The weather was as fierce as ______________________________.

**3.** An abandoned house is like ______________________________.

**4.** The newborn baby is as wrinkled as ______________________________.

Name ______________________ Class ______________ Date ______________

# Reading Strategy *(page 528)*

## Connect to Personal Experience

### Butterflies FAWZIYYA ABU KHALID

When you **connect to your personal experience,** you deepen your understanding and appreciation of the work. In "Butterflies," Saudi Arabian poet Fawziyya Abu Khalid writes about being abandoned, an experience with which most readers can sympathize. That sympathy draws readers into the poem and establishes a solid connection between the poet and her readers.

## ACTIVITY

**Directions** Recently you have read several poems. Consider the content of "Butterflies," "Elegy for a Woman of No Importance," "The Sound of Birds at Noon," and "The Diameter of the Bomb." Choose three passages from one or more of these poems that connect most closely to your personal experiences. Copy the passages and explain how each one relates to your personal experiences.

| Passage | Personal Experience |
|---|---|
| | |
| | |
| | |

## Selection Quick Check *(page 528)*

### Butterflies FAWZIYYA ABU KHALID

Use complete sentences to answer the following questions.

**1.** According to the speaker, what didn't she need when she was abandoned?

**2.** Whose path does the speaker follow?

**3.** According to the speaker, what does a bedouin know how to do?

Name ______________________ Class ______________ Date ______________

## Prueba Rápida *(pág. 528)*

### Mariposas FAWZIYYA ABU KHALID

Contesta las siguientes preguntas con oraciones completas.

**1.** Según la hablante, ¿qué no necesitó cuando la abandonaron?

______________________________________________

______________________________________________

______________________________________________

______________________________________________

**2.** La hablante sigue un camino, ¿el de quién?

______________________________________________

______________________________________________

______________________________________________

______________________________________________

**3.** De acuerdo con la hablante, ¿qué sabe hacer un beduino?

______________________________________________

______________________________________________

______________________________________________

______________________________________________

Name ______________________ Class ______________ Date ______________

## Summary/Resumen *(p. 532)*

### The Letter *from* Persepolis MARJANE SATRAPI

In this graphic story, Marji's family's maid, Mehri, falls in love with the neighbor and pretends she is Marji's sister. Marji writes him love letters on Mehri's behalf because Mehri cannot read or write. This goes on until Marji's father finds out. He explains to the neighbor that Mehri is their maid, not in an equal social class with him, so the affair ends. Marji is upset to learn that two people of unequal social classes cannot be in a relationship. She and Mehri, feeling sad and angry, decide to participate in a political demonstration. Marji's parents are extremely upset when they find out that they have been demonstrating, because the Iranian military killed many people on that historic day, "Black Friday," in 1978.

---

### La carta *de* Persépolis

En este cuento o historieta gráfica, Mehri, la mucama de la familia de Marji, se enamora del vecino y se hace pasar por la hermana de Marji. Marji le escribe cartas de amor en nombre de Mehri porque Mehri no sabe leer ni escribir. Esto continúa hasta que el padre de Marji lo descubre. Él explica al vecino que Mehri es su mucama y que no es de su misma clase social, así que la relación termina. Marji se disgusta mucho al ver que dos personas de distintas clases sociales no pueden entablar una relación. Ella y Mehri, sintiéndose tristes y airadas, deciden participar en una marcha de protesta política. Los padres de Marji se disgustan mucho al enterarse de que han estado en la protesta porque el ejército iraní había matado a muchas personas en ese día histórico, el "Viernes Negro" de 1978.

Name ______________________ Class ____________ Date ______________

# Tóm Tắt *(p. 532)*

## Lá Thư *trích từ* Persepolis MARJANE SATRAPI

Trong truyện tranh này, Marji nắm bắt được những vấn đề của các tầng lớp xã hội Iran khi cô đọc câu truyện của tác giả Ali Ashraf Darvishian về những đứa trẻ bị buộc phải lao động. Cũng chịu tình cảnh tương tự như vậy là cô hầu gia đình Marji tên là Mehri. Khi đến làm việc cho gia đình họ cô mới chỉ là một bé con. Mehri phải lòng người hàng xóm và giả vờ mình là em gái của Marji. Marji viết hộ Mehri những thư tình để gởi cho anh hàng xóm bởi vì Mehri không biết đọc biết viết. Chuyện cứ thế diễn ra cho mãi đến khi cha của Marji phát hiện ra. Cha của Marji giải thích với người hàng xóm rằng Mehri là người hầu nhà họ, không môn đăng hộ đối với anh, và chuyện yêu đương đến đây chấm dứt. Marji vô cùng buồn rầu khi biết được rằng hai người thuộc hai tầng lớp xã hội khác nhau không thể có mối quan hệ gì, vì vậy cô và Mehri cùng tham gia một cuộc biểu tình. Cha mẹ của Marji hết sức bối rối khi biết họ đã đi biểu tình, vì hồi năm 1978 quân đội Iran đã giết rất nhiều người vào cái ngày lịch sử đó, được gọi là "Ngày Thứ Sáu Tối".

Name ______________________ Class ______________ Date ______________

## Buod *(p. 532)*

### Sulat *mula sa* Persepolis MARJANE SATRAPI

Sa mapaglarawang kuwento na ito, natuklasan ni Marji ang mga problema sa lipunan ng Iran nang basahin niya ang mga kuwento ng awtor na si Ali Ashraf Darvishian tungkol sa mga batang sapilitáng pinagtrabaho. Tulad ng mga ito, ang katulong ng pamilya ni Marji na si Mehri ay bata pa lamang nang nagsimula siyang magtrabaho para sa kanila. Napa-ibig si Mehri sa kanilang kapitbahay, at nagkunwari siyang kapatid siya ni Marji. Nagsulat ng mga liham ng pag-ibig si Marji para kay Mehri dahil si Mehri ay hindi marunong magbasa o magsulat. Nagpatuloy ang mga ito hanggang nabisto sila ng ama ni Marji. Ipinaliwanag ng ama ni Marji sa kapitbahay na si Mehri ay katulong nila, at hindi tumbás ang kalagayan niya sa lipunan sa kalagayan ng lalaki, kaya nagtapós tuloy ang kanilang relasyón. Lubós na nabahala si Marji nang matutunan niya na ang dalawang tao na hindi magkatumbás ang kalagayan sa lipunan ay hindi maaaring magkaroon ng relasyón, kaya sumali silang dalawa ni Mehri sa isang demonstrasyón. Lubós na nabahala ang mga magulang ni Marji nang malaman nila ito dahil pumatáy ng maraming tao ang hukbong militar ng Iran noong makasaysayang araw na iyon, ang "Itim na Biyernes," noon taóng 1978.

Name ______________________ Class ______________ Date ______________

# 摘要 *(p. 532)*

## 來自 Persepolis 的《信》 MARJANE SATRAPI

在這個生動的故事中，Marji 在讀了 Ali Ashraf Darvishian 所著關於兒童被強迫去工作的故事後，瞭解到伊朗社會階層的問題。Marji 身邊便有一個類似的狀況，她家中的佣人 Mehri 剛來工作的時候，也只是一個小孩子。Mehri 愛上了一位他們的鄰居，而假裝是 Marji 的姐妹。因為 Mehri 不會讀書寫字，所以 Marji 幫 Mehri 寫情書給這個鄰居。這種情況一直延續到被 Marji 的父親發現之後才停止。Marji 的父親向鄰居解釋 Mehri 是他們的僕人，她和鄰居的社會階級不一樣；所以這段戀愛便結束了。Marji 發現兩個不同社會階級的人不能談戀愛而感到非常苦惱，所以和 Mehri 一起參加了一個示威。當 Marji 的父母發現她們去參加示威後感到非常震驚；在 1978 年「黑色星期五」的歷史性這一天，伊朗的軍隊殺了許多人。

Name ______________________ Class ______________ Date ______________

## Rezime Selekyson *(p. 532)*

### Lèt *nan* Persepolis MARJANE SATRAPI

Nan istwa grafik sa a, Marji aprann ki pwoblèm klas sosyal Iran genyen lè li istwa yon otè ki rele Ali Ashraf Darvishian ekri sou timoun yo fòse travay. Menm jan tou, bòn kay fanmi Marji a, Mehri, te yon timoun sèlman lè li te vin travay pou yo. Mehri te tonbe damou pou vwazen an epi te fè l panse se sè Marji li te ye. Marji te ekri lèt damou ba li sou non Mehri paske Mehri pat konn ni li ni ekri. Sa te kontinye jiskaske papa Marji te vin okouran. Papa Marji eksplike bay vwazen an Mehri se te bòn lakay li, li pat menm klas sosyal avèk li, epi bagay la te fini antre yo. Marji te fache anpil lè li te aprann moun ki pat menm klas sosyal pat kapab gen relasyon, kidonk li menm ak Mehri te patisipe nan yon manifestasyon. Manman ak papa Marji te fache anpil lè yo aprann Marji te nan manifestasyon sa a, paske sòlda Iranyen yo te touye plizyè moun jou istorik sa a, "Black Friday," nan ane 1978.

## Zuag Tswvyim *(p. 532)*

### Ntawv *los ntawm* Persepolis MARJANE SATRAPI

Hauv zaj dabneeg duab kos, Marji kawm txog cov teebmeem ntawm kev cais neeg hauv lub neej nyob Iran thaum nws nyeem txog kws sau ntawv Ali Ashraf Darvishian cov dabneeg sau txog cov menyuam raug yuam mus ua haujlwm. Tib yam li ntawd, Marji tsev neeg tus niam ua mov, Mehri, yog ib tus menyuam yaus thaum xub tuaj ua haujlwm rau lawv. Mehri muaj kev hlub nrog ib tus neeg nruab zos thiab ua txuj ua zoo li nws yog Marji tus niam laus. Marji sau ntawv hlub rau tus hluas nraug rau Mehri vim nws tsis txawj nyeem thiab sau ntawv. Qhov nov mus txog thaum Marji txiv paub thiab qhia qhov tseeb rau tus neeg nruab zos tias Mehri tsis nyob tib theem caj ces hauv lawv tsev neeg, ces Mehri txoj kev hlub xaus. Marji chim heev thaum paub tias tibneeg txawv theem tsis muaj cai sib txuas xov, ces nws thiab Mehri pib tawmtsam taug kev. Marji niam thiab txiv chim heev thaum paub txog nkawd txoj kev tawmtsam, vim tub rog Iranian tua ntau tus neeg nyob rau lub caij keebkwm ntawd, "Hnub Vas Xuv Dub," thaum 1978.

Name ______________________ Class ____________ Date ____________

# Literary Element *(page 532)*

## Symbol

## The Letter *from* Persepolis MARJANE SATRAPI

A **symbol** is a being or an object that stands for something beyond itself, often an abstract idea. For example, the dove is a common symbol of peace. The letter in this selection is a symbol of the class system in Iran at a time when social classes were strictly separated and people's class status was rigid.

## ACTIVITY

**Directions** Look for items in "The Letter" that you believe have symbolic meaning. On the chart, list three symbols and their meanings. Then write a paragraph to answer the question that follows the chart.

| Symbol | Meaning |
|---|---|
| | |
| | |
| | |

What does the use of symbolism add to "The Letter"?

_______________________________________________

_______________________________________________

_______________________________________________

_______________________________________________

_______________________________________________

Name ______________________ Class ______________ Date ______________

# Reading Strategy *(page 532)*

## Identify Genre

## The Letter *from* Persepolis MARJANE SATRAPI

A **genre** is a category or type of literature. Poetry, drama, essay, and short story are examples of various genres. Works in a genre share certain characteristics. Graphic novels such as *Persepolis* are works of fiction that resemble comic books visually and are like short novels in length, plot, and character development.

## ACTIVITY

**Directions** Answer the questions about the genre of "The Letter."

1. What is the relative importance of words compared to images in "The Letter"?

______________________________________________

______________________________________________

______________________________________________

2. What are some similarities and differences between comic books and graphic novels, such as *Persepolis?*

______________________________________________

______________________________________________

______________________________________________

3. How did "The Letter" affect you emotionally? How much of that feeling do you attribute to the genre?

______________________________________________

______________________________________________

______________________________________________

Name ______________________ Class ______________ Date ______________

# Selection Vocabulary Practice *(page 532)*

## The Letter *from* Persepolis MARJANE SATRAPI

**Vocabulary**

**clandestine** *adj.* secret
**devoted** *adj.* dedicated; feeling strong attachment
**demonstrate** *v.* to participate in a public display of group opinion; to rally or march

### EXERCISE A Practice with Synonyms and Antonyms

On the line, write whether the words in each pair are *synonyms* (words with the same or nearly the same meanings) or *antonyms* (words with opposite or nearly opposite meanings).

1. **devoted** — negligent ______________
2. **clandestine** — surreptitious ______________
3. **demonstrate** — protest ______________

### EXERCISE B Applying Meanings

Write the vocabulary word that answers each riddle.

1. I name something you might do if you were upset with government policy. Which word am I?

______________________________

2. I am a word often used to describe agencies like the FBI and CIA. Which word am I?

______________________________

3. I describe the way parents should feel toward their children. Which word am I?

______________________________

### EXERCISE C Responding to the Selection

On a separate sheet of paper, create a page from a graphic novel. Use the THREE vocabulary words on your page.

Name ______________________ Class ______________ Date ______________

## Vocabulary Strategy *(page 532)*

### Dictionary Use

### The Letter *from* Persepolis MARJANE SATRAPI

"Long live the republic! Down with the Shah!"
—*Marjane Satrapi,* "The Letter" *from* Persepolis

**Connecting to Literature** Marjane and Mehri are so carried away at the demonstration that Marjane yells, "Down with the Shah!" and Mehri shouts, "Long live the republic!" For a clearer understanding of what a republic is, look up the word *republic* in a dictionary.

Use guide words to find *republic* quickly. Guide words, the words in dark type at the top of each page of a dictionary, show the first and last entries on the page.

A dictionary entry gives the meanings of an entry word and much more information. Here is what one dictionary includes in the entry for *republic.*

Entry word is broken into syllables.

The pronunciation and stress are indicated.

The part of speech is shown.

**re•pub•lic** (rĭ pŭb′ lĭk) *n* [F *republique,* fr L *respublica,* fr *res* thing, wealth + *publica,* fem. of *publicus* public] **1 a:** a government having a chief of state who is not a monarch and who in modern times is usually a president **b :** a government in which supreme power resides in a body of citizens entitled to vote and is exercised by elected officers and representatives responsible to them and governing according to law **2 :** a body of persons freely engaged in a specified activity

The etymology gives the history of the word.

Example phrase demonstrates usage.



## ACTIVITY

**Directions** Use the dictionary entry above to answer the questions.

**1.** From which Latin words did *republic* come? What do the words mean?

______________________________________________

______________________________________________

**2.** How does knowing the etymology give you insight into the meaning of *republic?*

______________________________________________

______________________________________________

**3.** What part of speech is *republic?* ______________

**4.** Which meaning most closely fits *republic* as it is used in "The Letter"? ________

# Grammar Practice *(page 532)*

## Adverb Clauses

## The Letter *from* Persepolis MARJANE SATRAPI

An adverb clause is a subordinate clause that modifies a verb, an adjective, or an adverb. It tells when, where, why, to what extent, or under what conditions. A subordinating conjunction usually introduces an adverb clause.

Marjane sat on her bed stunned **after her parents slapped her.**

The subordinating conjunction *after* introduces the adverb clause *after her parents slapped her.*

An adverb clause that seems to have a missing word or words is called an elliptical adverb clause. The word or words that are left out are understood from the context.

Mehri was even more stunned **than Marjane.** (was)

## ACTIVITY

**Directions** Write an **X** on the line before each sentence that contains an adverb clause. Then underline the adverb clause.

____ **1.** Marjane felt ashamed to ride in the Cadillac after she realized what it stood for.

____ **2.** Because she was a sensitive child, her privileged status disturbed her.

____ **3.** Even though they got along, Marjane had more power than Mehri.

____ **4.** Mehri told Marjane scary stories at night before bedtime.

____ **5.** Marjane's mother tried to teach Mehri the alphabet, but Mehri was slow to learn.

____ **6.** Every night, Mehri and Hossein stared out the window at each other.

____ **7.** After Marjane's father found out about Hossein and Mehri, he told Hossein who Mehri was.

____ **8.** Because she was easily persuaded, Mehri let Marjane talk her into participating in a political demonstration.

____ **9.** They demonstrated against the Shah all day.

____ **10.** When they got home at night, they faced the wrath of Marjane's parents.

____ **11.** Her parents had reacted violently out of fear, but Marjane did not understand them.

____ **12.** Marjane Satrapi recalled her childhood adventures when writing "The Letter."

Name ______________________ Class ______________ Date ______________

## Selection Quick Check *(page 532)*

### The Letter *from* Persepolis MARJANE SATRAPI

Use complete sentences to answer the following questions.

**1.** What kinds of stories does Ashraf Darvishian, Marjane's favorite author, tell?

**2.** Who is Mehri, and what role does she play in Marjane's life?

**3.** What does Marjane do to encourage the romance between Mehri and Hossein?

**4.** Why does the romance fail?

**5.** What do Marjane and Mehri do next that gets them into trouble?

# Prueba Rápida *(pág. 532)*

## La carta *de* Persépolis MARJANE SATRAPI

Contesta las siguientes preguntas con oraciones completas.

**1.** ¿Qué tipo de historias relata Ashraf Darvishian, el autor favorito de Marjane?

**2.** ¿Quién es Mehri, y qué papel desempeña en la vida de Marjane?

**3.** ¿Qué hace Marjane para estimular el romance entre Mehri y Hossein?

**4.** ¿Por qué fracasa el romance?

**5.** ¿Qué hacen Marjane y Mehri después que las mete en problemas?

# Summary/Resumen *(p. 542)*

## TIME: Regarding Rania SCOTT MACLEOD

The Queen of Jordan, Rania al Abdullah, is a stylish, modern woman who has redefined the typically conservative role of queen. For example, she believes the veil worn by many Muslim women should be optional, so she usually does not wear one. Her stance on this and other controversial issues, as well as her expensive tastes for vacations and clothing, have earned praise from modernists and criticism from traditionalists. However, Rania has realized that she cannot bring about change that Jordanian society has not yet embraced, such as an equal role for women. Still, Rania continues to push her programs on human rights, women's rights, children's rights, education, and health in hopes that change will occur in the future.

---

## TIME: Sobre Rania

La reina de Jordania, Rania al Abdullah, es una mujer elegante y moderna que ha redefinido el papel habitualmente conservador de la reina. Por ejemplo, ella piensa que el velo que llevan muchas mujeres musulmanas debería ser opcional, así que muchas veces no lo utiliza. Su posición en esta y otras cuestiones controvertidas, además de sus gustos caros en cuanto a vacaciones y vestuario, le han ganado las alabanzas de los modernistas y las críticas de los tradicionalistas. Sin embargo, Rania se ha dado cuenta que ella no puede introducir cambios que la sociedad todavía no acepta, como por ejemplo un papel igualitario para las mujeres. De todas maneras, Rania sigue adelante con sus programas de defensa de los derechos humanos, los derechos de la mujer, los derechos del niño, la educación y la salud, con la esperanza de que se produzca el cambio en el futuro.

# Tóm Tắt *(p. 542)*

## TIME: Nói Về Rania SCOTT MACLEOD

Hoàng hậu Jordan, Rania al Abdullah, là một phụ nữ sành điệu, hiện đại, người đã định nghĩa lại vai trò bảo thủ điển hình của một hoàng hậu và đem lại những thay đổi chính trị. Ví dụ, bà cho rằng phụ nữ Hồi giáo nên được quyền lựa chọn có đeo mạng hay không, và bà thường không đeo mạng. Sự ảnh hưởng của bà với vấn đề này và những vấn đề gây tranh cãi khác, cũng như việc bà thích đi nghỉ mát ở các khu sang trọng và mua sắm quần áo đắt tiền, đã nhận được những lời ngợi khen từ phe theo khuynh hướng cách tân và lời chỉ trích của phe theo khuynh hướng truyền thống cũng như sự chú ý của cả thế giới. Tuy nhiên, Rania đã nhận ra rằng bà không thể đem lại những sự thay đổi mà xã hội vẫn chưa chấp nhận, như vai trò tự do và công bằng hơn cho phụ nữ. Dù vậy, Rania vẫn tiếp tục thúc đẩy những chương trình về quyền con người, quyền phụ nữ, quyền trẻ em, và các chương trình về giáo dục và y tế với hy vọng rằng sẽ có những thay đổi xảy ra trong tương lai.

Name ______________________ Class ______________ Date ______________

## Buod *(p. 542)*

### TIME: Ukol kay Rania SCOTT MACLEOD

Si Rania al Abdullah, ang Reyna ng Jordan, ay isang mapostura at modernang babae na siyang nakapagbago ng karaniwang konserbatibong papel ng reyna para magdalá ng mga pagbabago sa politikal na kalagayan. Halimbawa, naniniwala siya na ang pagsusuot ng belo ng marami sa mga babaeng Muslim ay dapat hindi sapilitán, at depende sa kagustuhan ng babae, kaya karaniwan siyang hindi nagsusuot nito. Ang impluwensiya niya tungkol dito at sa iba pang mga kontrobersiyál na isyu at ang kanyang mga maluhong bakasyón at pananamit ay pinupuri ng mga taong moderno, pinipintasan ng mga taong tradisyunál, at sinusubaybayan ng lipunang internasyonál. Gayunman, naiintindihan ni Rania na hindi siya maaaring makagawa ng pagbabagong hindi pa tinatanggap ng lipunan, tulad ng isang mas malaya at kapantay na papel para sa mga babae. Pero ipinagpapatuloy pa rin ni Rania ang kanyang mga programa para sa mga karapatan ng mga tao, sa karapatan ng mga kababaihan, sa karapatan ng mga bata, sa edukasyón, at sa kalusugan, at siya'y umaasang magaganap ang pagbabago sa darating na panahon.

## 摘要 *(p. 542)*

### TIME：關於 Rania SCOTT MACLEOD

約旦皇后 Rania al Abdullah 是一位摩登而時髦的女性；她重新定義了皇后的典型傳統角色，而帶來了政治上的改變。例如，她認為許多回教婦女所戴的面紗，應該由她們來決定是否要戴；所以她自己通常不戴。她在這個以及其他爭議性問題上的影響，以及她對於休假與衣著上的昂貴品味，除了引起國際的矚目之外，也受到現代主義者的讚揚，和傳統主義者的批評。但是，Rania 也瞭解她無法提倡社會尚未接納的改變，例如是一個更自由而平等的婦女角色。儘管如此，Rania 還是繼續地推動她在人權、婦女權利、兒童權利、教育、與衛生方面的計劃，希望在未來能實現改革。

Name ______________________ Class ______________ Date ______________

## Rezime Selekyson *(p. 542)*

### TIME: Osijè Rania SCOTT MACLEOD

Rèn Jouden an, Rania al Abdullah, se te yon fanm modèn ki te gen estil, ki te redefini wòl konsèvatè tipik yon rèn pou li te fè chanjman politik. Pa egzanp, li kwè vwal plizyè fanm mizilman pote dwe yon chwa, kidonk dabitid li pa mete youn sou li. Enfliyans li nan bagay sa a epitou sou lòt pwoblèm ki gen kontwovès ladan yo, menm jan tou ak lajan li depanse pou pase vakans epi abiye, fè modènis chante lwanj li, tradisyonalis yo kritike li, epi lemonn antye ap gade li. Men, Rania reyalize li pa kapab pote yon chanjman sosyete sa a pa pare pou aksepte, tankou yon wòl ki pi lib, pi egal ego pou fanm. Men kanmenm, Rania kontinye ap pouse pi devan pwogram pou dwa imen, dwa fanm, dwa timoun, edikasyon, ak sante, avèk lespwa va gen chanjman nan tan k ap vini yo.

## Zuag Tswvyim *(p. 542)*

### TIME: Hais txog Rania SCOTT MACLEOD

Tus poj Huabtais nyob Jordan, Rania al Abdullah, yog ib tus neeg siab, pojniam tshiab uas rov kho poj huabtais tes dejnum txog kam tebchaws. Xws li, nws ntseeg tias txhob yuam daim ntaub npog uas txhua tus pojniam Muslim siv, ces nws tsis lam npog. Nws lub meejmom nthuav mus deb thiab tsim tau ntau hom xwmtx-heej cov nyom, tib yam li nws tej yeebyam noj haus, hnav tsoos tsho, lub caij mus uasi, kuj tau txais ntau hom kev qhuas los ntawm cov kws tshiab, kev thuam los ntawm cov kws qub, thiab thoob plaws ntiajteb. Li ntawd, Rania paub tias nws yuav hloov tsis tau txhua yam uas tibneeg tseem mus tsis tau txog, xws li kev muaj vajhuam sib luag rau pojniam. Tabsis, Rania rau siab ntso txhawb cov cai pejxeem, pojniam cov cai, menyuam cov cai, kev kawm ntawv, thiab kev xisneej kom muaj kev cia siab rau kev hloov lawm yav tom ntej.

# Reading Strategy *(page 542)*

## Connect to Contemporary Issues

## TIME: Regarding Rania SCOTT MACLEOD

To connect to contemporary issues as you read, use your prior knowledge about current events to understand and evaluate the selection. As you read this article, you likely drew on your knowledge of the Middle East, a part of the world often in the news these days.

## ACTIVITY

**Directions** List three contemporary issues mentioned in "Regarding Rania." Then write something you know about each issue.

| Issue | "What I Know" |
|---|---|
| | |
| | |
| | |

Name ____________________ Class ____________ Date ____________

# Selection Quick Check *(page 542)*

## TIME: Regarding Rania SCOTT MACLEOD

Use complete sentences to answer the following questions.

**1.** Who is Rania al Abdullah?

**2.** What message lies behind Rania's manner of dress?

**3.** Why did Rania visit the Kamalia School for Girls?

**4.** What is Rania's most controversial work?

**5.** What did Rania talk about when she was invited to address the Economic Forum in Saudi Arabia?

## Prueba Rápida *(pág. 542)*

### TIME: Sobre Rania SCOTT MACLEOD

Contesta las siguientes preguntas con oraciones completas.

**1.** ¿Quién es Rania al Abdullah?

**2.** ¿Qué mensaje transmite Rania con sus atuendos?

**3.** ¿Por qué visitó Rania la Escuela de Niñas de Kamalia?

**4.** ¿Cuál es el trabajo más controvertido de Rania?

**5.** ¿De qué habló Rania cuando la invitaron a dar una conferencia en el Foro Económico de Arabia Saudita?

# PART 2

# South Central Asia: 3500 B.C.—Present

Name ______________________ Class ______________ Date ______________

# English Language Coach, Part 2

## Rhyming Words

When using rhyme, poets often stretch the rules a bit. Words don't have to end with the same letters to rhyme. Also, some words may not look as if they sound alike, but when pronounced correctly, they do sound alike. For example, the ending letters in *ties* and *size* are not the same, but they sound alike, so the words rhyme.

### ACTIVITY

**Directions** Read the word pairs below and decide whether they rhyme. If a pair does rhyme, write "yes." If a pair does not rhyme, write another word that does rhyme.

Example: four / shore ___*yes*___ below / willow ___*grow*___

1. night
   kite ____________
2. hear
   wear ____________
3. wise
   prize ____________
4. seem
   redeem ____________
5. break
   sneak ____________
6. team
   scheme ____________
7. hollow
   shallow ____________
8. weight
   fate ____________

Name ______________________ Class ____________ Date ____________

## Summary/Resumen *(p. 558)*

### *from the* Rig-Veda

The Creation Hymn describes the origins of the universe. All was nothing but darkness and there was an absence of sky and space. The heat of desire for knowledge caused the stirrings of life. The forces needed to create the universe came from above and below, but these forces are mysteries. The gods did not create the universe but instead arrived after it had been formed. The one god, who lives "in the highest heaven," may not even know how the universe was created.

---

### *del* Rig Veda

El Himno de la Creación describe el origen del universo. No había nada aparte de la tiniebla, y el cielo y el espacio eran una ausencia. El calor del ansia de conocimiento causó los primeros brotes de vida. Las fuerzas necesarias para crear el universo vinieron de arriba y de abajo, pero estas fuerzas son un misterio. Los dioses no crearon el universo, sino que aparecieron cuando ya éste había sido formado. Puede que ni el dios supremo, que reside "en el más alto de los cielos", sepa cómo fue creado el universo.

# Tóm Tắt *(p. 558)*

## ***trích từ*** **Rig Veda**

Trước khi vũ trụ được tạo ra, không có những khái niệm như sự tồn tại hay không tồn tại, và cũng không có không gian, bầu trời hoặc bất cứ thứ gì khác. Tác giả muốn biết ai là người chịu trách nhiệm cho sự hư vô này và vì sao lúc đó hoàn toàn không có gì dù sống hay chết. Trước khi vũ trụ ra đời, không có dấu hiệu nào của sự sống mãi cho đến khi sự ham muốn đã tạo ra cuộc sống—ham muốn sáng tạo và ham muốn kiếm tìm. Những lực cần thiết để tạo ra vũ trụ bắt nguồn từ cả trên cao và dưới thấp, nhưng những lực đó lại là những bí ẩn. Những vị thần linh không tạo ra vũ trụ, mà thay vào đó, họ xuất hiện sau khi vũ trụ đã thành hình. Có một vị thần cai quản mọi thứ, cai quản cả các vị thần khác. Vị thần tối cao này có thể đã tạo ra vũ trụ nhưng cũng có thể không, cũng như vũ trụ có thể đã tự tạo ra chính nó nhưng cũng có thể không. Có thể vị thần này, người sống "ở những tầng vũ trụ cao nhất," cũng không biết vũ trụ đã được tạo ra như thế nào.

Name ________________ Class ________________ Date ________________

## **Buod** *(p. 558)*

### *mula sa* Rig Veda

Bago nilikhâ ang sansinukob, walang matatawag na bagay na naroroon o wala roon, at walang kalawakan o espasyo, walang langit o himpapawid, walang kahit anuman. Nais malaman ng awtor kung sino ang may kagagawán ng pagkawala ng kahit anuman, at kung bakit walang kahit anong bagay na buháy o patáy. Bago nilikhâ ang sansinukob, walang bakás ng buhay hanggang nilikhâ ng pagnanais ang buhay—isang pagnanais na maglikhâ at isang pagnanais na malaman. Ang mga puwersang kinailangan upang ilikhâ ang sansinukob ay nanggaling mula sa itaas at sa ibabâ, pero ang mga puwersa na ito ay mga misteryo. Hindi ang mga diyos (pangmaramihan) ang lumikhâ ng sansinukob, kundi sila ay dumating lamang nang nabuô na ito. Mayroong isang diyos (iisa) na naghahari sa lahat, pati na rin sa mga ibang diyos. Maaaring ang pangkalahatang diyos na ito ang lumikhâ ng sansinukob, o maaari namang hindi siya ang may likhâ nito, at maaari rin na ang sansinukob mismo ay ang lumikhâ sa kanyang sarili. Maaaring hindi man nalalaman ng diyos na ito na siyang nakatirá sa "pinakamataas na langit" kung paano talaga nilikhâ ang sansinukob.

Name ______________________ Class ______________ Date ______________

# 摘要 *(p. 558)*

## 來自 Rig Veda

在宇宙被創造出來之前，並沒有什麼東西存在或是不存在，也沒有空間、天空、或是任何其他事物。作者想要知道這種不存在是誰造成的，而為什麼沒有東西是生或死。在宇宙被創造出來之前，沒有生命的跡象，直到慾望創造了生命：一個創造的慾望和一個尋找的慾望。創造宇宙所需的力量來自天上和地下，但這些力量是神祕而難以理解的。神（複數）並沒有創造宇宙，而是在宇宙形成之後才來到的。有一個神（單數）統治著一切，包括其他的神。這個總體的神可能或可能沒有形成宇宙，而宇宙可能或可能沒有形成宇宙的本身。這個住在「天國最高處」的神，可能也不知道宇宙是如何創造出來的。

## Rezime Selekyson *(p. 558)*

### *nan* Rig Veda

Anvan yo te kreye inivè a, pat gen anyen ki te egziste, ni pat gen anyen ki pat egziste non plis; pat gen ni lespas, ni syèl, ni ankenn lòt bagay. Otè a vle konnen kiyès ki te responsab pat gen anyen epi pou kisa anyen pat ni vivan ni mouri. Anvan yo te kreye inivè a, pat gen siy lavi jiskaske dezi te kreye lavi – yon dezi pou kreye epi yon dezi pou dekouvri. Fòs yo te bezwen pou kreye inivè a sòti ni anlè ni anba, men fòs sa yo se mistè. Dye yo (plizyè) pat kreye inivè a, men yo te vini apre li te fin kreye. Gen yon Bondye (yon sèl) ki kontwole tout bagay, sa enkli lòt dye yo. Bondye sa te kreye inivè a menm jan tou se gen dwa pat li ki te kreye li; pètèt inivè a te fòme tèt li poukont li menm jan tou se gen dwa pa sa. Bondye sa a, ki rete "pi wo nan syèl la," gen dwa pa menm konnen kijan inivè a te kreye.

## Zuag Tswvyim *(p. 558)*

### *los ntawm* Rig Veda

Ua ntej lub ntiajteb raug tsim, tsis xam tej yam muaj los tsis muaj, thiab nruab ntug, ntuj, lossis ib yam dabtsi li. Tus kws sau ntawv xav paub tias leej twg yog tus lees paub txog tej nruab nqhuab thiab vim licas tsis muaj yam dabtsi ciaj sia lossis tuag. Ua ntej lub ntiajteb raug tsim, tsis muaj yam dabtsi ciaj sia txog thaum txoj sia raug tsim—ib lub siab xav tsim thiab ib lub siab xav paub tseeb. Cov zog ntawm kev xav tsim tuaj saud thiab tuaj hauv tuaj, tabsis cov zog nov paub tsis tau. Cov vajtswv tsis yog cov tsim ntiajteb, tabsis lawv tuaj txog thaum lub ntiajteb twb raug tsim lawm. Muaj ib tug vajtswv uas tswj txhua yam, nrog rau lwm cov vajtswv. Tus thawj vajtswv nov tejzaum tau tsim lossis tsis tau tsim lub ntiajteb, uas tsis lam tsim tau los ntawm nws tus kheej. Tus vajtswv nov, uas nyob "saum ntuj ceebtsheej siab tshaj," tej zaum tsis paub tias lub ntiajteb tsim los licas thiab.

Name ______________________ Class ______________ Date ______________

# Literary Element *(page 558)*

## Paradox

## *from the* Rig-Veda

A **paradox** is a statement that seems self-contradictory, or even absurd, but reveals an unexpected truth. Writers often use paradox to help readers see something in a new way, or to emphasize a point.

For example, in the selection, the writer states "There was neither non-existence nor existence then." This is a paradox, because if there is non-existence, then it would follow that there is not existence. You can't have both at the same time. However, because of the seeming absurdity of the phrase, the writer underscores the sense of absolute nothingness.

## ACTIVITY

**Directions** Read the paradoxes, in boldface, from the *Rig-Veda*. In the second column, explain what the paradoxes mean.

| Paradox | Meaning |
|---|---|
| "**Darkness was hidden by darkness** in the beginning." | **1.** |
| "Poets seeking in their heart with wisdom **found the bond of existence in non-existence.**" | **2.** |

Name ______________________ Class ____________ Date ____________

## Reading Strategy *(page 558)*

### Analyze Connotation

### Creation Hymn *from the* Rig-Veda

Sometimes two or more words that have the same meaning can have different connotations. **Connotation** refers to the ideas or emotions that are associated with a word beyond its dictionary definition. For example, when you think of the synonyms *tired, exhausted,* and *weary,* different ideas or images most likely come to mind for each word.

## ACTIVITY

**Directions** Complete the chart. Write the meaning of the boldface word or words in the second column, and images or ideas that come to mind for the boldface word or words in the third column.

| Expression in the Rig-Veda | Meaning | Connotation |
|---|---|---|
| **1.** water, **bottomlessly deep** | | |
| **2.** Who here will **proclaim** it? | | |
| **3.** That was the first **seed** of mind. | | |

Name ______________________ Class ______________ Date ______________

# Selection Vocabulary Practice *(page 558)*

## *from the* Rig-Veda

**Vocabulary**

**distinguishing** *adj.* marking as different; characterizing
**impulse** *n.* a sudden desire or feeling that makes one want to act
**proclaim** *v.* to announce publicly; to make known; to declare

### EXERCISE A Practice with Analogies

Analogies are comparisons based on the relationships between words and ideas. Some analogies are based on synonyms or antonyms, and others are based on less obvious relationships: for example, a verb and the result of the action, such as "write : letter :: sing : song." Choose the word that best completes each analogy.

**1. impulse : act :: fatigue : ___________**

**a.** wakefulness **b.** sleep **c.** tired **d.** pillow

**2. proclaim : declaration :: run : ___________**

**a.** walk **b.** test **c.** shoes **d.** race

**3. lovely : unattractive :: distinguishing : ___________**

**a.** typical **b.** remark **c.** thought **d.** unique

### EXERCISE B Applying Meanings

Fill in the blanks below, using vocabulary words from the list.

**1.** Franklin Roosevelt addressed the nation to ___________ that the United States was now at war.

**2.** Canada's flag is easy to identify because of its ___________ maple leaf.

**3.** Our dog acts on its ___________ to bark every time someone comes to the door.

### EXERCISE C Responding to the Selection

Write a response to the "Creation Hymn" from the *Rig-Veda* in which you explain your own ideas about how the world came to be. Use the THREE vocabulary words in your response.

# Vocabulary Strategy *(page 558)*

## Thesaurus Use

## *from the* Rig-Veda

Who really knows? Who will here *proclaim* it?

Whence was it produced? Whence is this creation?

—from the *Rig-Veda*

**Connecting to Literature** The word *proclaim* has a very specific meaning—"to declare something publicly." However, there are other words that are very similar in meaning to *proclaim,* called synonyms. For example, *announce* means "to make known publicly," and *state* means "to express in words." Why did the author choose *proclaim* over these synonyms? The answer is that these three words do not have the same connotation, or the ideas or emotions associated with a word apart from its literal meaning. The word *proclaim,* for example, suggests saying something in a more certain, public, and forceful way than do the other two words. Replace *proclaim* in the reading with the two synonyms mentioned. How does it change the meaning of the sentence?

To learn more about synonyms, you can use a thesaurus. A thesaurus is a specialized dictionary of synonyms and antonyms. It can be organized in a dictionary style or a traditional style, in which you look up a word in the index and refer to the pages listed for the word's synonyms and antonyms.

## ACTIVITY

**Directions** Using a thesaurus, find two synonyms for each of the following words from the selection. Then write the connotations for each word.

| Word | Synonyms | Connotations |
|---|---|---|
| darkness | **1.** | |
| wisdom | **2.** | |
| desire | **3.** | |

Name ______________________________ Class ______________ Date ______________

# Grammar Practice *(page 558)*

## Noun Clauses

### *from the* Rig-Veda

A **noun clause** is a subordinate clause that acts as a noun.

A central belief of Hinduism is **reincarnation**. (noun)

A central belief of Hinduism is **that all living beings take part in a cycle of death and rebirth**. (noun clause)

The clause in the second sentence above replaces the predicate noun in the first sentence.

Noun clauses can be used in the same way as nouns—as subject, direct object, object of a preposition, and predicate noun.

**Whoever memorized the Vedas** preserved the sacred beliefs of Hinduism. (subject)

Brahmans knew **how to use special memorization techniques**. (direct object)

Hindus pay attention to **what is taught in the Vedas**. (object of a preposition)

Knowledge is **what *veda* means**. (predicate noun)

| WORDS THAT INTRODUCE NOUN CLAUSES | | | | |
|---|---|---|---|---|
| how | what | where | who | whomever |
| however | whatever | which | whoever | whose |
| that | when | whichever | whom | why |

## ACTIVITY

**Directions** Underline each noun clause. In the blank, indicate its use in the sentence: *S* (subject), *DO* (direct object), *OP* (object of a preposition), or *PN* (predicate noun).

_____ **1.** Hindus believe that you shouldn't eat meat.

_____ **2.** Hindu priests refer to whichever verses are appropriate for a ritual.

_____ **3.** The god Vindu defended against whatever evil forces he encountered.

_____ **4.** The Vedas are where you will find the sacred hymns of Hinduism.

_____ **5.** Whoever wrote this hymn had many questions about the creation of life.

_____ **6.** The state of liberation is where Hindus believe they will be released from the cycle of death and rebirth.

Name ______________________ Class ______________ Date ______________

## Selection Quick Check *(page 558)*

### *from the* Rig-Veda

Use complete sentences to answer the following questions.

**1.** What point in time does the first stanza describe?

______________________________________________

______________________________________________

______________________________________________

**2.** In the third stanza, by what was darkness hidden?

______________________________________________

______________________________________________

______________________________________________

**3.** What is "the first seed of mind" described in the fourth stanza?

______________________________________________

______________________________________________

______________________________________________

Name ______________________ Class ______________ Date ______________

# Prueba Rápida *(pág. 558)*

## *del* Rig Veda ANONYMOUS

Contesta las siguientes preguntas con oraciones completas.

**1.** ¿Qué punto en el tiempo describe la primera estrofa?

______________________________________________

______________________________________________

______________________________________________

**2.** En la tercera estrofa, ¿qué ocultaba a la obscuridad?

______________________________________________

______________________________________________

______________________________________________

**3.** ¿Cuál es "la primera semilla de la mente" descrita en la cuarta estrofa?

______________________________________________

______________________________________________

______________________________________________

# Summary/Resumen *(p. 563)*

## Hundred Questions *from the* Mahabharata

The Pandava brothers are chasing a deer through the forest and grow very tired and thirsty. One brother approaches a pond and is about to start drinking. Before he can do so, he is challenged by the voice of a yaksha, an invisible but semi-divine being, who insists the young man answer a series of questions before he can drink. Refusing, the brother is struck dead the moment he begins to drink. Each brother, in turn, is killed after similarly refusing to answer the questions. Finally the last brother, Yudhistira, arrives and he alone accepts the challenge, answers all the questions, and lives. Then yaksha—who is really Yudhistira's father—revives all the young men.

---

## Cien preguntas *del* Mahabharata

Los hermanos Pandava están persiguiendo un ciervo en el bosque y se cansan mucho y tienen sed. Uno de los hermanos se acerca a una laguna y está a punto de comenzar a beber. Antes de poder hacerlo, la voz de un yaksha, ser invisible pero semidivino, lo desafía e insiste en que el joven responda a una series de preguntas antes de poder beber. Habiéndose negado, el hermano cae muerto al momento en que comienza a beber. Cada hermano, a su turno, muere después de negarse de modo similar a responder a las preguntas. Finalmente, llega el último de los hermanos, Yudhistira, y acepta el desafío, contesta todas las preguntas y vive. Luego el yaksha, que es en realidad el padre de Yudhistira, revive a los jóvenes.

Name ______________________ Class ____________ Date ____________

# Tóm Tắt *(p. 563)*

## Một Trăm Câu Hỏi *trích từ* Thiên Sử Thi Mahabharata

Anh em Pandava đang đuổi theo một con hươu trong rừng và ngày càng bị mệt và khát. Một người đến gần một cái ao và định uống nước. Trước khi có thể thực hiện ý định, bị thách đố bởi một yaksha—một loài không thể nhìn thấy được nhưng là nửa người nửa tiên. Yaksha khăng khăng đòi chàng trai trẻ trả lời một loạt câu hỏi trước khi anh được uống nước. Vì từ chối nên chàng trai bị đánh chết khi bắt đầu uống. Anh em họ lần lượt bị giết chết sau khi từ chối trả lời các câu hỏi. Cuối cùng, người anh cả là Yudhistira đến và chỉ mình anh chấp nhận lời thách đố. Anh trả lời tất cả các câu hỏi và sống sót. Sau đó yaksha—chính là cha của Yudhistira—làm các chàng trai trẻ sống lại.

Name ______________________ Class ______________ Date ______________

## **Buod** *(p. 563)*

### Isang Daang Katanungan *mula sa* Mahabharata

Ang magkapatid na lalaking Pandava ay nanghahabol ng usa sa gubat at sila'y napagod nang husto at nauhaw. Lumapit ang isang kapatid sa isang maliit na lawa at iinom na sana siya. Bago niya ito magawa, hinamon siya ng boses ng isang yaksha, isang hindi nakikita pero halos maka-Diyos na tao, na nagpilit na sagutin niya ang ilang mga tanong bago siya makainom. Ayaw ito gawin ng kapatid at namatay ito kaagad nang nagsimula itong uminom. Ang bawat kapatid ay sunud-sunod na pinatay dahil ayaw nilang sagutin ang mga katanungan. Sa kahulihan, dumating ang huling kapatid na si Yudhistira, at siya lamang ang tumanggap sa hamon, sumagot sa lahat ng mga katanungan, at hindi namatay. Pagkatapos ay binuhay ni yaksha—na sa katotohanan ay ama ni Yudhistira—ang lahat ng mga batang lalaki.

# 摘要 *(p. 563)*

## 來自 Mahabharata 的《一百個問題》

Pandava 兄弟在森林中追趕一隻鹿，而感到又累又渴。有一個兄弟走向池塘，準備要開始喝水。在他喝水以前，他受到了一個夜叉 (yaksha) 的聲音的挑戰；這是一個看不見而半神的靈魂。這個夜叉堅持這個年輕人先回答一些問題才能喝水。這個兄弟拒絕了，而在他開始喝水的一瞬間被打死。接下來，每一個兄弟都在類似拒絕回答問題的情況下被殺了。最後，終於輪到最後一個兄弟 Yudhistira 前來，他接受了挑戰並回答了所有的問題而活了下來。然後，這個事實上是 Yudhistira 父親的夜叉，讓所有兄弟都復生了。

Name ______________________ Class ______________ Date ______________

## Rezime Selekyson *(p. 563)*

### San Keksyon *nan* Mahabharata

Frè Pandava yo ap chase yon sèf nan bwa a epi yo vin gen fatig ak swaf anpil. Youn nan frè yo apwoche yon ma dlo epi li pwal kòmanse bwè. Anvan li gen tan fè sa, vwa yaksha, yon kreyati envizib men ki mwatye dye, ba l yon defi, li ensiste pou jèn gason an reponn yon seri kesyon anvan li kapab bwè. Frè a refize, epi li tonbe mouri kou li kòmanse bwè. Chak frè mouri, youn dèyè lòt, apre yo fin refize reponn kesyon yo menm jan an. Finalman, dènye frè a, Yudhistira, rive, epi se li menm sèlman ki aksepte defi a, reponn tout kesyon yo, epi viv. Apre sa yaksha—ki an reyalite se papa Yudhistira—resisite tout jèn gason yo.

## Zuag Tswvyim *(p. 563)*

### Pua zaj Lus Nug *los ntawm* tus Mahabharata

Cov kwv tij Pandava tabtom caum ib tus kauv hauv ib thaj havzoov txog thaum nkees thiab nqhis dej heev. Ib tus tij los ze ib lub pas dej thiab yuav luag pib haus dej. Uantej kiag ntawd, ib tus yawg yaksha saum nta ntuj ua ib lub suab tawm tuaj cheem kom nws teb ib cov lus tso uantej yuav haus dej. Tsis quav ntsej, tus tij haus dej kiag ces tuag kiag thaum pib haus ntawd. Txhua leej kwv tij puav leej raug tua tas tibyam thaum tsis kam teb cov lus. Thaum kawg tus kwv ntxhawg, Yudhistira, los txog thiab nws lees cov lus, tebtau tas nrho, ces muaj sia nyob. Tomqab, yawg yaksha—uas, tiag mas, yog Yudhistira leej txiv rov muab siav rau tas nrho nws cov tub.

Name ______________________ Class ____________ Date ____________

# Literary Element *(page 563)*

## Epic Hero

## Hundred Questions *from the* Mahabharata

An **epic** is a long, narrative poem that relates the adventures and accomplishments of a hero. An **epic hero** is a larger-than-life legendary or historical figure. He demonstrates characteristics and performs acts that reflect the values that are held in high regard in a culture. Often, an epic hero is a warrior. He travels on a long journey or quest, faces enemies, and deals with gods or other supernatural forces. An epic hero exhibits qualities that set him apart from other men—he is usually stronger, wiser, and braver than ordinary humans and performs extraordinary feats. In the *Mahabharata,* Yudhistira is an epic hero.

## ACTIVITY

**Directions** Read the qualities of an epic hero in the web below. For each one, provide an example from the selection that shows how Yudhistira exhibits this quality.

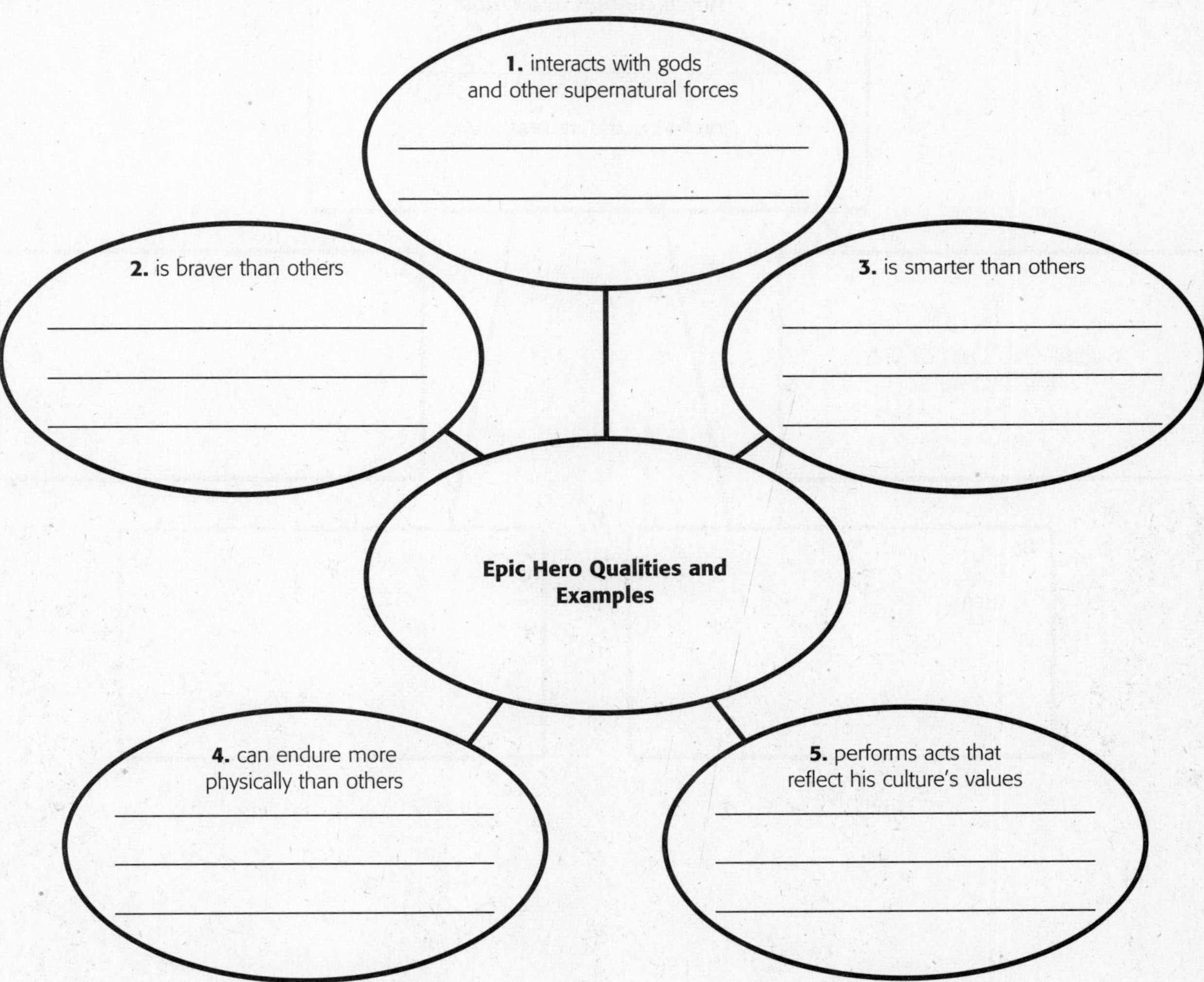

**1.** interacts with gods and other supernatural forces
**2.** is braver than others
**3.** is smarter than others
Epic Hero Qualities and Examples
**4.** can endure more physically than others
**5.** performs acts that reflect his culture's values

Name ______________________ Class ______________ Date ______________

# Reading Strategy *(page 563)*

## Apply Background Knowledge

## Hundred Questions *from the* Mahabharata

You can better understand a work of literature when you **apply background knowledge** of the historical and cultural events and beliefs that informed the work. You can interpret a character's actions and emotions more easily when you apply background knowledge.

### ACTIVITY

**Directions** Reread the *Before You Read* page about the *Mahabharata.* Study the section that discusses the Hindu concept of *dharma.* Use this information to complete the graphic organizer below. In the first square, paraphrase the Hindu concept of *dharma* and the Hindu beliefs about preserving the natural order. In the other squares, write the actions and emotions of the characters who exemplify these concepts. The first one is done for you.

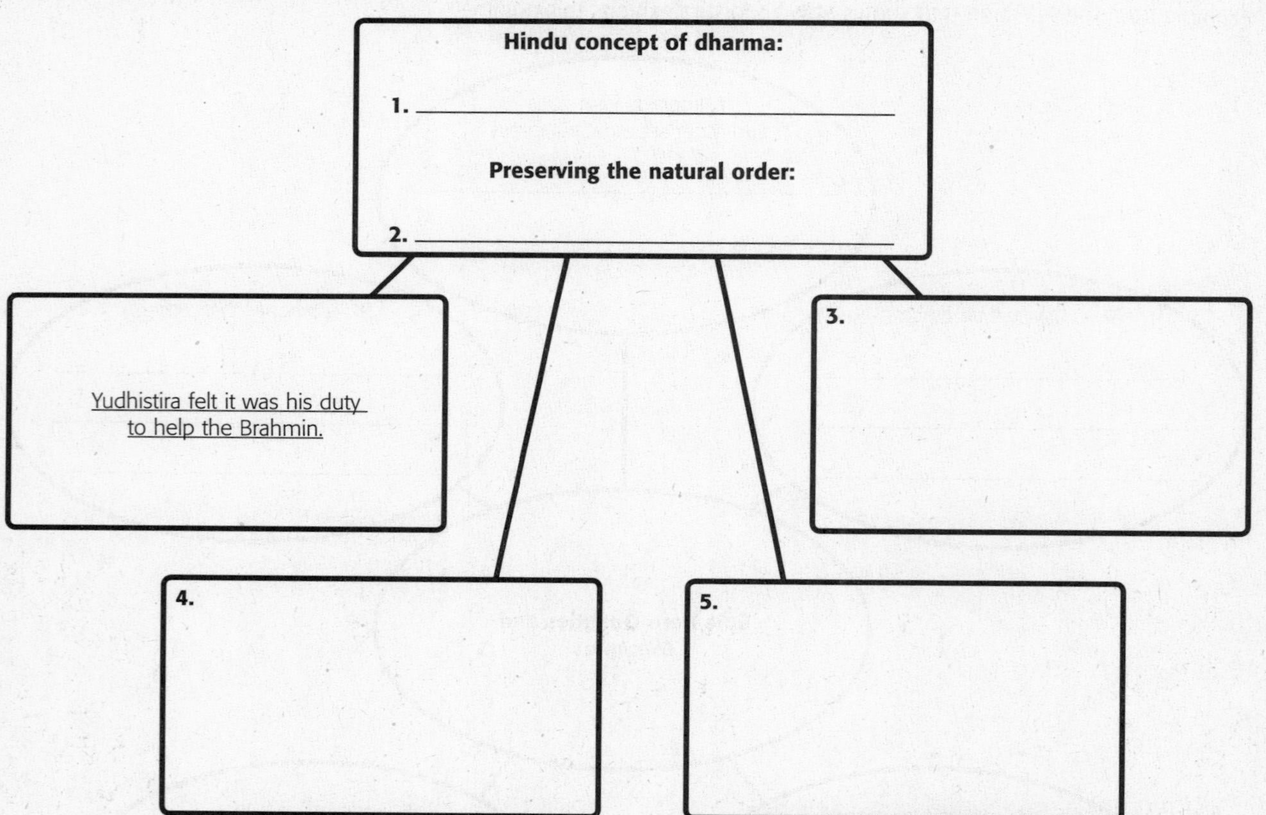

Hindu concept of dharma:
1. ______________________
Preserving the natural order:
2. ______________________
Yudhistira felt it was his duty to help the Brahmin.
3.
4.
5.

Name ______________________________ Class ______________ Date ______________

# Selection Vocabulary Practice *(page 563)*

## Hundred Questions *from the* Mahabharata

**Vocabulary**

**austerity** *n.* a morally strict act
**poignancy** *n.* the quality of painfully affecting one's feelings
**inordinate** *adj.* excessive
**fatuous** *adj.* silly; foolish
**avarice** *n.* greed

### EXERCISE A Practice with Synonyms and Antonyms

Synonyms are words with the same, or nearly the same, meaning. Antonyms are words with nearly opposite meanings. For each word or phrase below, write a synonym from the vocabulary list above, and then write an antonym ( a word or phrase) for the word.

| | Synonym from the List | Antonym |
|---|---|---|
| **1.** self-denying practice | ______________ | ______________ |
| **2.** ridiculous | ______________ | ______________ |
| **3.** deep feeling | ______________ | ______________ |
| **4.** selfishness | ______________ | ______________ |
| **5.** extreme | ______________ | ______________ |

### EXERCISE B Applying Meanings

On the line, write the letter of the word that best fits in each sentence below.

**1.** She showed her **avarice** by __________ her wealth.
**a.** sharing **b.** hoarding

**2.** The crowd __________ at the **fatuous** remark.
**a.** wept **b.** laughed

**3.** The **poignancy** of the play's ending made the audience __________.
**a.** cry **b.** sleep

**4.** An example of **austerity** may be to __________ all day.
**a.** fast **b.** eat

**5.** A man with **inordinate** strength could lift __________.
**a.** a paperclip **b.** a car

### EXERCISE C Responding to the Selection

Write an editorial in which you agree or disagree with the way in which the yaksha dealt with the brothers. Use at least FOUR vocabulary words in your editorial.

Name ______________________ Class ____________ Date ____________

# Vocabulary Strategy *(page 563)*

## Denotation and Connotation

## Hundred Questions *from the* Mahabharata

> "Yudhistira answered humbly, 'O yaksha, I will not covet what is yours. I will not touch this water without your sanction, in spite of my thirst.'"
>
> —"Hundred Questions" from Mahabharata

**Connecting to Literature** In the "Hundred Questions", the author uses words with denotations and connotations that add to the epic quality of the writing. A word's **denotation** is its literal meaning. A word's implied meaning is its **connotation**. For example, the author chose to use *covet* rather than "want," or "wish for." Why did the author choose *covet* over these synonyms? The answer is that *covet* is more formal and respectful and has religious undertones, which is in keeping with the epic and with a hero who is speaking to a supernatural being.

## ACTIVITY

**Directions** Complete the semantic features chart below to analyze words from "Hundred Questions" from the *Mahabharata.* Use a dictionary to find a definition, or denotation, for each word, and write its denotation in the second column. Record ideas, images, or feelings associated with the word in the third column. An example is proven.

| Word | Denotation | Connotation |
|---|---|---|
| sanction | give formal or official approval | the giving of approval from a higher, religious being |
| 1. | | |
| 2. | | |
| 3. | | |
| 4. | | |

Name ______________________ Class ____________ Date ____________

# Grammar Practice *(page 563)*

## Kinds of Sentences

## Hundred Questions *from the* Mahabharata

A **declarative sentence** makes a statement. It usually ends with a period.

The Pandava brothers lost their kingdom. Nakula said, "I hear the cries of cranes."

An **imperative sentence** gives a command or makes a request. The subject *you* is understood. Imperative sentences end with a period or an exclamation point.

Don't be foolhardy. Take care!

An **interrogative sentence** asks a question. It ends with a question mark.

What makes the sun rise? What remains immobile after being born?

An **exclamatory sentence** expresses strong emotions. It ends with an exclamation point.

Yudhistira couldn't believe his eyes! All of his brothers were dead!

## ACTIVITY

**Directions** Label each sentence *dec.* if it is declarative, *imp.* if it is imperative, *int.* if it is interrogative, and *exc.* if it is exclamatory.

____ **1.** Don't drink from the pond.

____ **2.** How would Yudhistira explain this tragedy?

____ **3.** The yaksha was Yama, the God of Justice.

____ **4.** Stop where you are!

____ **5.** Who is the friend of one about to die?

____ **6.** His brothers came back to life!

____ **7.** The yaksha was impressed with Yudhistira's answers.

____ **8.** The Mahabharata is one of the longest literary works in the world.

____ **9.** Why did the brothers drink from the pond?

____ **10.** Listen to the voice.

Name ________________ Class ________________ Date ________________

# Selection Quick Check *(page 563)*

## Hundred Questions *from the* Mahabharata

Use complete sentences to answer the following questions.

**1.** Why does Yudhistira feel duty-bound to help the brahmin?

**2.** What sound alerts the brothers to the possible location of a water source?

**3.** What warning do the first four Pandava brothers ignore?

**4.** In what form does the voice by the lake materialize before Yudhistira?

**5.** Who does the yaksha turn out to be?

Name ______________________ Class ______________ Date ______________

## **Prueba Rápida** *(pág. 563)*

### Cien preguntas *del* Mahabharata

Contesta las siguientes preguntas con oraciones completas.

**1.** ¿Por qué Yudhistira se siente obligado a ayudar al brahmín?

______________________________________________

______________________________________________

______________________________________________

**2.** ¿Qué sonido avisa a los hermanos que posiblemente encuentren una fuente de agua?

______________________________________________

______________________________________________

______________________________________________

**3.** ¿Qué aviso ignoran los primeros cuatro hermanos Pandava?

______________________________________________

______________________________________________

______________________________________________

**4.** ¿Qué forma toma la voz al materializarse ante Yudhistira?

______________________________________________

______________________________________________

______________________________________________

**5.** ¿Qué resulta ser el yaksha?

______________________________________________

______________________________________________

______________________________________________

## Summary/Resumen *(p. 576)*

### *from* Homer in India WILLIAM DALRYMPLE

The author is surprised to learn that the Hindu epics of Rajasthan continue to live on in oral traditions centuries after Classical epics, such as the *Iliad* and the *Odyssey,* have long disappeared from oral practices and exist only as written texts. The epics of Rajasthan are "preserved by a caste of wandering *bhopas*—shamans and bards—who traveled from village to village, staging performances." The author attends a performance by a *bhopa* and learns that the Hindu epics survive in oral form because the poems are religious rituals. The *bhopas* who relay the epics transmit the gods' messages. These gods are not inaccessible, metaphysical gods, but ones that are "deified locals with whom herders could relate and who could understand their needs" and "the ebb and flow of daily life." Therefore, the need for *bhopas* to transmit the epics orally is as strong as ever.

---

### *de* Homero en la India

El autor se sorprende de que la epopeya hindú de Rajasthan continúe existiendo en forma oral siglos después de que las epopeyas clásicas, como la *Ilíada* y la *Odisea,* han desaparecido de la transmisión oral y sólo existen como texto escrito. La epopeya de Rajasthan permanece "preservada por una casta de *bhopas* errantes, chamanes y bardos que viajaban de aldea en aldea haciendo actuaciones". El autor asiste a la actuación de un *bhopa* y aprende que las epopeyas hindúes sobreviven en forma oral porque los poemas son rituales religiosos y los *bhopas* que los relatan están transmitiendo los mensajes de los dioses. No hay dioses inaccesibles ni metafísicos, sino dioses que son "paisanos deificados con los que los pastores pueden identificarse, y que pueden comprender las necesidades humanas" y "el flujo y reflujo de la vida diaria". Por lo tanto, la necesidad de *bhopas* para transmitir oralmente la epopeya es tan firme como siempre.

Name ______________________________ Class _____________ Date _______________

# Tóm Tắt *(p. 576)*

## *trích từ* Homer Ở Ấn Độ WILLIAM DALRYMPLE

Nhà văn William Dalrymple đến Ấn Độ để nghe sử thi Rajasthan, những bài thơ sử thi của đạo Hinđu được truyền khẩu. Không giống như sư thi Illiad và Odyssey, những tác phẩm đã từng được truyền khẩu nhưng giờ đây chỉ còn ở dạng văn viết, sử thi Rajasthan vẫn tồn tại ở dạng truyền khẩu. Sử thi Rajasthan được "bảo tồn bởi một tầng lớp những bhopas lãng du—những pháp sư và nghệ sĩ chuyên hát các bài hát co—đi từ làng này sang làng khác trình diễn". Dalrymple phát hiện ra rằng lý do vì sao những bài thơ này vẫn được truyền khẩu là vì chúng được đọc trong các nghi lễ tôn giáo, và người bhopas đọc lại các bài thơ này để chuyển tải thông điệp của các thần linh. Đó không phải là những vị thần xa xôi, siêu hình mà là những vị thần "xuất thân từ người địa phương mà những người chăn gia súc có thể gắn bó vì những vị thần này thống hiểu mọi nhu cầu của họ" cũng như "những vui buồn của cuộc sống đời thường". Chính vì vậy, nhu cầu nghe bhopas truyền khẩu các trường sử thi vẫn không hề suy giảm.

## Buod *(p. 576)*

### *mula sa* Si Homer sa India WILLIAM DALRYMPLE

Nagpunta ang manunulát na si William Dalrymple sa India para pakinggan ang mga epiko ng Rajasthan, ang mga epiko ng mga Hindu na ipinasa-pasa sa salita. Hindi tulad ng Illiad at ng Odyssey, mga epiko na dati ay pinasa-pasa sa salita, pero ngayon ay makikita na lamang bilang mga nakasulat na teksto, ang mga epiko ng Rajasthan ay pinapasa-pasa pa rin sa pasalitang anyô. Ang mga epiko ng Rajasthan ay "pinanatili ng isang caste o uri ng mga nagbibiyaheng bhopas—mga shaman at mga kumakantang manunulá—na naglakbay sa mga iba't-ibang bayan para magbigay ng mga pagganap sa entablado." Natutunan ni Dalrymple na nanatili ang mga ito sa pasalitang anyô dahil ang mga tuláng ito ay mga ritwál ng relihiyón, at ang mga bhopas na nagpapasa-pasa nito ay nagpapahiwatig ng mga mensahe galing sa mga diyos. Ang mga ito ay hindi mga diyos na 'di-maabot at metapisikál, kung hindi mga "lokal na tao na kinikilalang mga diyos, na maaaring kausapin ng mga tagapagpastol, at nakakaunawa ng kanilang mga pangangailangan" at "ng pagbabâ at pagtaas ng agos ng pang-araw-araw na buhay." Samakatwid, ang pangangailangan ng mga bhopas na magpasa ng mga tuláng ito sa kasalukuyang panahon ay kasing-lakas pa rin ng dati.

# 摘要 *(p. 576)*

## 來自《印度的荷馬》WILLIAM DALRYMPLE

作家 William Dalrymple 到印度去聽 Rajasthan 史詩，這是一種口頭流傳的印度史詩。Illiad 和 Odyssey 也曾一度透過口頭流傳，而現在只有書面的形式存在；但 Rajasthan 史詩則不一樣，至今仍只有口頭的形式存在。Rajasthan 史詩「保存在印度種姓制度的流浪 bhopas 的身上，這些僧人和流浪詩人在各個村落之間往返做出演出。」Dalrymple 瞭解到他們之所以能以口頭的形式流傳下來，是因為這些詩是宗教上的儀式，而 bhopas 用他們來傳遞神的訊息。這些不是難以接近而抽象的神；這些神是「牧人所認同而能瞭解百姓需求而被奉若神明的本地人」以及「日常生活的落潮與流動」。因此，透過 bhopas 來口頭流傳這些史詩的必要性，直到現今都很重要。

Name ______________________ Class ______________ Date ______________

## Rezime Selekyson *(p. 576)*

### *nan* Homer nan Peyi Lèzenn WILLIAM DALRYMPLE

Yon ekriven yo rele William Dalrymple t ale nan peyi End pou tande istwa epik Rajasthan, ki se powèm epik Hindu moun rakonte pa bouch. Kontrèman avèk Illiad ak Odyssey yo te konn rakonte pa bouch men ki sou papye sèlman kounye a, istwa epik Rajasthan yo egziste sou fòm oral jiska prezan. Istwa epik Rajasthan "se yon klas moun eran yo rele bhopas— chaman avèk bad— ki te prezève yo; yo te vwayaje sòti nan yon vilaj al nan yon lòt, epi yo te monte prezantasyon." Dalrymple te aprann yo te siviv sou fòm oral paske powèm yo se rityèl relijye, epi bhopas ki rakonte yo a se mesaj dye yo y ap transmèt. Sa yo se pa dye ki inaksesib oswa metafizik, men se dye "lokal ki konekte avèk moun yo epi konprann sa yo bezwen" epitou "ki konprann kijan lavi toulejou ye." Kidonk, bezwen bhopas yo genyen pou transmèt epik sa yo pa vwa oral pi fò pase lontan.

Name ______________________ Class ______________ Date ______________

## Zuag Tswvyim *(p. 576)*

### *los ntawm* Homer nyob India WILLIAM DALRYMPLE

Kws sau ntawv William Dalrymple mus rau India mus mloog kwvhuam ntawm Rajasthan, uas muab txhais ua pajhuam Hindu. Tsis zoo li Illiad thiab Odyssey uas raug muab coj los hais ua dabneeg tabsis muaj rau ntaub ntawv thiab, cov kwvhuam ntawm Rajasthan tseem muaj nyob ua lus hais. Cov kwvhuam nov raug "tshwj cia rau ib theem neeg lojleeb bhopas—cov txiv neeb thiab txiv sau ntawv—uas keev tsiv zos dhau zos, seev cev ua yeebyam." Dalrymple kawm tias cov kwvhuam nyob taus ua lus hais vim cov kws pajhuam coj kev cai dab qhuas nruj, thiab cov bhopas siv lawv ua lus vajtswv tawm. Cov nov tsis yog dab ua, yog cov vajtswv pom tau, tabsis yog cov vajtswv uas "leej heev rau cov mej zeeg ntseeg lawv hauv zos thiab lawv ho totaub yam mejzeeg xav tau" thiab "kev mus-los hauv lub neej." Li ntawd, kev xav tau bhopas txhais tawm ua kwvhuam thiaj li tseem-ceeb tshaj plaws.

Name _______________ Class _______________ Date _______________

# Reading Strategy *(page 576)*

## Analyze Cultural Context

### *from* Homer in India WILLIAM DALRYMPLE

When you **analyze cultural context,** you examine how a culture influenced a literary tradition or text. The history, beliefs, and daily life of a culture help to shape a literary text. For example, in this selection, we learn that an extremely important aspect of Indian culture was the way in which people made their living—through herding and farming. Farmers and herders looked for ways to keep their animals healthy. They believed attending the performance of a *bhopa,* who could invoke the spirit of Pabuji, could cure sickness in animals.

## ACTIVITY

**Directions** For each detail about the Indian culture that Dalrymple describes, write how it shaped the oral tradition of the *bhopas.*

| Detail | How It Shaped the Oral Tradition of the *Bhopas* |
|---|---|
| Many of the Indian villagers were illiterate. | **1.** |
| The Indian villagers believed in the power of the gods to help them in their work. | **2.** |
| Oral storytelling was an integral part of Indian life. | **3.** |
| The Indian villagers were mostly herders and farmers. | **4.** |

Name ______________________ Class ______________ Date ______________

# Selection Quick Check *(page 576)*

## *from* Homer in India WILLIAM DALRYMPLE

Use complete sentences to answer the following questions.

**1.** How were the epics of Rajasthan originally kept alive?

______________________________________________

______________________________________________

______________________________________________

**2.** How did Laxmi Kumari Chundawat help to preserve Rajasthani epic poems?

______________________________________________

______________________________________________

______________________________________________

**3.** What is a *phad?*

______________________________________________

______________________________________________

______________________________________________

**4.** Why did Mohan's fellow villagers want Mohan to perform for them?

______________________________________________

______________________________________________

______________________________________________

**5.** How does Dalrymple explain the answer to the question of how the epics were kept alive?

______________________________________________

______________________________________________

______________________________________________

Name ______________________ Class ______________ Date ______________

## Prueba Rápida *(pág. 576)*

### *de* Homero en la India WILLIAM DALRYMPLE

Contesta las siguientes preguntas con oraciones completas.

**1.** ¿Cómo se mantuvieron vivos en un principio los poemas épicos de Rajasthan?

**2.** ¿De qué manera ayudó Laxmi Kumari Chundawat a preservar los poemas épicos de Rajasthani?

**3.** ¿Qué es un *phad?*

**4.** ¿Por qué los aldeanos vecinos de Mohan querían que él ejecutara para ellos?

**5.** ¿De qué manera Dalrymple explica la respuesta a la pregunta sobre cómo se mantuvieron vivos los cuentos épicos?

Name ____________________ Class ____________ Date ____________

## Summary/Resumen *(p. 582)*

### Rama and Ravana in Battle *from the* Ramayana

Ravana's warriors are quickly dying in their battle against Rama's camp, so Ravana decides to fight Rama himself. When the gods see Ravana's fierce determination to destroy Rama, they give Rama a special chariot. Ravana sees that the gods are helping the mere mortal Rama and resigns to kill Rama in the face of the gods. But Ravana's efforts are foiled and Rama injures him badly. Acting with honor, Rama waits until Ravana is well enough to fight him again instead of killing him while he is deeply injured. When Ravana recovers, Rama finally kills him. As Rama looks at Ravana's body, he requests that Ravana have an honorable burial "befitting his grandeur." The story emphasizes the importance of morality, honor, and integrity.

---

### Rama y Ravana en combate *del* Ramayana

Los guerreros de Ravana están muriendo rápidamente en la batalla contra el campamento de Rama, por lo que Ravana decide pelear personalmente con Rama. Cuando los dioses observan que Ravana está ferozmente decidido a destruir a Rama, le dan a éste un carruaje especial. Ravana ve que los dioses están ayudando al simple mortal Rama y se resigna a matar a Rama frente a los dioses. Pero los esfuerzos de Ravana fracasan y Rama lo hiere gravemente. Actuando con honor, Rama espera hasta que Ravana esté lo suficientemente bien como para pelear de nuevo contra él en lugar de matarlo mientras está herido. Cuando Ravana se recupera, Rama finalmente lo mata. Observando el cadáver de Ravana, Rama ordena que le den un entierro honorable "digno de su grandeza". El cuento enfatiza la importancia de la moral, el honor y la integridad.

Name ______________________ Class __________ Date __________

# Tóm Tắt *(p. 582)*

## Rama và Ravana Trên Chiến Trường *trích từ* Ramayana

Những chiến binh của Ravana hy sinh hàng loạt trong trận chiến chống lại phe Rama, vậy nên Ravana quyết định tự mình sẽ chiến đấu với Rama. Khi thấy quyết tâm sắt đá của Ravana nhằm hủy diệt Rama, các vị thần liền tặng cho Rama một chiến xa đặc biệt. Tức giận, Ravana lao nhanh tấn công về phía Rama. Ngược lại, Rama ra lệnh cho chiến binh điều khiển chiến xa lái thật chậm và bình tĩnh. Ravana thấy rõ rằng các vị thần đang giúp đỡ Rama, người chỉ có một lần chết, và quyết tâm giết Rama trước mặt các vị thần. Nhưng những nỗ lực của Ravana đã thất bại và Ravana bị Rama đánh trọng thương. Rama hành động một cách đầy danh dự và đợi cho đến khi Ravana đủ sức khỏe để chiến đấu mới tiếp tục đánh Ravana chứ không giết Ravana ngay khi đang bị thương nặng. Khi Ravana hồi phục, Rama cuối cùng cũng đã giết được Ravana. Khi nhìn thi thể của Ravana, Rama yêu cầu chôn cất cho ông thật trang trọng "cho xứng đáng với sự vĩ đại của ông." Câu truyện này nhấn mạnh tầm quan trọng của đạo đức, danh dự và sự chính trực.

## Buod *(p. 582)*

### Si Rama at si Ravana sa Labanán *mula sa* Ramayana

Madalíng nagsisimatayan ang mga mandirigma ni Ravana sa kanilang paglaban sa kampo ni Rama, kaya nagpasiya si Ravana na labanan mismo si Rama. Nang makita ng mga diyos ang malakas na determinasyón ni Ravana na patayín si Rama, binigyan nila si Rama ng isang natatanging sasakyang karo. Nagalit si Ravana, at sumugod siya patungo kay Rama. Hindi tulad niya, inutusan ni Rama ang nagpapatakbô ng kanyang sasakyang karo na kumilos nang mabagal at sa kalmadong paraan. Nakita ni Ravana na tinutulungan ng mga diyos ang hamak lamang na taong si Rama, at nais niyang patayín si Rama sa harap ng mga diyos. Pero nabigô ang mga pagsisikap ni Ravana, at malubha siyang nasugatan ni Rama. Marangal ang kilos ni Rama, at sa halip na patayín niya si Ravana habang lubhang sugatán ito, hinintay niya hanggang sapát na magaling ná at maaari nang makipaglaban muli si Ravana. Nang gumalíng na si Ravana, saka na lamang siya pinatáy ni Rama. Habang tinitingnan niya ang bangkay ni Ravana, hiniling ni Rama na bigyan ito na marangal na libíng na "nababagay sa kanyang karangalan." Binibigyan-diin ng kuwento ang kahalagahan ng moralidád, karangalan, at integridad.

# 摘要 *(p. 582)*

## 來自 Ramayana 的《Rama 和 Ravana 的戰鬥》

Ravana 的戰士在對於 Rama 陣營的戰鬥中死傷很快，所以 Ravana 決定自己和 Rama 搏鬥。當神看到 Ravana 要消滅 Rama 的強烈決心，祂們給了 Rama 一部特別的戰車。生氣的 Ravana 向前衝向 Rama。對比起來，Rama 命令他的戰車駕駛緩慢而鎮靜地移動。Ravana 看到神在幫助臨死的 Rama，而決定要在神的面前把 Rama 殺死。可是 Ravana 的努力受到了挫折，Rama 讓他受了重傷。Rama 為了保持榮譽，等到 Ravana 恢復夠了才繼續和他搏鬥，而沒有趁他受重傷的時候把他殺了。當 Ravana 恢復之後，Rama 終於殺了他。Rama 看著 Ravana 的屍體，下令給他一個「能配合他的莊嚴」的光榮葬禮。這個故事強調了道德、榮譽、和正直的重要性。

Name ______________________ Class ______________ Date ______________

## Rezime Selekyson *(p. 582)*

### Batay Rama ak Ravana *nan* Ramayana

Gèrye Ravana yo mouri byen vit nan batay yo kont kan Rama a, kidonk Ravana deside pou li batay ak Rama li menm. Lè dye yo wè detèminasyon Ravana genyen pou li detwi Rama, yo bay Rama yon charyo espesyal. Ravana fache, li derape pou l al koresponn ak Rama. Rama, okontrè, pase chofè charyo li a lòd pou li deplase san mache prese. Ravana wè dye yo ap ede yon senp mòtèl tankou Rama epi deside l ap touye Rama nan figi dye yo. Men efò Ravana yo pa jwenn siksè epi Rama blese li grav. Rama aji avèk onè; li tann jiskaske Ravana refè pou batay avèk li ankò olye pou li touye li pandan li tou blese a. Lè Ravana refè, Rama finalman touye li. Pandan Rama ap gade kò Ravana, li mande pou yo antere Ravana yon fason onorab "dapre grandè li." Istwa a mete aksan sou enpòtans moralite, onè, ak entegrite.

Name ______________________ Class ______________ Date ______________

## Zuag Tswvyim *(p. 582)*

### Rama thiab Ravana hauv Tshav Rog *los ntawm* Ramayana

Ravana cov tub rog tuag sai sai tom tsav rog nrog Rama, ces Ravana txiav txim siab ntaus nrog Rama tus kheej. Thaum cov vajtswv pom Ravana kev npau taws los rhuav Rama, lawv muab ib lub tsheb nees tshwjxeeb rau Rama. Chim dhau, Ravana tuam ya ceev ceev rau Rama. Rama, txawv qhov ntawd, maj mam tshem nws lub tsheb qeeb qeeb thiab txias txias. Ravana pom tias cov vajtswv pab tus neeg txawj tuag Rama ces nws tsum tsis tua Rama ntawm lawv qhov muag. Tabsis Ravana lub zog raug Rama txo ces nws raug mob hnyav heev. Siv meejmoom los tswj, Rama tos kom Ravana zoo mob tso mam rov sib tua dua. Thaum Ravana zoo los, Rama muab nws tua tuag. Thaum Rama ntsia Ravana lub cev, nws hais kom ua ib lub ntees muaj meejmom rau Ravana "kom tsim nyog nws lub meejmom." Zaj dabneeg hais txog qhov tseemceeb ntawm kev tuag, meejmom, thiab kev haumxeeb.

Name ______________________ Class ______________ Date ______________

# Literary Element *(page 582)*

## Conflict

### Rama and Ravana in Battle *from the* Ramayana

**Conflict** plays a central role in most epics. Conflict is the struggle between opposing forces in a story. Stories often have both internal and external conflicts.

An **internal conflict** is the struggle that takes place within a character's mind, when he or she wrestles with opposing thoughts, emotions, or goals. For example, Mahodara, Ravana's assistant, struggles with obeying Ravana's orders not to engage Rama and with his own desire to fight Rama himself.

An **external conflict** is a struggle between a character or characters and an outside force, such as another character, or an intangible force, such as society in general. The conflict at the beginning of the excerpt, between the armies of Rama and Ravana, is an external conflict.

## ACTIVITY

**Directions** In the chart below, identify an internal and external conflict for the characters of Rama and Ravana. Do not use the examples given above.

| Character | Conflict | Internal or External? |
|---|---|---|
| Rama | **1.** | |
| Rama | **2.** | |
| Ravana | **3.** | |
| Ravana | **4.** | |

Name ____________________ Class ____________ Date ____________

## Reading Strategy *(page 582)*

### Monitor Comprehension

### Rama and Ravana in Battle *from the* Ramayana

When you **monitor comprehension**, you make sure that you have understood what you have read. Passages with lengthy sentences, many clauses, and unfamiliar words may be difficult to understand. You should reread a difficult passage, breaking down any difficult sentences or phrases it contains. Then summarize or restate the passage in your own words. You may also use background knowledge or illustrations to help you understand what you read.

## ACTIVITY

**Directions** Read each passage from the selection and summarize it or restate it in your own words to make sure you understand it. Refer back to the text if necessary.

| Passage | Summary or Restatement |
|---|---|
| "Cries and shouts and the wailings of the widows of warriors came over the chants and songs of triumph that his courtiers arranged to keep up at a loud pitch in his assembly hall." | **1.** |
| "After much thought, [Rama] decided to use 'Brahamasthra,' a weapon specially designed by the Creator Brahma on a former occasion, when he had to provide one for Shiva to destroy Tripura, the old monster who assumed the forms of flying mountains and settled down on habitations and cities, seeking to destroy the world." | **2.** |
| "Then the chariot horses of Ravana and Rama glared at each other in hostility, and the flags topping the chariots—Ravana's ensign of the Veena and Rama's with the whole universe on it—clashed, and one heard the stringing and twanging of bow-strings on both sides, overpowering in volume all other sound." | **3.** |

Name ______________________ Class ______________ Date ______________

# Selection Vocabulary Practice *(page 582)*

## Rama and Ravana in Battle *from the* Ramayana

**Vocabulary**

**magnitude** *n.* great size or importance
**intermittently** *adv.* on and off again; coming at intervals
**primordial** *adj.* original; existing from the beginning
**pristine** *adj.* pure; unspoiled

### EXERCISE A Practice with Connotation

A word's connotation is the ideas and feelings associated with it. For each vocabulary word, write a synonym. Then write the connotation for each.

| Vocabulary Word | Connotation | Synonym and Connotation |
|---|---|---|
| **1.** magnitude | | |
| **2.** primordial | | |
| **3.** pristine | | |

### EXERCISE B Applying Meanings

Complete each analogy.

**1.** pristine : dirty :: immense : __________

**a.** huge **b.** tiny **c.** mountain

**2.** knowledge: __________ :: magnitude : significance.

**a.** wisdom **b.** stupidity **c.** read

**3.** intermittently : continuously :: slowly : __________

**a.** walk **b.** gradually **c.** swiftly

### EXERCISE C Responding to the Selection

Write the story of Ravana attacking the divine elephants which Vibishana refers to at the end of the epic. Include a description of the way in which Ravana was gored in the back. Use at least THREE of the vocabulary words in your story.

Name ______________________ Class ____________ Date ____________

# Vocabulary Strategy *(page 582)*

## Greek and Latin Word Origins

## Rama and Ravana in Battle *from the* Ramayana

"Groans and wailings reached his ears with deadly clarity; and he noticed how the monkey hordes reveled in their bloody handiwork.

—"Rama and Ravana in Battle" *from* the Ramayana

**Connecting to Literature** Some of the words in these lines from the *Ramayana* have their roots in Greek or Latin. For example, *clarity* comes from the Latin root *clar*, which means "clear." Many words in the English language have their roots in Greek or Latin. Knowing the meaning of these roots can help you figure out the meanings of unfamiliar words.

Many prefixes and suffixes also come from Greek or Latin. By knowing the meaning of a word's prefix or suffix, along with the meaning of its root, you can decode the meaning of a word.

Here are some common Latin and Greek root words, prefixes, suffixes, and their meanings.

| Prefix | Root | Suffix |
|---|---|---|
| ***pre-*** before | ***dict*** say | ***-ion*** state or quality of |
| ***in-*** not *or* in | ***vert*** turn | |
| ***bene-*** good | ***fac*** make *or* do | ***-or*** one who |
| | ***aero*** air | ***-ate*** to make |
| ***re-*** back, again | ***ject*** throw | |
| ***in-*** not *or* in | ***spec*** see | |

## ACTIVITY

**Directions** Use a dictionary and the chart above to find the word parts, and their meanings, of the words below. Then write the definition of each.

**1.** spectator ______________________

**2.** aerial ______________________

**3.** averted ______________________

**4.** benediction ______________________

**5.** dejectedly ______________________

Name ______________________ Class ______________ Date ______________

# Grammar Practice *(page 582)*

## Sentence Fragments

## Rama and Ravana in Battle *from the* Ramayana

A **sentence fragment** is an incomplete sentence. It may lack a subject, a verb, or both. It might also be a subordinate clause that cannot stand alone. Correct sentence fragments by adding the missing words or phrases.

Ravana and his army. (missing a verb)

Couldn't stand the destruction. (missing a subject)

Into his chariot in search of Rama. (missing subject and verb)

## ACTIVITY

**Directions** Write *F* for each group of words that is a fragment and *S* for each group of words that is a complete sentence. Revise the fragments to make them complete sentences.

____ **1.** Shot arrows from a dozen bows.

____ **2.** In a chariot sent by the gods.

____ **3.** Rama and Ravana used supernatural weapons.

____ **4.** Rama and his army of monkeys.

____ **5.** Could ever win the battle?

____ **6.** Mahodara begged Ravana.

____ **7.** Unsure of what to do next.

____ **8.** Although he had prayed for his arms and heads to be indestructible.

____ **9.** Rama watched Ravana fall.

____ **10.** Surrounded by his brothers and all his other war chiefs.

Name ______________________ Class ______________ Date ______________

# Selection Quick Check *(page 582)*

## Rama and Ravana in Battle *from the* Ramayana

Use complete sentences to answer the following questions.

**1.** Why does Ravana decide to join the battle at the beginning of the excerpt?

______________________________________________

______________________________________________

______________________________________________

**2.** What does Ravana intend to do, once he has joined the battle?

______________________________________________

______________________________________________

______________________________________________

**3.** What do the gods send to Rama? Why?

______________________________________________

______________________________________________

______________________________________________

**4.** What weapons do Ravana and Rama fight with at first? What kinds of weapons do they later resort to?

______________________________________________

______________________________________________

______________________________________________

**5.** What does Rama tell Vibishana to do with Ravana?

______________________________________________

______________________________________________

______________________________________________

Name ______________________ Class ______________ Date ______________

## Prueba Rápida *(pág. 582)*

### Rama y Ravana en combate *del* Ramayana

Contesta las siguientes preguntas con oraciones completas.

**1.** ¿Por qué Ravana decide unirse a la batalla al comienzo del pasaje?

**2.** ¿Qué intenta hacer Ravana después de unirse a la batalla?

**3.** ¿Qué le envían los dioses a Rama? ¿Por qué?

**4.** ¿Cuáles son las armas con las que pelean Ravana y Rama al comienzo? ¿Qué tipos de armas usan después?

**5.** ¿Qué le dice Rama a Vibishana que debe hacer con Ravana?

Name ______________________ Class ______________ Date ______________

# Comparing Literature About Lessons *(page 594)*

## Graphic Organizer

## The Lion-Makers *from the* Panchatantra

## The Dog and the Wolf AESOP

## The Oak and the Reed JEAN DE LA FONTAINE

## The Elephant Who Challenged the World JAMES THURBER

Use the graphic organizer below to record how characters change and learn valuable lessons from the beginning of a story to its end.

**Directions** For each selection, use the first box to record which character appears foolish and which appears wise at the beginning of each story. In the second box, record which character appears foolish and which appears wise at the end of each story. This comparison can help you analyze how lessons are taught in each of the stories.

**1. The Lion-Makers**

Beginning of story

Foolish: ______________

Wise: ______________

End of story

Foolish: ______________

Wise: ______________

**2. The Dog and the Wolf**

Beginning of story

Foolish: ______________

Wise: ______________

End of story

Foolish: ______________

Wise: ______________

**3. The Oak and the Reed**

Beginning of story

Foolish: ______________

Wise: ______________

End of story

Foolish: ______________

Wise: ______________

**4. The Elephant Who Challenged the World**

Beginning of story

Foolish: ______________

Wise: ______________

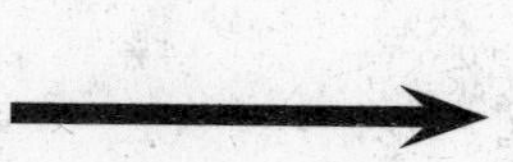

End of story

Foolish: ______________

Wise: ______________

Name ______________________ Class ______________ Date ______________

## Summary/Resumen *(p. 595)*

### The Lion-Makers *from the* Panchatantra

Four men—three of whom have great scholarship but lack sense and one who has only sense—set out to make their fortune. Coming across the remains of a dead lion, the three scholars decide—against the advice of the sensible man—to bring the lion back to life. The sensible man hides in a tree. When the lion is brought to life, it kills the three scholars. Only the man of sense survives.

---

### Los brahmanes y el león *del* Panchatantra

Cuatro hombres, tres de los cuales tenían muchos conocimientos pero nada de sentido común y uno que sólo tenía sentido común, se lanzan a buscar fortuna. Al encontrarse con los restos de un león muerto, los tres eruditos deciden revivir al león, en contra del consejo del hombre sensato, que se oculta en un árbol. Cuando el león revive, mata a los tres eruditos, y solamente se salva el hombre con sentido común.

Name ______________________ Class ____________ Date ______________

# Tóm Tắt *(p. 595)*

## Những Người Mang Lại Mạng Sống Cho Sư Tử *trích từ* Tập Truyện Ngụ Ngôn Panchatantra

Bốn người đàn ông—ba người học nhiều nhưng thiếu sự hiểu biết thông thường và một người thì ngược lại—lên đường đi tìm vận may. Đi ngang qua xác của một con sư tử chết, ba người nhiều chữ quyết định làm con sư tử sống lại—bất chấp lời khuyên của người đàn ông khôn ngoan. Người khôn ngoan nấp trên một cái cây. Khi con sư tử được cứu sống lại, nó giết chết ba người nhiều chữ. Chỉ có mỗi người có hiểu biết thông thường là sống sót.

Name ______________________________ Class _______________ Date _______________

## **Buod** *(p. 595)*

### Mga Tagagawa ng Leon *mula sa* Panchatantra

Apat na lalaki—na ang tatlo sa kanila ay matatalino pero walang sentido-komún at ang isa ay may sentido-komún —ay nagsimulang maghanap-buhay upang yumaman. Nang natuklasan nila ang bangkay ng isang patay na leon, nagpasiya ang tatlong iskolar — laban sa payô ng taong may sentido-komún— na buhayin muli ang leon. Nagtago ang taong may sentido-komún sa likod ng isang punô. Nang ang leon ay nabuhay muli, pinatay nito ang tatlong iskolar. Ang naligtas lamang ay ang taong may sentido- komún.

# 摘要 *(p. 595)*

## 來自 Panchatantra 的《獅子的復生》

有四個人一起出去碰運氣；他們之中有三個人具有豐富的學識但沒有常識，而另一人則僅有常識。當他們碰到一隻死去獅子的屍體時，這三個學者不顧有常識者的反對，決定要讓獅子起死回生。那個有常識的人躲到樹上。當獅子復生了以後，它殺了那三個學者。只有那個有常識的人活了下來。

Name ______________________ Class ______________ Date ______________

## **Rezime Selekyson** *(p. 595)*

### Moun Ki t ap Fè Lyon yo *nan* Panchatantra

Kat mesye—twa nan yo gen anpil konesans men pa gen yo bon sans, epi youn sèlman gen bon sans—antreprann fè fòtin. Le yo rankontre rès yon lyon mouri, twa save yo deside—malgre konsèy mesye sansib la—pou yo resisite lyon an. Mesye sansib la al kache nan yo pyebwa. Lè lyon an retounen vivan, li touye twa save yo. Sèl mesye ak bon sans la siviv.

## Zuag Tswvyim *(p. 595)*

### Tus Tsim Tsov Ntshuav *los ntawm* tus Panchatantra

Plaub tus neeg—peb tug kawm tau ntau tabsis tsis ntse thiab ib tug mas ntse heev—pib tawm mus nrhiav ua neej. Thaum los txog ntawm ib tus tsov ntxhuav tuag lawm, peb tug paub hais tias—tsis quav ntsej tus ntse cov lus—cia pab kom tus tsov ntxhuav rov ciaj sia. Tus ntse khiav nkaum saum ib tsob ntoo. Thaum tus tsov ntxhuav ciaj rov los, nws muab peb tug ntawd tom tuag tas. Tus ntse thiaj tseem nyob.

## Literary Element *(page 595)*

### Moral

### The Lion-Makers *from the* Panchatantra

In "The Lion-Makers," the writer includes the moral of the story both at the beginning and at the end of the story. A **moral** is a message, or a practical lesson, that the writer conveys to the reader about right and wrong. In some cases, the moral is not stated clearly, and it is up to the reader to figure it out. In other cases, as in fables such as "The Lion-Makers," the moral is stated clearly in an epigram or a maxim—a short verse or saying. Applying the epigram to the characters' actions allows readers to gain a deeper understanding of the lesson being taught and to apply it to their own lives.

## ACTIVITY

**Directions** Match each story summary or event with its epigram. Then for each epigram, write a short paragraph on a separate sheet of paper about an experience you or someone you know has had that fits with each lesson.

**1.** You stay up late playing computer games and do poorly on your math test.

**2.** A girl applies for a job, but the manager notices that the friends she is with are loud and disrespectful. She is turned down for the job.

**3.** A new family moves into the neighborhood, but because they wear strange clothes and speak a different language, no one talks to them. Finally, one of the neighbors strikes up a conversation with the parents, and the two families, finding they have much in common, become fast friends.

**4.** A small boy with few friends gets a new game that no one on the block has. Kids who used to make fun of him are soon coming over to his house to play. But when one of them breaks the game, they never come over again and resume making fun of him.

**a.** Fair weather friends are not worth much.

**b.** Acquaintance softens prejudices.

**c.** You are judged by the company you keep.

**d.** Early to bed and early to rise, makes a man healthy, wealthy, and wise.

Name ____________________ Class ____________ Date ____________

# Reading Strategy *(page 595)*

## Preview

## The Lion-Makers *from the* Panchatantra

When you are looking for a book at the library, chances are that you first **preview** the book. This means that you look at the title and cover art, the summary of the book on the back, the author, and the chapter titles. You get a good idea about the topic of the work, how it is organized, and its plot or theme.

When you preview a text, you know what to expect from it before you read it. Because you have a frame of reference, you are better able to understand the text as you read it.

## ACTIVITY

**Directions** Using the first row of the chart as a model, complete the second column as you preview the fable "The Lion-Makers." Include ideas about what each detail leads you to expect from the text.

| Detail | Previewing |
|---|---|
| Title: "The Lion-Makers" | The poem must be about people who make lions, although that sounds implausible. This text must not be realistic fiction. |
| Genre or type of writing | **1.** |
| Saying at the beginning: "Scholarship is…" | **2.** |
| Illustrations and captions | **3.** |
| Italic text, or other text that is set off | **4.** |

Name ____________________ Class ____________ Date ____________

# Selection Vocabulary Practice *(page 595)*

## The Lion-Makers *from the* Panchatantra

**Vocabulary**

**scholarship** *n.* academic achievement or knowledge
**attainment** *n.* accomplishment
**nullity** *n.* mere nothing; something insignificant

### EXERCISE A Practice with Word Parts

Word parts are root words, prefixes, and suffixes. If you are uncertain of the meaning of a word part, think of other words that contain the part. For example, if you are unsure of what the word *savagery* means but you know that *savage* means "fierce," think of other words that have the suffix *-ery,* such as *bravery*. You most likely know that *bravery* means "the quality of being brave," so the suffix *-ery* must mean "the quality of." Therefore you can conclude that *savagery* means "the quality of being savage."

For each vocabulary word, think of two other words whose meaning you know that contain the same suffix. Then write the meaning of the suffix.

| | Other Words | Meaning of Suffix |
|---|---|---|
| **1. scholarship** | ____________ | ____________ |
| **2. attainment** | ____________ | ____________ |
| **3. nullity** | ____________ | ____________ |

### EXERCISE B Applying Meanings

Complete each analogy.

**1.** learning : scholarship :: rage : ____________

**a.** calm **b.** fury **c.** disgust

**2.** huge : ____________ :: nullity : significant

**a.** enormous **b.** large **c.** tiny

**3.** attainment : achievement :: happiness : ____________

**a.** joy **b.** sadness **c.** smile

### EXERCISE C Responding to the Selection

Write a letter to the three eldest brothers explaining why you think having common sense is more important than learning things from books. Use all THREE vocabulary words in your letter.

Name ______________________ Class ______________ Date ______________

# Vocabulary Strategy *(page 595)*

## Homonyms and Homophones

## The Lion-Makers *from the* Panchatantra

> "Scholarship is less than sense; / Therefore seek intelligence:
> Senseless scholars in their pride / Made a lion; then they died."
>
> —"The Lion-Makers" *from the* Panchatantra

**Connecting to Literature** In this epigram from "The Lion-Makers," the writer uses the words *sense, pride,* and *died*. These words are homonyms or homophones. **Homonyms** are words that sound alike and are spelled alike but that have different meanings. For example, in the text, *pride* means "arrogance" or "self-importance." But another meaning for *pride* is "a group of lions." **Homophones** are words that sound alike but are spelled differently and have different meanings. In the excerpt, *died* means "passed away." But *dyed*, which has the same pronunciation, means "colored" or "stained."

To determine the correct definition of a homonym or homophone, use context clues: examine the word's part of speech within the sentence and the words that surround it.

## ACTIVITIES

**Directions** For each homonym, write the letter of the correct definition.

____ **1.** The termite **bored** through the wood.
- **a.** made weary
- **b.** made a hole

____ **2.** Did she just **bat** her eyes at you?
- **a.** wink
- **b.** hit the ball

____ **3.** I want to **bowl** tomorrow.
- **a.** play a bowling sport
- **b.** rounded dish

____ **4.** That dog is very **fast.**
- **a.** refrain from eating
- **b.** quick; speedy

____ **5.** Don't do anything **rash.**
- **a.** skin condition
- **b.** hasty

**Directions** Circle the correct homophone in each sentence.

**6.** She wrote on flowered (stationary/stationery).

**7.** The coal (minor/miner) was covered in soot.

**8.** You shouldn't (metal/meddle) in other people's affairs.

**9.** Mrs. Alvarez is the (principle/principal) of our school.

**10.** Please (wring/ring) out that wet towel and hang it up.

Name ______________________ Class ______________ Date ______________

## Grammar Practice *(page 595)*

### Run-On Sentences

### The Lion-Makers *from the* Panchatantra

A run-on sentence is two or more complete sentences written as though they were one sentence. A comma splice is perhaps the most common kind of run-on sentence. It occurs when two main clauses are separated by a comma rather than a semicolon or a period. Another kind of run-on sentence is formed when there is no punctuation between two main clauses. A third kind of run-on sentence is formed when there is no comma before a coordinating conjunction that joins two main clauses.

> Three of the Brahman were scholars with no sense, the fourth had sense but no scholarship. (Correct the run-on sentence by adding a coordinating conjunction, such as *and,* by replacing the comma with a semicolon, or by making each main clause a separate sentence.)
>
> The Brahmans went on a journey they wanted to use their scholarship to earn money. (Correct by adding a comma and a coordinating conjunction, by adding a semicolon, or by making each main clause a separate sentence.)
>
> The eldest Brahman wanted to leave the fourth behind but the third Brahman thought he should stay. (Correct by adding a comma before *but.*)

## ACTIVITY

**Directions** Correct each run-on sentence.

1. The *Panchatantra* is a collection of Indian fables they contain lessons about living wisely.
2. The stories in the *Panchatantra* were written down around 200 B.C., they were passed down through oral tradition.
3. The fourth Brahman had sense however, he found scholarship distasteful.
4. Scholarship is less than sense therefore seek intelligence.
5. They traveled in the forest, they came upon a lion's skeleton.
6. Three of the Brahmans wanted to bring the lion to life the fourth Brahman did not.
7. The *Panchatantra* was translated into many languages it was translated into English in 1570.
8. The lion came to life but the fourth Brahman did not die.
9. The first three Brahmans were great scholars, the fourth had sense.
10. The fourth Brahman warned the others they did not listen.

Name ______________________ Class ______________ Date ______________

## Selection Quick Check *(page 595)*

### The Lion-Makers *from the* Panchatantra

Use complete sentences to answer the following questions.

**1.** What do three of the Brahmans have in common?

______________________________________________

______________________________________________

______________________________________________

**2.** For what do the Brahmans think accomplishments should be used?

______________________________________________

______________________________________________

______________________________________________

**3.** Why do the first three Brahmans call the fourth Brahman a "dullard"?

______________________________________________

______________________________________________

______________________________________________

**4.** What reason does the third Brahman give for including the fourth Brahman on their journey and sharing any wealth with him?

______________________________________________

______________________________________________

______________________________________________

**5.** What warning does the fourth Brahman give the other three in the forest?

______________________________________________

______________________________________________

______________________________________________

Name ______________________ Class ______________ Date ______________

## Prueba Rápida *(pág. 595)*

### Los brahamanes y el león *del* Panchatantra

Contesta las siguientes preguntas con oraciones completas.

**1.** ¿Qué tienen en común los tres brahmanes?

______________________________________________

______________________________________________

______________________________________________

**2.** Según los brahmanes, ¿para qué deben usarse los logros?

______________________________________________

______________________________________________

______________________________________________

**3.** ¿Por qué los primeros tres brahmanes llaman "tonto" al cuarto bramán?

______________________________________________

______________________________________________

______________________________________________

**4.** ¿Qué rázon da el tercer brahmán para incluir al cuarto brahmán en su viaje y compartir la riqueza con él?

______________________________________________

______________________________________________

______________________________________________

**5.** ¿Qué aviso da el cuarto brahmán a los otros tres en el bosque?

______________________________________________

______________________________________________

______________________________________________

Name ______________________ Class ______________ Date ______________

## Summary/Resumen *(p. 607)*

### The Kabuliwallah RABINDRANATH TAGORE

The Kabuliwallah, a peddler from Kabul, becomes fast friends with the narrator's five-year-old daughter Mini in Calcutta. When the peddler is jailed for attacking a man who owes him money, both the narrator and Mini forget him. Eight years later, released from jail, the Kabuliwallah appears on Mini's wedding day. The Kabuliwallah is shocked at how different Mini is from the small child he remembered. Seeing Mini grown reminds the Kabuliwallah that his own daughter, far away in Afghanistan, must also be quite different from when he had last seen her. The narrator feels compassion for what both he and the Kabuliwallah have lost—the precious youth of their daughters.

---

### El Kabuliwallah

En Calcuta el Kabuliwallah, un vendedor ambulante de Kabul, establece una estrecha amistad con Mini, la hija de cinco años del narrador. Cuando el vendedor va a prisión por atacar a un hombre que le debía dinero, el narrador y Mini se olvidan de él. Ocho años más tarde, puesto en libertad, el Kabuliwallah aparece el día de la boda de Mini. El Kabuliwallah queda impresionado por lo diferente que es Mini de la pequeña niña que él recordaba. Ver a Mini ya crecida le recuerda al Kabuliwallah que su propia hija, que está lejos en Afganistán, también debe haber cambiado mucho desde la última vez que la vio. El narrador se compadece de lo que tanto él como el Kabuliwallah han perdido: la preciosa juventud de sus hijas.

Name ________________________________ Class _______________ Date ________________

# Tóm Tắt *(p. 607)*

## Người Kabuliwallah RABINDRANATH TAGORE

Một người Kabuliwallah, có nghĩa là người bán hàng rong đến từ Kabul, trở thành bạn tốt của cô con gái năm tuổi Mini của người thuật truyện ở Calcutta. Khi người bán hàng rong bị bắt giam vì tội tấn công một người nợ tiền mình, cả người thuật truyện và Mini quên luôn ông. Tám năm sau, khi được thả ra khỏi tù, Kabuliwallah xuất hiện ở đám cưới của Mini. Kabuliwallah cảm thấy choáng váng trước sự thay đổi của Mini so với hồi cô bé còn nhỏ. Nhìn thấy Mini trưởng thành khiến Kabuliwallah nhớ rằng con gái mình đang ở đất nước Afghanistan xa xôi hẳn cũng khác rất nhiều so với lần cuối ông nhìn thấy nó. Người thuật truyện cảm thấy thương hại cho những gì cả mình và người bán hàng rong vừa mất, đó chính là—tuổi thanh xuân quý giá của con gái họ.

## Buod *(p. 607)*

### Ang Kabuliwallah RABINDRANATH TAGORE

Ang Kabuliwallah, isang maglalako mula sa Kabul, ay naging matalik na kaibigan sa Calcutta ng limang-taong-gulang na babaeng anak ng nagsasalaysay na nagngangalang Mini. Nang ang maglalako ay nabilanggo dahil inatake niya ang isang lalaking may utang sa kanya, nakalimutan siya ng kapwa nagsasalaysay at ni Mini. Makaraan ang walong taon, pagkalabas sa bilangguan, dumating ang Kabuliwallah sa araw ng kasal ni Mini. Nagulat ang Kabuliwallah sa malaking pagbabago ni Mini mula nang ito'y maliit na bata. Nang nakita ng Kabuliwallah si Mini na malaki na, naalala niya na ang kanyang sariling anak na babae, na nasa Afghanistan, ay malamáng na talagang ibang-iba na ngayon simula nang huli niyang nakita ito. Ang nagsasalaysay ay nakaramdam ng awa para sa nawala sa kanya at sa Kabuliwallah —ang mahalagang kabataan ng kanilang mga anak na babae.

Name ______________________ Class ______________ Date ______________

# 摘要 *(p. 607)*

## Kabuliwallah 的故事 RABINDRANATH TAGORE

Kabuliwallah 是一個來自喀布爾的小販；他在加爾各答市很快地和敘述者的五歲女兒 Mini 成為朋友。當這個小販因為攻擊一個欠他錢的人而被關進監獄，敘述者和 Mini 都忘記了他。八年之後，當 Kabuliwallah 出獄後，他在 Mini 結婚的那一天出現了。Kabuliwallah 感到非常震驚，他所記得的 Mini 和現在的她非常不一樣。看到了長大成人的 Mini，讓 Kabuliwallah 想到他在遙遠阿富汗的自己的女兒，一定也和他上一次見到她的時候很不一樣了。敘述者對於他和 Kabuliwallah 同樣失去的一件事情而感到很惋惜 — 自己女兒的可貴青春時期。

Name ______________________ Class ______________ Date ______________

## Rezime Selekyson *(p. 607)*

### Kabuliwallah RABINDRANATH TAGORE

Kabuliwallah, yon kòlpòtè ki sòti Kaboul, vin zanmi byen vit ak pitit fi senkan moun k ap rakonte istwa a, Mini, nan Calcutta. Lè yo mete kòlpòtè a nan prizon poutèt li atake yon mesye ki dwe l lajan, ni moun k ap rakonte istwa a ni Mini bliye l. Witan pita, lè li sòti nan prizon, Kabuliwallah parèt jou maryaj Mini. Kabuliwallah choke pou jan Mini diferan te timoun li sonje a. Lè li wè Mini grandi, sa fè Kabuliwallah sonje pwòp pitit fi pa li, byen lwen nan Afganistan, dwe byen diferan de jan li te ye dènye fwa li te wè li. Moun k ap rakonte istwa a santi konpasyon pou sa ni li ni Kabuliwallah pèdi—jenès presye pitit fi yo.

Name ______________________ Class ______________ Date ______________

## Zuag Tswvyim *(p. 607)*

### Tus Neeg Lag Luam Kabuliwallah RABINDRANATH TAGORE

Tus Kabuliwallah, ib tus neeg lag luam tuaj Kabul tuaj, tig los ua phoojywg nrog tus hais zaj lus tus ntxhais tsib xyoo Mini nyob Calcutta. Thaum tus neeg lag luam raug coj mus kaw vim ntaus ib tus neeg tshuav nws nqi, Mini thiab nws txiv nov pab tug neeg lawm. Yim xyoo tomqab, tawm tsev nkauj los, tus Kabuliwallah tshwm tom Mini lub tshoob. Tus Kabuliwallah ceeb tas thaum pom Mini txawv thaum tseem yau uas nws nco tau. Pom Mini loj hlob tuaj ua rau Kabuliwallah nco nws tus ntxhais, nyob deb deb tim Afghanistan uas ntshai yuav txawv tshaj thaum nws pom zaum dhau los. Tus hais zaj lus mob siab txog kev hlub ntawm nkawd ob leeg, nws thiab Kabuliwallah uas tau ploj—yam nkawd muaj zoo tshaj hauv lub neej ntawm ob tus ntxhais.

Name ______________________ Class ______________ Date ______________

# Literary Element *(page 607)*

## Characterization

## The Kabuliwallah RABINDRANATH TAGORE

A writer uses **characterization** to reveal the personality of a character. One method writers use to reveal a character is by directly stating a character's traits. Other ways writers reveal a character are through the character's words, thoughts, and actions and by the way in which other characters interact and feel about that character. For example, at the beginning of "The Kabuliwallah," Mini goes into her father's room, takes her father's hand, and asks question after question. Her words and actions show that she is an inquisitive, talkative child who has a good relationship with her father.

## ACTIVITY

**Directions** Read the character's words, thoughts, or actions listed in the first column of the chart. Write in the second column what the words tell you about that character's personality.

| Character's Words, Thoughts, or Actions | What Is Revealed about the Character's Personality |
|---|---|
| **1.** The Kabuliwallah listens to Mini and gives her raisins, almonds, and a coin. | |
| **2.** At first Mini runs away, terrified of the Kabuliwallah. A few days later she is laughing with him. | |
| **3.** Mini's mother thinks that anyone who comes toward the house is a person who wants to harm them. | |
| **4.** Tears come to the narrator's eyes after he sees the Kabuliwallah's daughter's handprint. | |

Name ______________________ Class ______________ Date ______________

# Reading Strategy *(page 607)*

## Analyze Cultural Context

## The Kabuliwallah RABINDRANATH TAGORE

The **cultural context** includes the values, traditions, customs, and beliefs of the people and places in a story. Recognizing a story's cultural context can help you better understand the thoughts and actions of the characters. For example, outsiders were looked down upon in Indian culture. This knowledge helps explain why Mini had false fears about the Kabuliwallah at first.

## ACTIVITY

**Directions** Read the passages in the Cultural Context column. For each passage, write two examples from the story that illustrate how this information explains a character's thoughts, feelings, behaviors, or actions in the story.

| Cultural Context | Example |
|---|---|
| Outsiders were looked down upon in Indian society. | **1.**<br><br>**2.** |
| When Indian women marry, they go to live with their husband's family. | **3.**<br><br>**4.** |
| The narrator is a Hindu. | **5.**<br><br>**6.** |

Name ______________________ Class ____________ Date ____________

## Selection Vocabulary Practice *(page 607)*

### The Kabuliwallah RABINDRANATH TAGORE

**Vocabulary**

**demur** *n.* a hesitation or an objection
**formidable** *adj.* tending to inspire awe, wonder, or alarm
**arid** *adj.* excessively dry
**fettered** *adj.* chained; tied up
**sordid** *adj.* dirty; squalid; wretched

### EXERCISE A Practice with Word Origins

Knowing a word's origin can help you remember and understand its definition. Look at the word origins and their meanings. Write the vocabulary word next to its origin.

**1.** Latin word that comes from *formido:* terror ____________

**2.** Middle English word that comes from Old English *fot:* foot ____________

**3.** Latin word that comes from *arere:* to be dry ____________

**4.** Latin word that comes from *morari:* to linger ____________

### EXERCISE B Applying Meanings

Write the vocabulary word that is a synonym for each pair of words below.

**1.** fearsome, frightening, ____________

**2.** objection, protest, ____________

**3.** restrained, bound, ____________

**4.** filthy, grimy, ____________

**5.** parched, scorched, ____________

### EXERCISE C Responding to the Selection

Write one journal entry, choosing from the following: from the Kabuliwallah's point of view when he first sees Mini in her wedding dress; from the narrator's point of view when he first sees the Kabuliwallah after he has gotten out of prison; or from Mini's point of view when she sees the Kabuliwallah after he has gotten out of prison. Include the thoughts and feelings of the character at that point in time. Use at least THREE vocabulary words.

Name ______________________ Class ______________ Date ______________

# Vocabulary Strategy *(page 607)*

## Dictionary Use

## The Kabuliwallah RABINDRANATH TAGORE

> "I was hard at work on my seventeenth chapter, where Protrap Singh, the hero, . . . was about to escape with her by the third story window . . .
>
> So precarious was the position of my hero and my heroine that my first impulse was to stop and buy something since the man had been called."
>
> —*Rabindranath Tagore,* "The Kabuliwallah"

**Connecting to Literature** In this excerpt from "The Kabuliwallah," Rabindranath Tagore explains how his work was interrupted by his daughter's calling the Kabuliwallah. You may not be familiar with the meanings of some words, such as *precarious.* If you are unsure of a word's meaning, a dictionary can help.

**Find a Word** The guide words at the top of each page tell you the first and last words on that page. Use these words to help you quickly locate the word you want.

**The Main Entry** In addition to a word's definition, the main entry shows you how the word is broken into syllables, its pronunciation and part of speech, example sentences to show how a word is used, and the word's etymology, or history.

## ACTIVITY

**Directions** Use the dictionary entry below to answer the questions that follow.

**pre•car•i•ous** (pri kar' ə əs) *adj.* **1.** dependent on chance or unknown conditions; uncertain: *The queen's rule was precarious because she was extremely unpopular with her people.* **2.** dependent on chance conditions; doubtful: *The research was based on precarious generalizations.* **3.** dangerous; perilous: *The huge storm put the sailors in a precarious position.* [Latin *precarious* obtained by prayer or begging]

**1.** What part of speech is precarious? ______________________

**2.** How many meanings are given for *precarious?* Which meaning does Tagore use in the lines at the top of the page? How can you tell?

__________________________________________________________________

__________________________________________________________________

**3.** What is the history of the word *precarious?* How does this help you better understand the word?

__________________________________________________________________

__________________________________________________________________

__________________________________________________________________

Name ______________________ Class ______________ Date ______________

# Grammar Practice *(page 607)*

## Regular Verbs

## The Kabuliwallah RABINDRANATH TAGORE

All verbs have four principal parts—a base, or present form, a present participle, a past form, and a past participle. All verb tenses are formed from these principal parts.

Different types of verbs form their past participles differently. A regular verb forms its past and past participle by adding *-ed* or *-d* to the base form. In some regular verbs that end in *y*, the *y* is changed to *i*. In some regular verbs that end in a vowel and then a consonant, the final consonant is doubled.

**Principal Parts of Regular Verbs**

| Base | Present Participle | Past | Past Participle |
|---|---|---|---|
| chatter | chattering | chattered | chattered |
| cry | crying | cried | cried |
| throb | throbbing | throbbed | throbbed |

Used alone, the base form (except the base form of *be*) and the past form are the main verbs. However, one or more auxiliary verbs are required for the present participle and the past participle to function as the simple predicate.

Adults **murmur.** (base form) Adults **murmured.** (past form)

Adults are **murmuring.** (present participle with the auxiliary verb *are*)

Adults have **murmured.** (past participle with the auxiliary verb *have*)

## ACTIVITY

**Directions** Complete each sentence by writing the form of the verb shown in parentheses.

1. The Kabuliwallah __________ Mini's company. (past form of *enjoy*)
2. Mini is __________ with the Kabuliwallah. (present participle of *laugh*)
3. The narrator has __________ that the Kabuliwallah is a father, too. (past participle of *realize*)
4. Mini __________ for her wedding day. (past form of *prepare*)
5. The Kabuliwallah __________ almonds in paper. (past form of *wrap*)
6. The narrator is __________ what life is like in distant lands. (present participle of *imagine*)
7. Mini and her fiancé were __________ that night. (past participle of *marry*)
8. The narrator __________ the Kabuliwallah after eight years. (past form of *recognize*)

Name ______________________ Class ______________ Date ______________

## Selection Quick Check *(page 607)*

### The Kabuliwallah RABINDRANATH TAGORE

Use complete sentences to answer the following questions.

**1.** According to the narrator, what can five-year-old Mini not live without?

**2.** How does the Kabuliwallah try to win Mini's affections?

**3.** How do Mini and the Kabuliwallah spend their visits together?

**4.** Of whom does Mini remind the Kabuliwallah?

**5.** What present does the narrator give to the Kabuliwallah at the end of the story?

Name ______________________ Class ______________ Date ______________

# Prueba Rápida *(pág. 607)*

## El Kabuliwallah RABINDRANATH TAGORE

Contesta las siguientes preguntas con oraciones completas.

**1.** De acuerdo con el narrador, ¿qué no puede dejar de hacer Mini, la niña de cinco años?

______________________________________________

______________________________________________

______________________________________________

**2.** ¿Qué hace el Cabuliwallah para ganar el afecto de Mini?

______________________________________________

______________________________________________

______________________________________________

**3.** ¿Qué hacen Mini y el Cabuliwallah durante sus vistas?

______________________________________________

______________________________________________

______________________________________________

**4.** ¿A quién le recuerda Mini al Cabuliwallah?

______________________________________________

______________________________________________

______________________________________________

**5.** ¿Qué regalo da el narrador al Cabuliwallah al final del cuento?

______________________________________________

______________________________________________

______________________________________________

## Summary/Resumen *(p. 619)*

### Like the Sun R. K. NARAYAN

Sekhar, a teacher, vows to spend one day telling the complete truth. In the process, he insults his wife's cooking and his headmaster's musicianship. He finds that, as with the sun, it is hard for people to look truth straight in the face. His wife sulks, and the headmaster insists that Sekhar grade 100 papers overnight. Still, Sekhar concludes that the luxury of telling the untempered truth is worth the punishment.

---

### Como el Sol

Sekhar, un maestro, promete pasar un día diciendo toda la verdad. En el transcurso, insulta la comida hecha por su esposa y la música que toca su director. Descubre que, al igual que con el Sol, a las personas les resulta difícil enfrentarse cara a cara con la verdad. Su esposa se enfada y el director insiste en que Sekhar califique cien trabajos de un día para el otro. Aún así, Sekhar llega a la conclusión de que el placer de decir la verdad sin tapujos bien vale el castigo.

# Tóm Tắt *(p. 619)*

## Giống Như Mặt Trời R. K. NARAYAN

Sekhar, một giáo viên, thề sẽ dành một ngày chỉ để nói sự thật. Trong ngày thực hiện lời thề, anh chê khả năng nấu nướng của vợ mình và khả năng chơi nhạc của ông hiệu trưởng. Anh nhận thấy rằng, mọi người đều thấy nhìn thẳng vào sự thật cũng khó như nhìn thẳng lên ánh mặt trời. Vợ anh hờn dỗi còn vị hiệu trưởng nhất quyết yêu cầu Sekhar chấm 100 bài một đêm. Tuy vậy, Sekhar kết luận rằng việc nói ra sự thật không che đậy mang lại cảm giác rất hài lòng và do đó vẫn là điều đáng làm cho dù bị trừng phạt.

Name ______________________ Class ______________ Date ______________

## **Buod** *(p. 619)*

### Tulad ng Araw R. K. NARAYAN

Nangako si Sekhar, isang guro, na balang-araw ay sasabihin niya ang kompletong katotohanan. Kapag isinagawa niya ito, iinsultuhin niya ang pagluluto ng kanyang asawa at ang kaalaman ng kanyang punung-guro sa musika. Natuklasan niya na, tulad ng araw, mahirap tingnan ng mga tao nang deretsa ang katotohanan. Nagtampo ang kanyang asawa, at nagpumilit ang punung-guro na mag-gragrado si Sekhar ng isang daang papeles buong gabi. Gayunpaman, napag-isipan ni Sekhar na ang pagkakaroon ng pagkakataong sabihin ang masakit na katotohanan ay kasing-halaga ng parusa.

# 摘要 *(p. 619)*

## 和太陽一樣 R. K. NARAYAN

當老師的Sekhar誓言要一整天都直言無悔地完全說實話。在這個過程中，他侮辱了他太太的烹飪能力和他校長的音樂技巧。他發覺，直接面對實話就和直接看著太陽一樣困難。他的太太很生氣，而校長則堅持Sekhar連夜批改一百份作業。可是，Sekhar仍結論認為無節制說實話的樂趣，值得所受到的懲罰。

Name ______________________ Class ______________ Date ______________

## Rezime Selekyson *(p. 619)*

### Tankou Solèy R. K. NARAYAN

Sekhar, yon pwofesè, fè ve pou li pase yon jounen ap di laverite sèlman. Nan fè sa, li ensilte manje madanm li fè ak talan mizisyen direktè li. Li dekouvri, menm jan ak solèy, li di pou moun gade laverite nan fas. Madanm li fache, epi direktè a ensiste pou Sekhar korije san devwa yon sèl lannwit. Malgre sa, Sekhar konkli plezi di laverite san moderasyon vo pinisyon an.

## Zuag Tswvyim *(p. 619)*

### Zoo li lub Hnub R. K. NARAYAN

Sekhar, ib tus xibfwb, lees siv ib hnub los qhia tas nrho qhov tseeb. Thaum hais tawm, nws tau thuam nws pojniam ua noj thiab thuam nws tus kws qhia paj nkauj. Nws paub tias, ib yam li lub hnub, tibneeg muab ntsej muag ntsia nacj ncaj lub hnub nyuaj heev. Nws poj niam thiab tus xibfwb txaus siab los kom Sekhar ua haujlwm txheeb ib puas tus menyuam kev kawm ntawv ib hmo. Li ntawd los, Sekhar xaus tias kev lees txhaum los hais qhov tseeb tsim nyog kev rau txim lawm.

# Literary Element *(page 619)*

## Analogy

## Like the Sun R. K. NARAYAN

A writer uses an **analogy** to make comparisons of two things that are otherwise dissimilar. In using an analogy, writers help readers to better understand something that might be new or unfamiliar by comparing it to something that is familiar. For example, the analogy that is demonstrated repeatedly in "Like the Sun" is that hearing the truth is like looking at the sun because, just as people can't bear to look at the sun because it is so blinding, people don't like to hear the truth because it's too much to bear.

## ACTIVITY

**Directions** The following are other analogies that compare hearing a painful truth to something else. Tell whether or not you think each analogy works and why.

| Hearing the truth is like . . . | Reasons the Analogy Does or Does Not Work |
|---|---|
| listening to pleasant music. | **1.** |
| getting a punch in the stomach. | **2.** |
| diving into ice-cold water. | **3.** |
| gazing at a star-filled sky. | **4.** |

Name ______________________ Class ____________ Date ____________

# Reading Strategy *(page 619)*

## Activate Prior Knowledge

### Like the Sun R.K. NARAYAN

When you **activate prior knowledge,** you use what you already know—your own experiences, knowledge, and personal background—to understand the events, characters, and themes in a piece of literature. Even if a story takes place in a different time and culture, as in "Like the Sun," you can still use your prior knowledge to help you gain a better understanding of what you read. For example, you don't need to have been a teacher in an Indian school to know how telling the truth all of the time might affect friends and family.

| Prior Knowledge | Events in the Story |
|---|---|
| I was very hurt when my friend told me I was a bad athlete. | Sekhar tells his wife that he doesn't like her cooking, so I can understand that she feels hurt and angry. |

## ACTIVITY

**Directions** Complete the chart. For the event listed on the right, write an example from your own experience, or of people you know, that help you understand the event.

| Prior Knowledge | Helps me understand . . . |
|---|---|
| **1.** | how Sekhar feels when asked to tell the truth about his headmaster's singing. |
| **2.** | how Sekhar feels about putting off grading his papers for so long. |
| **3.** | why the headmaster chose to punish Sekhar after Sekhar told him the truth about his singing. |

Name ______________________ Class ____________ Date ____________

# Selection Vocabulary Practice *(page 619)*

## Like the Sun R. K. NARAYAN

**Vocabulary**

**shirk** *v.* to evade or avoid one's duty
**stupefied** *adj.* stupid, groggy, or insensible
**increment** *n.* something gained or added in a series, usually at regular intervals
**scrutinize** *v.* to examine with close attention to detail

### EXERCISE A Practice with Multiple-Meaning Words

Some words have more than one meaning. For example, the word *common* is used in "Like the Sun." It has several meanings, two of which are "shared by two or more people," and "ordinary." Circle the correct meaning of the bold-faced vocabulary word, based on context clues.

**1.** The **stupefied** audience watched the magician's incredible tricks.

**a.** stupid or groggy **b.** astonished

**2.** Don't **shirk** your duty to get to work on time.

**a.** avoid **b.** sneak

**3.** Her salary increased in normal **increments** every year.

**a.** things gained in a series at regular intervals

**b.** the rate at which something changes

### EXERCISE B Applying Meanings

Write the vocabulary word that best matches the situation.

**1.** A lazy boy might do this with his job of taking out the trash: ____________

**2.** Careful jury members do this with the evidence: ____________

**3.** A person might be this after a long, boring speech: ____________

### EXERCISE C Responding to the Selection

On a separate sheet of paper, write a journal entry describing a typical day, during which you told the absolute truth to everyone you met. Use at least TWO vocabulary words.

Name ______________________ Class ____________ Date ____________

# Vocabulary Strategy *(page 619)*

## Jargon

## Like the Sun R. K. NARAYAN

"I've engaged a drummer and a violinist to accompany me."
—*R.K. Narayan,* Like the Sun

**Connecting to Literature** In this excerpt from "Like the Sun," Narayan uses words that deal with the field of music. For example, in music, *accompany* means "to perform an instrumental or vocal part that supports a melody." *Accompany* also has a more common meaning: "to go with as a companion or associate." If you are not familiar with musical terms, you might not realize that the first meaning is the appropriate one for this passage. However, by studying the context, you can determine the word's meaning as Narayan used it.

Words that are related to a specific field or occupation, like *accompany,* are called **jargon.** In some cases, the words also have other, more common meanings.

## ACTIVITIES

**Directions** The phrases below are from "Like the Sun." Define the boldfaced words, which are jargon, based on their context. Use a dictionary if necessary.

| Jargon | Field or Occupation | Meaning |
|---|---|---|
| ". . . when he was teaching geography for **Third Form A** . . ." | education | **1.** |
| ". . . sing a full song **composed** by Thyagaraja . . ." | music | **2.** |
| "Sekhar received a note from the **headmaster.**" | education | **3.** |
| ". . . this is the first time I am doing it **full-dress** . . ." | the performing arts | **4.** |

**Directions** On a separate sheet of paper, write a sentence for each word listed below, based on its use as jargon in the field stated next to the word.

1. **chorus**—music
2. **private**—the military
3. **average**—mathematics

Name ______________________ Class ______________ Date ______________

## Grammar Practice *(page 619)*

### Irregular Verbs

### Like the Sun R. K. NARAYAN

An **irregular verb** forms its past and past participle in some way other than by adding *-ed* or *-d* to the base form. Following are some common irregular verbs.

**Principal Parts of Irregular Verbs**

| Base | Past | Past Participle | Base | Past | Past Participle |
|---|---|---|---|---|---|
| be | was, were | been | lie | lay | lain |
| become | became | become | lose | lost | lost |
| buy | bought | bought | see | saw | seen |
| choose | chose | chosen | seek | sought | sought |
| drink | drank | drunk | sell | sold | sold |
| drive | drove | driven | sing | sang | sung |
| fly | flew | flown | steal | stole | stolen |
| give | gave | given | swing | swung | swung |
| keep | kept | kept | take | took | taken |
| know | knew | known | tear | tore | torn |
| lay | laid | laid | think | thought | thought |
| lead | led | led | throw | threw | thrown |

**Directions** Complete each sentence by writing the form of the verb shown in parentheses.

1. Sekhar __________ to tell the truth for a day. (past form of *choose*)
2. The headmaster has __________ Sekhar's opinion. (past participle of *seek*)
3. The headmaster had __________ horribly for hours. (past participle of *sing*)
4. Sekhar's wife __________ angry with her husband. (past form of *become*)
5. The headmaster had __________ Sekhar ten days to grade the tests. (past participle of *give*)
6. Sekhar has __________ how truth affects people. (past participle of *see*)
7. Had Sekhar __________ how truth would affect people? (past participle of *know*)
8. Sekhar was worried as he __________ home. (past form of *drive*)

Name ______________________ Class ______________ Date ______________

## Selection Quick Check *(page 619)*

### Like the Sun R. K. NARAYAN

Use complete sentences to answer the following questions.

**1.** To what does Sekhar compare truth?

______________________________________________

______________________________________________

______________________________________________

**2.** According to Sekhar, why do people temper the truth?

______________________________________________

______________________________________________

______________________________________________

**3.** How does Sekhar respond to his wife's wince of pain when he tells her the truth about her culinary masterpiece?

______________________________________________

______________________________________________

______________________________________________

**4.** What work has Sekhar avoided completing in a number of weeks?

______________________________________________

______________________________________________

______________________________________________

**5.** How does Sekhar feel walking home from the headmaster's house?

______________________________________________

______________________________________________

______________________________________________

Name ________________ Class ________ Date ________

## Prueba Rápida *(pág. 619)*

### Como el Sol R. K. NARAYAN

Contesta las siguientes preguntas con oraciones completas.

**1.** ¿Con qué compara Sekhar la verdad?

**2.** Según Sekhar, ¿por qué la gente suaviza la verdad?

**3.** ¿Cómo responde Sekhar al gesto de dolor de su esposa cuando le dice la verdad acerca de su obra maestra culinaria?

**4.** ¿Qué trabajo pospone Sekhar durante varias semanas?

**5.** ¿Cómo se siente Sekhar en el camino de regreso dela casa del director?

## Summary/Resumen *(p. 625)*

### By Any Other Name SANTHA RAMA RAU

The narrator of this memoir of colonial times in India recalls how, when she was five and her sister eight, they were sent to a school run by the British. Without making any effort to learn the children's real names, the headmistress gives both girls English names. All the Indian children at the school are treated similarly: they are assigned seats in the last row, associate only with each other, and finally are assumed to be cheaters. This last indignity leads the older sister to march her sister home, never to return to the school.

---

### Con cualquier otro nombre

La autora de estas memorias de los tiempos coloniales en la India recuerda cómo, cuando tenía cinco años y su hermana ocho, fueron enviadas a una escuela que dirigían los británicos. Sin hacer ningún esfuerzo por aprender los nombres reales de las niñas, la directora les puso a las niñas nombres ingleses. Todos los niños indios en la escuela eran tratados de modo similar: los sentaban en la última fila, se relacionaban sólo entre ellos y finalmente, se suponía que hacían trampas. Esta última humillación hace que la mayor se lleve a su hermana a casa, para no regresar nunca a la escuela.

Name ______________________________ Class ______________ Date ______________

# Tóm Tắt *(p. 625)*

## Bằng Bất Kể Cái Tên Nào Khác SANTHA RAMA RAU

Đây là một hồi ký về thời kỳ thuộc địa ở Ấn Độ. Người thuật truyện nhớ lại khi mình năm tuổi và chị gái tám tuổi được đưa đến một trường học của người Anh. Không hề cố công để biết tên bọn trẻ, bà hiệu trưởng đặt cho hai cô bé những cái tên bằng tiếng Anh. Tất cả trẻ em Ấn Độ ở trường học đều bị đối xử giống như nhau: các em bị chỉ định ngồi xuống dãy bàn cuối, chỉ kết giao với nhau, và rồi bị cho là những kẻ gian lận. Sự sỉ nhục này khiến cho cô chị gái dắt em mình chạy một mạch về nhà và không bao giờ quay trở lại trường nữa.

# Buod *(p. 625)*

## Anuman ang Pangalan SANTHA RAMA RAU

Natatandaan ng nagsasalaysay ng buhay noong kolonyal na panahon sa India na noong siya'y limang-taong-gulang at ang kapatid niya ay walong-taong gulang, pinapunta sila sa isang paaralan na pinatatakbo ng British. Nang wala mang pagsisikap na matutunan ang mga tunay na pangalan ng mga bata, ang dalawang babae ay binigyan ng punung-guro ng mga Ingles na pangalan. Ganoon din ang pagtrato sa lahat ng mga Indian na bata sa paaralan: sila'y binigyan ng mga upuan sa huling hanay, nakipaghalubilo lamang sa isa't-isa, at sa kahulihan ay ipinalagay na mandaraya. Dahil sa huling insulto na ito, inuwi ng mas matandang kapatid na babae ang kanyang kapatid na babae, at hindi sila kailanman bumalik sa paaralan.

Name ______________________ Class ______________ Date ______________

# 摘要 *(p. 625)*

## 隨便取個名字 SANTHA RAMA RAU

這篇印度殖民地時期回憶錄的敘述者，描寫她五歲的時候，和她八歲的姐姐一起被送到英國人管理的學校上學。學校根本沒有想要知道這些小孩的姓名；女校長直接給這兩個小女孩取了英文的名字。學校裡面所有的印度小孩都受到相似的待遇：永遠坐在最後一排、只能在印度小孩之間互相來往、並被認為是作弊者。最後的一項屈辱，導致姐姐帶著妹妹回家，再也不去這個學校了。

Name ______________________ Class ______________ Date ______________

## Rezime Selekyson *(p. 625)*

### Ak Nenpòt Ki Lòt Non SANTHA RAMA RAU

Moun k ap rakonte memwa li sou tan kolonyal nan peyi Lenn ap sonje kijan, lè li te gen senkan epi sè li te gen witan, yo te voye yo nan yon lekòl Angle t ap dirije. San li pa fè okenn efò pou li aprann vre non timoun yo, direktris la bay toude tifi yo non angle. Tout timoun endyen nan lekòl la resevwa menm tretman an: yo ba yo plas nan dènye ranje a, ti Endyen yo rete sèlman antre yo, epi finalman yo sipoze ti Endyen yo triche. Dènye endiyite sa a fè pi gran sè a mennen ti sè li lakay, epi pa janm tounen nan lekòl la ankò.

## Zuag Tswvyim *(p. 625)*

### Rau lub Npe Twg Los Tau SANTHA RAMA RAU

Tus hais zaj kwvhuam, rau lub caij teb chaws Aakiv tseem tswj India, nco thaum nws muaj tsib xyoos hos tus niam laus muaj yim xoo; nkawd kawm tom lub tsev kawm ntawv neeg Aakiv tswj. Tsis tas yuav nyuaj kawm cov menyuam lub npe, tus poj xibfwb cia li tis npe Aakiv tsuag tsuag rau cov ntxhais. Cov menyuam India ces raug zaum kab rooj nram kawg; lawv sib tham heev ces ua rau tus xib fwb xav tias lawv sib nyiag. Qhov nov rhuav ntsej muag heev ces ua rau tus niam laus coj tus niam hluas tawm khiav tsis rov mus kawm ntawv ntxiv lawm.

Name ______________________ Class ______________ Date ______________

# Literary Element *(page 625)*

## Autobiography

## By Any Other Name SANTHA RAMA RAU

An **autobiography** is the story of a person's life that is written by that person. Autobiographies reveal a lot about authors and often include details that help you understand what life was like during the time and in the place they lived. Writers of autobiographies often write about the times in their lives that were the most meaningful to them and to their purpose for writing. For example, Rau wrote about her time in the Anglo-Indian school not only because it made such an impression on her but also because it illustrates larger, more global issues that others can relate to.

## ACTIVITY

**Directions** The following are details from "By Any Other Name." For each one, write how the detail was important to the author's life, the impact it had on you as the reader, and the author's purpose for including the detail. The first one is done for you.

| Detail | Importance to Author | Impact on Reader | Purpose |
|---|---|---|---|
| The headmistress won't use Indian names. | felt her identity was taken away; didn't feel responsible for "Cynthia's" actions | I felt indignation for Santha at the unfairness of her "renaming." | to show people how people's prejudices affect others |
| The Indian children are isolated at the back of the classroom. | **1.** | **2.** | **3.** |
| British children eat sandwiches. Premila asks to bring sandwiches. | **4.** | **5.** | **6.** |
| Premila leaves school after being told Indian children cheat. | **7.** | **8.** | **9.** |

Name ______________________ Class ______________ Date ______________

## Reading Strategy *(page 625)*

### Connect to Contemporary Issues

### By Any Other Name SANTHA RAMA RAU

In many pieces of literature, the themes, characters, and events are meaningful not only during the time in which the work was written, but today as well. Rau touches on many issues in her story "By Any Other Name" that are meaningful today. By **connecting what you read to contemporary issues**, you can gain a deeper understanding of the text you are reading, as well as the issues that face us today.

For example, in "By Any Other Name," Premila tells her mother they should have sandwiches for lunch. This is an example of how people reject their own traditions to fit in with the cultures of others. You can connect this issue to a contemporary issue such as the following: People who come to our country learn English to fit in with our culture.

## ACTIVITY

**Directions** Complete the chart. For the issue listed on the left, write in the second column an example from "By Any Other Name" that illustrates this issue. In the last column, write an example from contemporary times that illustrates this issue. Consult the Internet or a newspaper, if necessary.

| Issue | Example from "By Any Other Name" | Example from Contemporary Times |
|---|---|---|
| People are judged by the prejudices of others. | **1.** | **2.** |
| People stand up for their rights when they think they have been mistreated. | **3.** | **4.** |
| Some people believe that their culture is superior to that of other people and try to impose it on others. | **5.** | **6.** |

Name ______________________ Class ______________ Date ______________

# Selection Vocabulary Practice *(page 625)*

## By Any Other Name SANTHA RAMA RAU

**Vocabulary**

**provincial** *adj.* belonging or peculiar to a particular province; local; lacking sophistication or polish
**insular** *adj.* isolated; narrow-minded
**incomprehensible** *adj.* unintelligible; indiscernible; not understood
**sedately** *adv.* in a dignified or serious manner; calmly; solemnly
**tepid** *adj.* lukewarm; halfhearted

### EXERCISE A Practice with Context Clues

To better understand the meaning of an unfamiliar word, you should look at the context, or the words that surround it. By studying the context carefully, you can figure out the word's meaning. Write the word from the vocabulary list that best completes each sentence.

**1.** The headmistress ignored __________ customs and traditions.

**2.** The __________ way of thinking of the English teachers was insulting to the Indian children.

**3.** Santha had a __________ interest in the Anglo-Indian school.

### EXERCISE B Applying Meanings

Write the vocabulary word that is an antonym for each boldfaced word or phrase.

**1.** The headmistress said their Indian names were **easy to understand.** __________

**2.** The children played the game very **boisterously.** __________

**3.** Premila's reaction to the school was **enthusiastic.** __________

### EXERCISE C Responding to the Text

On the back of this page, write a journal entry from Premila's point of view on the day of the test. Include dialogue, responses of her teacher and classmates, as well as her thoughts and feelings. Use at least THREE of the vocabulary words.

Name ______________________ Class ______________ Date ______________

# Vocabulary Strategy *(page 625)*

## Multiple-Meaning Words

## By Any Other Name SANTHA RAMA RAU

"She had long, glossy-black braids and wore a cotton dress..."

—*Santha Rama Rau,* "By Any Other Name"

**Connecting to Literature** In this excerpt from "By Any Other Name," there are a few words that could have more than one meaning. For example, *long* can be an adjective that means the "opposite of short," or it can be a verb that means "to yearn." The word *long* is a multiple-meaning word. Multiple-meaning words have two or more definitions.

To determine the correct definition of a multiple-meaning word in a sentence, use context clues: examine the word's part of speech within the sentence and the words that surround it.

Here are some common multiple-meaning words:

| Word | Denotation | Connotation |
|---|---|---|
| mean | • intend<br>• unkind | They *mean* to win the game.<br>The *mean* dog growled at everyone. |
| rest | • relax<br>• remainder | Let's *rest* before the race.<br>Write the *rest* of the report tomorrow. |



## ACTIVITY

**Directions** Circle the correct definition for the multiple-meaning word in each sentence. Use a dictionary if necessary.

**1.** The thirsty children drank the **punch.** **a.** sweet drink **b.** to strike with a fist

**2.** When will the plane **land?** **a.** part of Earth's surface **b.** set down

**3.** The farmer put the pigs in the **pen.** **a.** small enclosure **b.** writing instrument

**4.** Put the jewelry in the **safe.** **a.** secure **b.** protected place for keeping valuables

**5.** Our state **borders** three others. **a.** touches at the boundaries **b.** designs at the edge of a fabric, rug, or piece of art

**6.** Let's **reflect** on what we read. **a.** think about **b.** mirror

**7.** I will **press** that wrinkled shirt. **a.** member of the news media **b.** iron

**8.** The fish **snapped** at the bait. **a.** grabbed quickly with the mouth **b.** said abruptly

Name ______________________ Class ______________ Date ______________

# Grammar Practice *(page 625)*

## Verb Tenses: Present, Past, and Future

## By Any Other Name SANTHA RAMA RAU

Verb tenses help to show when events take place—in the present, the past, or the future.

The **present tense** expresses a constant, repeated, habitual, or customary action or condition. It can also express a general truth or an action or condition that is happening right now.

At home, Santha and Premila **take** a nap in the afternoon. (habitual action)

Santha **feels** uncomfortable. (not always but just now)

The **past tense** expresses an action or condition that was started and completed in the past.

The headmistress **gave** Santha and Premila English names.

Use the **future tense** to express an action or condition that will occur in the future. Use *will* or *shall* before the base form of the verb to form the future tense. Future time can also be expressed using the present tense with an adverb or adverb phrase that states a future time.

Premila **will** go home. Santha **shall** take a siesta. They **will** leave next week.

## ACTIVITY

**Directions** Complete each sentence with the correct verb in the tense shown in parentheses.

**1.** The girls ____________ Indian food for lunch. (*eat,* past)

**2.** Santha ____________ her first day of school. (*remember,* present)

**3.** They ____________ competitive games at school. (*play,* future)

**4.** Their mother ____________ them they didn't have to go back. (*tell,* past)

**5.** Santha ____________ a wonderful evening outside. (*have,* past)

**6.** Santha ____________ about her first day of school. (*write,* future)

**7.** She ____________ kohl around her eyes. (*wear,* present)

Name ______________________ Class ______________ Date ______________

## Selection Quick Check *(page 625)*

### By Any Other Name SANTHA RAMA RAU

Use complete sentences to answer the following questions.

**1.** Who is the narrator of the memoir?

**2.** What "pretty English names" does the headmistress give to Santha and Premila?

**3.** How do the sisters' lunches differ from the other students' lunches?

**4.** Why is the narrator accused of "not being a good sport" during play?

**5.** At the end, why is the narrator able to put the experience "happily away"?

Name ______________________ Class ____________ Date ____________

## Prueba Rápida *(pág. 625)*

### Con cualquier otro nombre SANTHA RAMA RAU

Contesta las siguientes preguntas con oraciones completas.

**1.** ¿Quién es la narradora de las memorias?

**2.** ¿Qué "nombres ingleses bonitos" da la directora a Santha y a Premila?

**3.** ¿En qué se diferencian los almuerzos de las hermanas de los almuerzos de las otras estudiantes?

**4.** ¿Por qué la narradora es acusada de "no ser buena jugadora" durante el juego?

**5.** Al final, ¿por qué la narradora puede olvidar la experiencia "con fellicidad"?

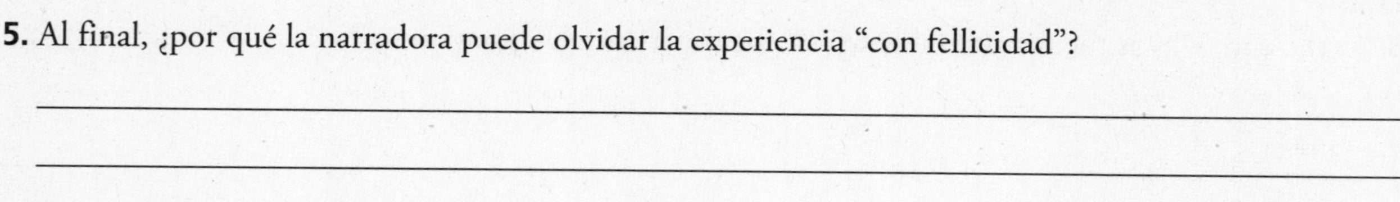

Name ____________________ Class ____________ Date ____________

## Summary/Resumen *(p. 636)*

### The Wagon KHALIDA ASGHAR

A man sees three strange men on a bridge watching the sunset. People in the city gradually begin to notice that the sky blazes blood red, even at nightfall. The city's residents begin to experience waves of a pungent smell, apparently coming from wagonloads of garbage that roll through the city. One day the three strange men, who had been the first to notice the unusual color of the sun, look inside one of the garbage wagons. They are struck dumb with horror at what they see and then flee, never to be seen again. The stench abates, but the man never learns what the three men had seen inside the wagon.

---

### La carreta

El autor ve a tres hombres extraños sobre un puente mirando la puesta del Sol. Las personas de la ciudad comienzan a advertir gradualmente que el cielo se tiñe de rojo sangre, aún al anochecer. Los residentes de la ciudad comienzan a percibir oleadas de un olor penetrante, que aparentemente proviene de la carga de las carretas de basura que atraviesan la ciudad. Un día los tres hombres extraños, que habían sido los primeros en advertir el color inusual del Sol, miran dentro de las carretas de basura. Quedan mudos del horror por lo que ven y huyen, sin ser vistos nunca más. El hedor disminuye, pero el autor nunca descubre que fue lo que vieron dentro de la carreta los tres hombres.

# Tóm Tắt *(p. 636)*

## Xe Chở Rác KHALIDA ASGHAR

Người thuật truyện nhìn thấy ba người đàn ông lạ trên một cây cầu xem mặt trời lặn. Mọi người trong thành phố dần dần phát hiện ra rằng bầu trời chiếu màu đỏ như máu, ngay cả lúc màn đêm buông xuống. Cư dân trong thành phố bắt đầu liên tục ngửi thấy mùi hăng cay, hình như tỏa ra từ những xe chất đầy rác đi qua thành phố. Một ngày kia, ba người lạ mặt, những người đầu tiên nhận ra màu sắc không bình thường của mặt trời, nhìn vào một trong số các xe chở rác. Họ kinh hãi không thốt ra lời trước những gì họ nhìn thấy, bèn bỏ chạy và không ai còn nhìn thấy họ nữa. Mùi hôi thối bớt dần, nhưng người thuật truyện không bao giờ biết được ba người đàn ông đó đã nhìn thấy gì trong xe chở rác.

Name ______________________ Class ______________ Date ______________

# Buod *(p. 636)*

## Ang Karo KHALIDA ASGHAR

Nakakita ang nagsasalaysay ng tatlong di-kilalang lalaki sa tulay, nanonood ng paglubog ng araw. Unti-unting napapansin ng mga tao sa siyudad na ang langit ay nagiging pula, tulad ng dugo, kahit sa gabi. Nagsimulang makaamoy ang mga naninirahan sa siyudad ng amoy na sumusuot sa ilong, tila mula sa mga karo ng basura na nagdaraan sa siyudad. Isang araw, ang tatlong taong ito na hindi kilala, na unang nakapansin sa di-karaniwang kulay ng araw, ay tumingin sa loob ng isa sa mga karo ng basura. Nasindak sila sa kanilang nakita, at sila'y tumakbo, at hindi sila kailanman nakita muli. Nawala ang amoy, pero hindi kailanman natuklasan ng nagsasalaysay kung ano ang nakita ng tatlong lalaki sa loob ng karo.

Name ______________________ Class ______________ Date ______________

# 摘要 *(p. 636)*

## 恐怖的馬車 KHALIDA ASGHAR

敘述者看到三個奇怪的男子，在橋上觀賞日落。城市的居民漸漸注意到，即使在傍晚的時候天空也會呈現明亮的血紅色。這個城市的居民開始聞到一陣陣的辛辣刺激味道；很明顯是來自於穿過市區的很多垃圾馬車。有一天，這三個首先注意到太陽不正常顏色的奇怪男子，往一部垃圾馬車裡面看。他們對所看到的東西恐怖地目瞪口呆；然後他們逃跑了，再也沒有出現過。這個惡臭後來減弱了；可是敘述者一直都不知道這三個人到底在馬車裡看到了什麼東西。

Name ________________ Class ________________ Date ________________

## Rezime Selekyson *(p. 636)*

### Vagon an KHALIDA ASGHAR

Moun k ap rakonte istwa a wè twa zòm etranj sou yon pon k ap gade solèy la k ap kouche. Moun nan vil la pezape kòmanse remake syèl la yon wouj san briyan, menm lè lannwit tonbe. Rezidan vil la kòmanse pran yon sant dezagreyab, ki sanble sòti nan chajman fatra ki nan vagon k ap woule nan vil la. Yon jou twa zòm etranj yo, ki te remake koulè inabityèl solèy la an premye, gade anndan youn nan vagon fatra yo. Yo wè yon bagay terib ki rann yo bèbè epi yo sove, moun pa janm wè yo ankò. Odè repousan an ale, men moun k ap rakonte istwa a pa janm konnen kisa twa zòm yo te wè anndan vagon an.

## Zuag Tswvyim *(p. 636)*

### Lub Tsheb KHALIDA ASGHAR

Tus hais zaj lus pom peb tug neeg txawv saum ib tug choj saib lub hnub poob. Tib neeg hauv zos pib pom zujzus tias lub ntuj ci liab ploog li ntshav, txawm poob mus rau yav tsaus ntuj zus. Cov neeg nruab zos pib ntsib tej nthwv pa tsw phem, ncho los ntawm cov khibnyawb uas ntog raws hauv nroog. In hnub, peb tus neeg kws yog cov xub pom cov xim txawvtxav ntawm lub hnub, mus xauj hauv cov tsheb khibnyawb. Lawv ceeb vwm tas rau yam lawv pom thiab ntsib, ces lawv khiav tawm, tsis xav pom ntxiv lawm. Cov pa nqig zuj zus, tabsis tus hais zaj lus paub tsis tau tias peb tus neeg ntawd pom dabtsi hauv lub tsheb.

Name ________________ Class ________ Date ________

# Literary Element *(page 636)*

## Narrator

## The Wagon KHALIDA ASGHAR

The **narrator** of a story is the person who tells the story. A writer's choice of narrator can make a big difference in how a reader understands and interprets the story. A narrator who is a character in the story uses *I* or *me* to talk about himself or herself and tells the story in the first-person point of view. We know only what the narrator knows and perceives about the world and only the narrator's thoughts and feelings.

When reading a story with first-person point of view, we have to judge the narrator, to decide if he or she is **reliable** or **unreliable**. Our opinion is based on the events and other characters in the story. For example, at one point in "The Wagon," the narrator is at the bookstore and is deeply affected by the smell, but the other characters smell nothing. Therefore, we must decide whether there actually is a smell and only the narrator is affected by it, or whether the narrator is just imagining it.

## ACTIVITY

**Directions** For each detail, tell how the experience of the narrator of "The Wagon" differs from those around him. Then write what you think the actual truth is.

| Detail | Narrator's Experience vs. Other Characters | Actual Truth |
|---|---|---|
| The narrator is sickened and consumed by thoughts of the muck-wagon. | **1.** | **2.** |
| The narrator has frequent encounters with the three men on the bridge. | **3.** | **4.** |
| The cityfolk are no longer bothered by the odor, but narrator is still affected. | **5.** | **6.** |

Name ______________________ Class ______________ Date ______________

# Reading Strategy *(page 636)*

## Identify Ambiguities

### The Wagon KHALIDA ASGHAR

An **ambiguity** is a statement or description that can be interpreted in more than one way or that cannot be explained in any one, clear way. Identifying ambiguities can help you discover hidden meanings in a text.

> "I found nothing extraordinary in the scene; so I looked back at them instead. Their faces, although not at all similar, still looked curiously alike."

There are ambiguities in this passage from "The Wagon." For example, how can the men look alike if their faces are "not at all similar"? By thinking more deeply about this discrepancy, the reader may come to the conclusion that although they are not related by blood, they may look alike because they do the same kind of work, or they are concerned about the same things. This information gives us insight into not only how the men are related but also their larger role in the story.

## ACTIVITY

**Directions** For each excerpt, tell what the ambiguity is and explain the ambiguity.

"I turned around to look at the stretch of sky over the distant Ravi. I was stunned: it was glowing red despite the darkness.

'You are right,' I said, to hide my puzzlement, 'we really did fail to notice that.'"

**1.** ambiguity: ______________________

**2.** explanation: ______________________

"My condition frightened Zakiya, who asked, 'What's the matter—you look so pale?'

'I'm all right. God knows what that smell is,' I said. . .

Zakiya also sniffed the air, then said. 'Must be coming from the house of Hakim Sahib. . . . Or else it's from burnt food.'"

**3.** ambiguity: ______________________

**4.** explanation: ______________________

"The cityfolk are no longer bothered by the slashing stench. They have become immune to it and think it has died. . .

But it continues to torment my body. . ."

**5.** ambiguity: ______________________

**6.** explanation: ______________________

Name ______________________ Class ____________ Date ____________

# Selection Vocabulary Practice *(page 636)*

## The Wagon KHALIDA ASGHAR

### Vocabulary

**impervious** *adj.* not easily affected or disturbed
**inexorable** *adj.* relentless; unyielding
**pungent** *adj.* having a sharp or stinging quality, especially affecting the sense of taste or smell
**surge** *n.* a strong, sudden increase or flow

### EXERCISE A Practice with Context Clues

To better understand the meaning of an unfamiliar word, look at the context, or the words that surround it. Write the vocabulary word that completes each sentence, based on the context.

**1.** The __________ cheese had a sharp, cutting taste.

**2.** __________ to the noise, the girl finished the test unaffected by her surroundings.

**3.** The houses were overcome by the __________ of water from the breach in the dam.

### EXERCISE B Applying Meanings

Complete each analogy.

**1.** inexorable : avoidable :: clean : __________

**a.** spotless **b.** filthy **c.** wipe

**2.** bland : white rice :: pungent: __________

**a.** water **b.** rotten eggs **c.** spicy

**3.** surge : gush :: throw : __________

**a.** toss **b.** ball **c.** drop

### EXERCISE C Responding to the Text

On the back of this page, write additional paragraphs to the end of the story in which the narrator discovers what is inside the wagon. Use descriptive language and include the narrator's thoughts and feelings. Use at least TWO of the vocabulary words.

Name ______________________ Class ____________ Date ____________

# Vocabulary Strategy *(page 636)*

## Thesaurus Use

## The Wagon KHALIDA ASGHAR

"Wrecked by insomnia and exhaustion, people strained . . . to appear carefree and cheerful."

"Damaged by restlessness and drowsiness, people tried hard . . . to look untroubled and glad."

—*Khalida Asghar,* from "The Wagon"

**Connecting to Literature** In the first passage, from "The Wagon," the narrator describes how people were affected by whatever was causing the odor. In the second passage, several words have been replaced by synonyms, or two words that are similar in meaning. Notice how the meaning of the passage has changed slightly. That is because the connotation, or ideas and emotions associated with a word, for each synonym is different.

To learn more about synonyms, you can use a thesaurus. A thesaurus is a specialized dictionary of synonyms and antonyms. It can be organized in dictionary style or in traditional style in which you can look up a word in the index and refer to the pages listed for synonyms and antonyms for the word.

## ACTIVITY

**Directions** Using a thesaurus, find two synonyms for each of the following words from the selection. After each synonym, write the meaning of the synonym.

| Word from the Selection | Synonyms | Meanings of Synonyms |
|---|---|---|
| trudged | **1.** | **3.** |
| | **2.** | **4.** |
| uncanny | **5.** | **7.** |
| | **6.** | **8.** |
| odor | **9.** | **11.** |
| | **10.** | **12.** |

Name ______________________ Class ______________ Date ______________

# Grammar Practice *(page 636)*

## Perfect Tenses: Present, Past, and Future

### The Wagon KHALIDA ASGHAR

There are three perfect tenses in the English language: the present perfect, the past perfect, and the future perfect.

The **present perfect tense** expresses an action or condition that occurred at some indefinite time in the past. This tense also shows an action or condition that began in the past and continues into the present. To form the present perfect tense, use *has* or *have* with the past participle of the verb.

> He **has seen** the three men before. (past indefinite action)
>
> We **have smelled** the odor for days (action begins in past, continues into present.)

Use the **past perfect tense** to indicate that one past action or condition began and ended before another past action started. To form the past perfect tense, use *had* with the past participle of a verb.

> By the time the show began (past), people **had waited** for hours. (past perfect)

Use the **future perfect tense** to express one future action that will begin and end before another future action begins. To form the future perfect tense, use *will have* or *shall have* with the past participle of a verb.

> By nightfall, the three men **will have arrived** at the bridge.

## ACTIVITIES

**Directions** Underline each perfect tense verb and identify it by writing *present perf., past perf.,* or *future perf.* in the blank.

**1.** The men had trudged for miles before they reached the bridge.
______________

**2.** The people have become sick in just a few weeks. ______________

**3.** How many will have died by next year? ______________

**4.** The price of sleeping pills has skyrocketed. ______________

**Directions** Complete each sentence by writing the verb in the tense shown in parentheses.

**5.** He ______________ to his knees from the pain. (*fell,* present perfect)

**6.** Zakiya ______________ worried after he threw himself on the bed. (*became,* past perfect)

**7.** By spring, the odor ______________ around for months. (*be,* future perfect)

**8.** The cityfolk ______________ that the odor is gone. (*decide,* present perfect)

Name ______________________ Class ______________ Date ______________

## Selection Quick Check *(page 636)*

### The Wagon KHALIDA ASGHAR

Use complete sentences to answer the following questions.

**1.** At the beginning of the story, what are the three men watching from the bridge?

**2.** What happens to the sky, even after the sun sets?

**3.** Where does the narrator often stop for a friendly chat?

**4.** What happens to the pungent stench at sundown?

**5.** Where does the narrator see the three strange men again?

Name ______________________ Class ______________ Date ______________

## Prueba Rápida *(pág. 636)*

### La carreta KHALIDA ASGHAR

Contesta las siguientes preguntas con oraciones completas.

**1.** Al principio del cuento, ¿qué observan los tres hombres desde el puente?

______________________________________________

______________________________________________

______________________________________________

**2.** ¿Qué sucede en el cielo, aun después de que se oculta el sol?

______________________________________________

______________________________________________

______________________________________________

**3.** ¿Dónde se detiene el narrador con frecuencia para una conversación amigable?

______________________________________________

______________________________________________

______________________________________________

**4.** ¿Qué sucede con el olor desagradable durante el anochecer?

______________________________________________

______________________________________________

______________________________________________

**5.** ¿Dónde ve de nuevo el narrador a los tres extraños?

______________________________________________

______________________________________________

______________________________________________

Name ______________________ Class ______________ Date ______________

# Spelling Practice

## Similar-Looking Words

Some words are easy to confuse because they look alike in some way. Learn to distinguish words by spelling them correctly.

## ACTIVITY

**Directions** These pairs of unit words have at least one syllable in common or appear similar in some other way. In the sentences that follow, write the correct pair of words.

| | |
|---|---|
| abate—abandoned | inexorable—incur |
| fatuous—treacherous | conspire—considerably |
| pristine—clandestine | pugnacious—pungent |
| demur—murmur | restore—redeem |

1. Her __________ behavior on the hike put the group in danger. She did not pay attention to the slippery and __________ sections of the trail.
2. The seaside cove was beautiful and __________. It was an isolated, __________ meeting place, so the landscape went virtually untouched.
3. Neighborhood residents wanted to __________ the park's dilapidated basketball court. They raised money to __________ the land from developers to make improvements.
4. When she accepted the committee's recommendation without __________, there was a __________ of surprise at her decision.
5. If it feels threatened, a bear may become __________, but a skunk simply releases a strong, __________ odor.
6. The __________ effects of the drought severely damaged the crops. The farmers would __________ great losses when harvest time arrived.
7. It was apparent that the rain would not __________, so we __________ our plans for a picnic.

Name ______________________ Class ____________ Date ____________

# Writing Workshop *(page 652)*

## Reflective Essay

## Graphic Organizer

A reflective essay explores the meaning of a personal experience.

### ACTIVITY

**Directions** Determine a subject for your reflective essay. Then use the graphic organizer below to help you develop the content. Write your topic in the center oval. Fill in the surrounding ovals with narrative details you might want to include in your essay. Use these suggestions to generate ideas for those supporting details:

- Note precise details and use word pictures that *show* what happened.
- Add comments that explain why the experience was meaningful to you.
- Use specific sensory images—how something looked, felt, tasted, smelled, or sounded.
- Include background details to explain how you felt before the experience.

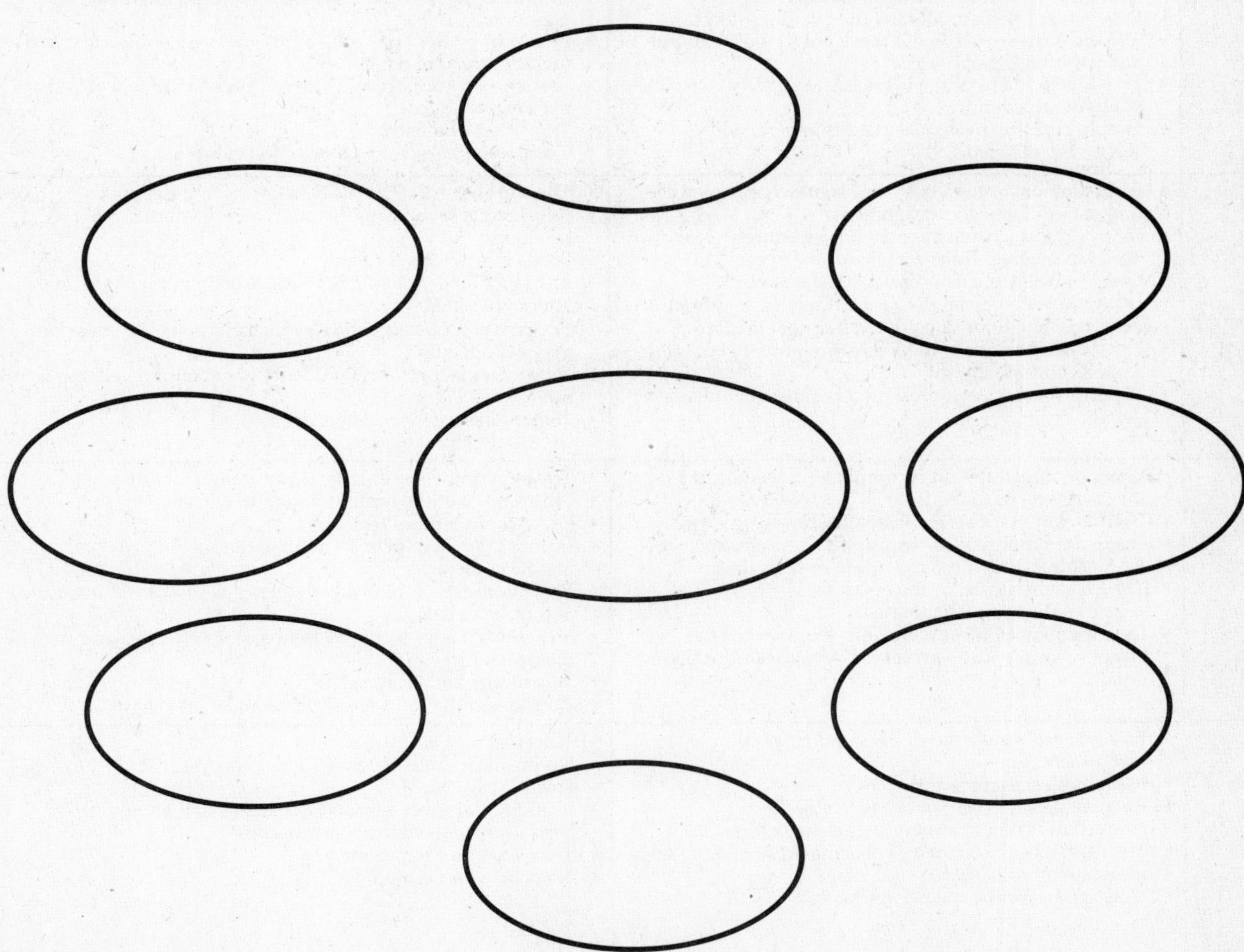

# Writing Workshop Rubric

## Reflective Essay

| | Ideas | Organization |
|---|---|---|
| **6** | • Essay demonstrates a clear, complete understanding of the assignment.<br>• Essay's dominant theme is clear and very well articulated.<br>• Essay makes a clear, insightful point about the subject.<br>• Essay shows a deep, well-considered understanding of the subject.<br>• The ideas presented in the essay are completely thought out and well elaborated.<br>• The development of the ideas is thorough and logical.<br>• Support for the ideas presented is highly specific and very detailed. | • The significance of the title is clear and very insightful.<br>• Essay clearly states a position about the topic.<br>• Focus is very clear and effective throughout the essay.<br>• Introduction is exceptionally clear, effective, and compelling—it grabs the reader's attention.<br>• Presentation of supporting evidence is exceptionally clear and thorough, with details that are explicit and vivid.<br>• Sequence of supporting evidence is highly logical and exceptionally effective.<br>• Transitions provide a seamless progression from point to point.<br>• Conclusion very effectively reaffirms the focus of the essay. |
| **5** | • Essay demonstrates a general, essentially complete understanding of the assignment.<br>• Essay's dominant theme is clear and well articulated.<br>• Essay makes a clear point about the subject.<br>• Essay shows a considered understanding of the subject.<br>• The ideas presented in the essay are thought out and elaborated.<br>• The development of the ideas is mostly thorough and generally logical.<br>• Support for the ideas presented is specific and detailed. | • The significance of the title is clear and meaningful.<br>• Essay states a position about the topic.<br>• Focus is clear and effective throughout the essay.<br>• Introduction is clear, effective, and catches the reader's attention.<br>• Presentation of supporting evidence is clear and complete, with strong details.<br>• Sequence of supporting evidence is logical and generally effective.<br>• Transitions provide a progression from point to point.<br>• Conclusion reaffirms the focus of the essay. |
| **4** | • Essay demonstrates a basic understanding of the assignment.<br>• Essay's dominant theme is clear and generally well expressed.<br>• Essay makes a point about the subject.<br>• Essay shows some understanding of the subject.<br>• The ideas presented in the essay are thought out but not completely elaborated.<br>• The development of the ideas is not entirely complete but generally logical.<br>• Support for the ideas presented is general and somewhat detailed. | • The significance of the title is generally clear but not explicitly so.<br>• Essay implies a position about the topic.<br>• Focus is generally clear.<br>• Introduction is clear and attempts to grab the reader's attention.<br>• Presentation of supporting evidence is generally clear and includes details.<br>• Sequence of supporting evidence is generally effective but not always logical.<br>• Transitions are used.<br>• Conclusion recalls the focus of the essay. |
| **3** | • Essay demonstrates a basic but somewhat incomplete understanding of the assignment.<br>• Essay's dominant theme may not be entirely clear and needs to be more fully expressed.<br>• Essay makes a vague point about the subject.<br>• Essay shows a partial understanding of the subject.<br>• Ideas presented are considered but not elaborated.<br>• The development of the ideas is not entirely complete and not entirely logical.<br>• Support for the ideas presented is general but lacks detail. | • The significance of the title is not entirely clear.<br>• Essay suggests a position about the topic, but it may be vague.<br>• Focus is not always clear.<br>• Introduction is not entirely clear or may not include an attention-getter.<br>• Presentation of supporting evidence is generally clear but may lack details.<br>• Sequence of supporting evidence is not entirely effective and not always logical.<br>• Transitions are inconsistently used.<br>• Conclusion may not recall the focus of the essay. |
| **2** | • Essay demonstrates an incomplete understanding of the assignment.<br>• Essay's dominant theme is not clear or fully expressed.<br>• Essay does not make a clear point about the subject.<br>• Essay shows little understanding of the subject.<br>• The ideas presented in the essay are not fully considered and not elaborated.<br>• Development of ideas is incomplete and illogical.<br>• Support for the ideas presented is vague and lacks detail. | • The significance of the title is not clear.<br>• Position about the topic is not entirely clear.<br>• Focus is sometimes lacking.<br>• Introduction is not clear and may not include an attention-getter.<br>• Presentation of supporting evidence is somewhat unclear and lacks details.<br>• Sequence of supporting evidence is not effective and may be illogical.<br>• Transitions are rarely used.<br>• Conclusion does not recall the focus of the essay. |
| **1** | • Essay demonstrates no understanding of the assignment.<br>• Essay has no dominant theme.<br>• Essay makes no point about the subject.<br>• Essay shows no understanding of the subject.<br>• The ideas presented are not considered or elaborated.<br>• Ideas are not developed.<br>• No support for the ideas is presented. | • The essay has no title.<br>• No position about the topic is demonstrated.<br>• Focus is absent.<br>• Introduction is unclear and does not catch attention.<br>• No supporting evidence is presented.<br>• Transitions are not used.<br>• No conclusion is included. |

| Voice | Word Choice & Sentence Fluency | Conventions |
|---|---|---|
| • Writer's voice is clear, consistent, and effective throughout the essay.<br>• Writer's voice is perfectly attuned to the subject matter.<br>• Writer's voice is perfectly attuned to the audience.<br>• Essay's tone demonstrates exceptional sensitivity to the subject.<br>• Writer uses first-person point of view accurately throughout. | • Essay displays great precision and accuracy in word choices.<br>• Descriptive phrasing is vivid and highly effective.<br>• Sentences and paragraphs flow smoothly together.<br>• Sentences vary in length and structure.<br>• Ideas are clearly connected using transition words and phrases.<br>• Essay shows an excellent balance between emotional reflection and reasoned observations. | • All words are spelled correctly.<br>• The essay contains no errors in English usage or grammar.<br>• The essay contains no errors in punctuation.<br>• The essay contains no errors in capitalization. |
| • Writer's voice is generally consistent and effective throughout the essay.<br>• Writer's voice is appropriate to the subject matter.<br>• Writer's voice is appropriate for the audience.<br>• Essay's tone demonstrates sensitivity to the subject.<br>• Writer generally uses first-person point of view. | • Essay displays generally precise and accurate word choices.<br>• Descriptive phrasing is engaging and generally effective.<br>• Sentences and paragraphs generally flow smoothly together.<br>• Sentences vary somewhat in length and structure.<br>• Ideas are generally connected using transition words and phrases.<br>• Essay shows good balance between emotional reflection and reasoned observations. | • Almost all words are spelled correctly.<br>• The essay contains almost no errors in English usage or grammar.<br>• The essay contains almost no errors in punctuation.<br>• The essay contains almost no errors in capitalization. |
| • Writer's voice is somewhat consistent throughout the essay.<br>• Writer's voice is generally appropriate to the subject matter.<br>• Writer's voice is generally appropriate for the audience.<br>• Essay's tone demonstrates some sensitivity to the subject.<br>• Writer uses first-person point of view a few times. | • Word choices reflect thought but are not always precise or accurate.<br>• Descriptive phrasing is attempted but is not always effective.<br>• An effort is made to flow sentences and paragraphs, but not always effectively.<br>• Sentences vary somewhat in length and structure but could use more variation.<br>• Ideas are usually connected using transition words and phrases, but not always.<br>• Essay shows some balance between emotional reflection and reasoned observations. | • Some spelling errors occur, but not enough to impede understanding.<br>• The essay contains some errors in usage or grammar, but not enough to impede understanding.<br>• The essay some errors in punctuation, but not enough to impede understanding.<br>• The essay contains a few errors in capitalization. |
| • Writer's voice is not always consistent.<br>• Writer's voice is not always appropriate to the subject matter.<br>• Writer's voice is not always appropriate for the audience.<br>• Essay's tone demonstrates only occasional sensitivity to the subject.<br>• Writer mixes first-person point of view with other points of view. | • Word choices reflect thought but are often not precise or accurate.<br>• Descriptive phrasing is occasionally attempted but is not effective.<br>• Sentences and paragraphs may not flow together.<br>• Sentences only occasionally vary in length and structure.<br>• Ideas are only occasionally connected using transition words and phrases.<br>• Essay includes both emotional reflection and observation but is overly reliant on one approach. | • Some spelling errors may impede understanding.<br>• Errors in usage or grammar may impede understanding at times.<br>• Errors in punctuation may impede understanding at times.<br>• Errors in capitalization may intrude on understanding. |
| • Writer's voice is generally inconsistent.<br>• Writer's voice is sometimes inappropriate to the subject matter.<br>• Writer's voice is sometimes inappropriate for the audience.<br>• Essay's tone demonstrates little sensitivity to the subject.<br>• Writer uses first-person point of view only once. | • Word choices are generally not precise or accurate.<br>• Descriptive phrasing is rarely used.<br>• Sentences and paragraphs may not flow together.<br>• Sentences rarely vary in length and structure.<br>• Ideas are rarely connected using transition words and phrases.<br>• Essay includes only emotional reflection or observation, but not both. | • Spelling errors impede understanding.<br>• The essay contains numerous errors in usage or grammar.<br>• Errors in punctuation often impede understanding.<br>• The essay contains numerous errors in capitalization. |
| • Writer's voice is not consistent.<br>• Writer's voice is not appropriate to the subject matter.<br>• Writer's voice is not appropriate for the audience.<br>• Essay's tone demonstrates no sensitivity to the subject.<br>• Writer never uses first-person point of view. | • Word choices are haphazard and inappropriate.<br>• Descriptive phrasing is not used.<br>• Sentences and paragraphs do not flow together.<br>• Sentences do not vary in length and structure.<br>• Ideas are not connected using transition words and phrases.<br>• Essay includes declarations but no reflection or observation. | • Numerous spelling errors prevent understanding.<br>• Numerous errors in usage or grammar impede understanding.<br>• Numerous errors in punctuation impede understanding.<br>• Numerous errors in capitalization. |

Name ______________________ Class ____________ Date ____________

# Speaking, Listening, and Viewing *(page 660)*

## Reflective Presentation

Practice your listening skills as your classmates present their essays. Make sure you understand the subject of the presentation and notice any visual aids. Evaluate how the presenter uses both verbal and nonverbal techniques to engage the audience.

## ACTIVITY

**Directions** Use the following checklist to sharpen your awareness of speaking techniques and the use of visual aids. Answer the questions on the lines provided or circle the response that best describes your opinion. Offer suggestions for each point.

What is the speaker's topic and main idea?

_______________________________________________

### VISUAL AIDS

What visual aids does the speaker use?

_______________________________________________

| The speaker's use of visual aids is<br>**a.** very well timed<br>**b.** mostly well timed<br>**c.** poorly timed and distracting | Suggestions/Comments: |
|---|---|
| The content of the visual aids is<br>**a.** very appropriate<br>**b.** somewhat appropriate<br>**c.** not at all appropriate | Suggestions/Comments: |
| The quality of the visual aids is<br>**a.** high quality<br>**b.** acceptable quality<br>**c.** poor quality | Suggestions/Comments: |



### VERBAL TECHNIQUES

| The speaker's tone of voice was<br>**a.** appropriate<br>**b.** acceptable<br>**c.** inappropriate | Suggestions/Comments: |
|---|---|

| The speaker's pronunciation was<br>**a.** excellent **b.** good **c.** poor | Suggestions/Comments: |
|---|---|
| The volume of the speaker's voice was<br>**a.** loud and steady throughout<br>**b.** too soft or too loud at times<br>**c.** too soft or too loud throughout | Suggestions/Comments: |
| The pace of the presentation was<br>**a.** slow and steady<br>**b.** mostly slow but sometimes rushed<br>**c.** rushed throughout | Suggestions/Comments: |

## NONVERBAL TECHNIQUES

| The speaker's eye contact was<br>**a.** consistent throughout<br>**b.** occasional<br>**c.** no eye contact | Suggestions/Comments: |
|---|---|
| The speaker's posture was<br>**a.** relaxed but straight<br>**b.** stiff<br>**c.** slouched | Suggestions/Comments: |
| The speaker's gestures were<br>**a.** natural, appropriate<br>**b.** awkward, sometimes inappropriate<br>**c.** too few or too many | Suggestions/Comments: |

What was the most effective part of the speaker's presentation? Why?

_______________________________________________

What part of the speaker's presentation do you think could be improved? How?

_______________________________________________

# Speaking, Listening, and Viewing Rubric

## Reflective Presentation

| | Stance & Posture | Handling of Notes & Gestures | Vocal Variety |
|---|---|---|---|
| **6** | • Stance is alert and in tune with vocal delivery.<br>• Stance and posture enhance the content of the reflection. | • Use of notes is fluid and does not detract from reflection delivery.<br>• Gestures complement verbal delivery of reflection and add dramatic emphasis, empathy, or emotional power to the reflection. | • Pitch, rate, volume and tone quality vary to add dramatic power to the reflection.<br>• Pitch, rate, volume, and quality are appropriate to the content of the reflection and are conversational in cadence and tone.<br>• There are no vocalized pauses (um, like, etc.).<br>• The reflection contains no mispronunciations. |
| **5** | • Stance is in tune with vocal delivery.<br>• Stance and posture generally assist the content of the reflection. | • Use of notes is not fluid but does not detract from reflection delivery.<br>• Gestures are attempted when appropriate and enhance delivery. | • Pitch, rate, and volume vary somewhat and add dramatic texture to the reflection at times.<br>• Pitch, rate, volume, and quality are generally appropriate, with some effort at a conversational tone.<br>• There are a few vocalized pauses but not enough to break the flow of the narrative.<br>• The reflection contains few mispronunciations. |
| **4** | • Stands straight throughout reflection.<br>• Stance and posture vary somewhat to support the content of the reflection. | • Consults notes but is not overly reliant.<br>• Attempts to gesture when appropriate. | • Pitch, rate, and volume vary only a little and add little support to the content of the reflection.<br>• Some effort at a conversational tone is made.<br>• Some vocalized pauses may hinder the flow of the reflection.<br>• Some mispronunciations may detract from reflection. |
| **3** | • Some shifting of weight occurs during reflection.<br>• Stance and posture vary little to support the content of the reflection. | • Reads from notes often; some uncertainty is evident.<br>• Only a few gestures are used. | • There is little variety in pitch, rate, and volume.<br>• Conversational tone is rare.<br>• Some vocalized pauses break the flow of the reflection.<br>• Frequent mispronunciations detract from the reflection. |
| **2** | • Frequent shifting of weight occurs during reflection.<br>• Stance and posture rarely relate to the content of the reflection. | • Reads from notes more frequently than not and delivery is unsure.<br>• Gestures are rarely used. | • Speaks in a partial monotone, at a low volume, or too fast or too slow.<br>• Natural rhythm is lacking.<br>• Frequent vocalized pauses break the flow of the reflection.<br>• Frequent mispronunciations distract the listener. |
| **1** | • Shifts weight from foot to foot throughout presentation.<br>• Slumped or slouching throughout reflection. | • Is completely reliant on notes—reading the reflection.<br>• Delivery is stumbling.<br>• No gestures are used; hand is in pocket or fidgeting. | • Speaks in a monotone, at a low volume, or too fast or too slow.<br>• There is no natural rhythm.<br>• Frequent vocalized pauses interrupt the reflection.<br>• Frequent mispronunciations interfere with meaning. |

| Facial Expression & Eye Contact | Content of Reflection |
|---|---|
| • Face is animated and attuned to the content of the reflection.<br>• Eye contact is comprehensive, direct, and sustained. | • The reflection demonstrates a clear, complete understanding of the assignment.<br>• A single incident or event is thoroughly presented and analyzed, with the analysis revolving around a powerful, central theme.<br>• The presentation sets a clear, evocative mood for the reflection.<br>• The reflection makes a clear and insightful point about the incident or event.<br>• Development of ideas is thorough and completely complementary to the tone of the reflection.<br>• Ideas are fully elaborated, with specific, detailed support that powerfully enhances thematic unity.<br>• No mistakes in grammar, and vocabulary is always appropriate.<br>• Reflection is highly engaging to the audience and precisely tuned to the subject.<br>• Presentation is exactly tuned to the audience. |
| • Face reflects the content of the reflection.<br>• Eye contact is comprehensive, and direct. | • The reflection demonstrates a clear understanding of the assignment.<br>• A single incident or event is presented and analyzed, and the analysis has a clear central theme.<br>• The presentation sets a consistent mood for the reflection.<br>• The reflection makes a point about the incident or event.<br>• Development of ideas is thorough and complements the tone of the reflection.<br>• Ideas are elaborated, with support that generally enhances thematic unity.<br>• Reflection contains few mistakes in grammar; vocabulary is appropriate.<br>• Reflection engages the audience and is tuned to the subject.<br>• Presentation is generally tuned to the audience. |
| • Face is expressive most of the time.<br>• Eye contact made with all segments of audience. | • The reflection demonstrates a basic understanding of the assignment.<br>• A single incident or event is presented with a central theme.<br>• The presentation sets a mood for the reflection, but it is not maintained at all times.<br>• The reflection makes a point about the incident or event, but it is not always clear.<br>• Development of ideas complements the tone of the reflection.<br>• Ideas are elaborated, but supporting details may not enhance thematic unity.<br>• The reflection contains a few mistakes in grammar and word choice, but not enough to detract from the presentation.<br>• The presentation is generally engaging and appropriate to the reflection.<br>• Presentation is mostly appropriate to the audience, but not always. |
| • Face is infrequently expressive.<br>• Eye contact is haphazard and not sustained. | • The reflection demonstrates some understanding of the assignment, but it is not complete.<br>• A single incident or event is presented but without a unifying theme.<br>• The presentation sets only a partial, inconsistent mood for the reflection.<br>• Reflection's point about the incident or event is unclear; no message develops.<br>• Development of ideas is not always in keeping with the tone of the reflection.<br>• Ideas may not be expanded, and supporting details may be inappropriate or incomplete.<br>• The reflection contains a few distracting mistakes in grammar and word choice.<br>• The presentation is somewhat engaging but not always appropriate to the reflection.<br>• Presentation is only occasionally appropriate to the audience. |
| • Face is inexpressive.<br>• Eye contact is rare. | • The reflection demonstrates little understanding of the assignment.<br>• The incident or event that is the focus of the reflection is not clear.<br>• The mood of the reflection is not clear.<br>• The reflection makes no meaningful point about the incident or event.<br>• Development of ideas is rarely in keeping with the tone of the reflection.<br>• Support for ideas is attempted but is generally inappropriate and incomplete.<br>• The reflection is harmed by distracting mistakes in grammar and word choice.<br>• The presentation is rarely engaging and often not appropriate to the reflection.<br>• The presentation is often inappropriate to the audience. |
| • There is little or no expression—face is uninvolved.<br>• Little or no eye contact with audience. | • The assignment is not understood.<br>• The reflection's subject is not understood.<br>• No mood is created in the reflection.<br>• No point it made in the reflection.<br>• No tone is established.<br>• No support for ideas is presented.<br>• Mistakes in grammar and word choice distract from the reflection.<br>• The presentation is not engaging and not appropriate to the subject.<br>• Presentation is not appropriate to the audience. |

Name ______________________ Class ______________ Date ______________

# Two-Column Table Graphic Organizer

| | |
|---|---|
| | |

Name ________________________ Class ______________ Date ______________

## Three-Column Table Graphic Organizer

| | | |
|---|---|---|
| | | |

Name ______________________________ Class ______________ Date ______________

# Three-Column Grid Graphic Organizer

| | | | |
|---|---|---|---|
| | | | |
| | | | |
| | | | |

Name ______________________ Class ______________ Date ______________

## Sequence Graphic Organizer

Name ______________________ Class ______________ Date ______________

## Supporting Details Graphic Organizer

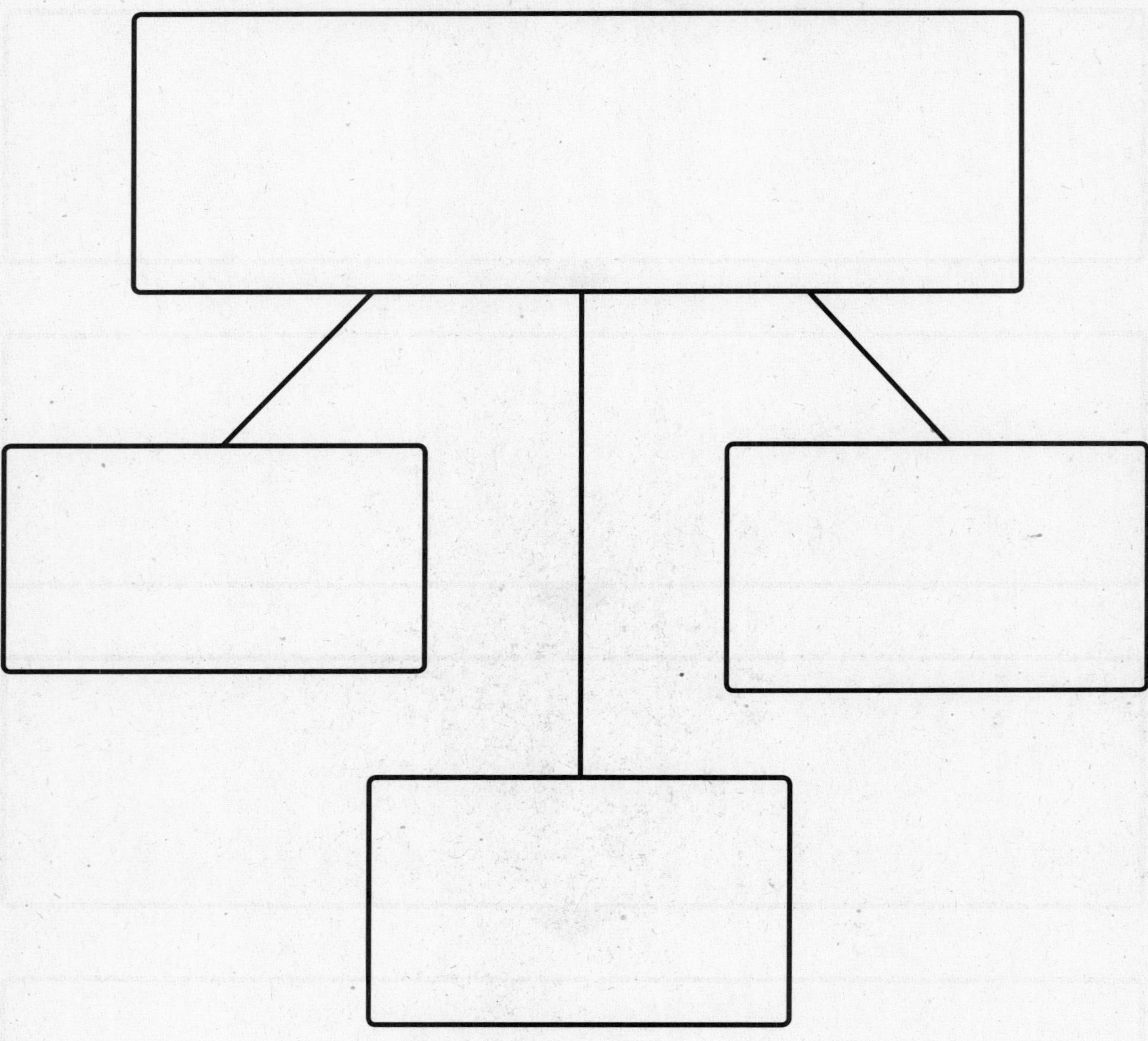

## Cluster Graphic Organizer

Name ________________________ Class ______________ Date ______________

## If-Then Graphic Organizer

Name ______________________ Class ____________ Date ____________

## Compare-and-Contrast Graphic Organizer

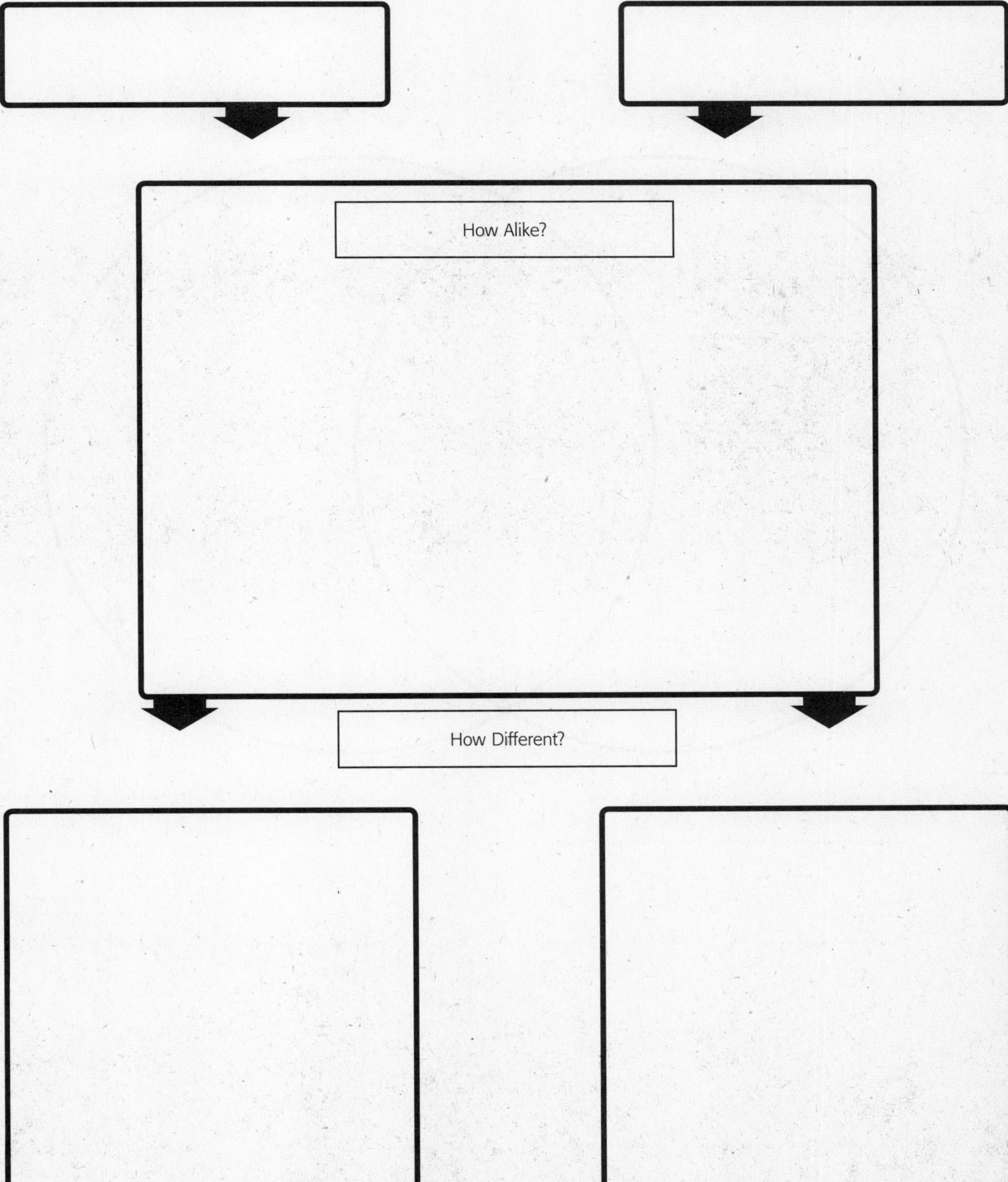

Name ______________________ Class ______________ Date ______________

## Venn Diagram

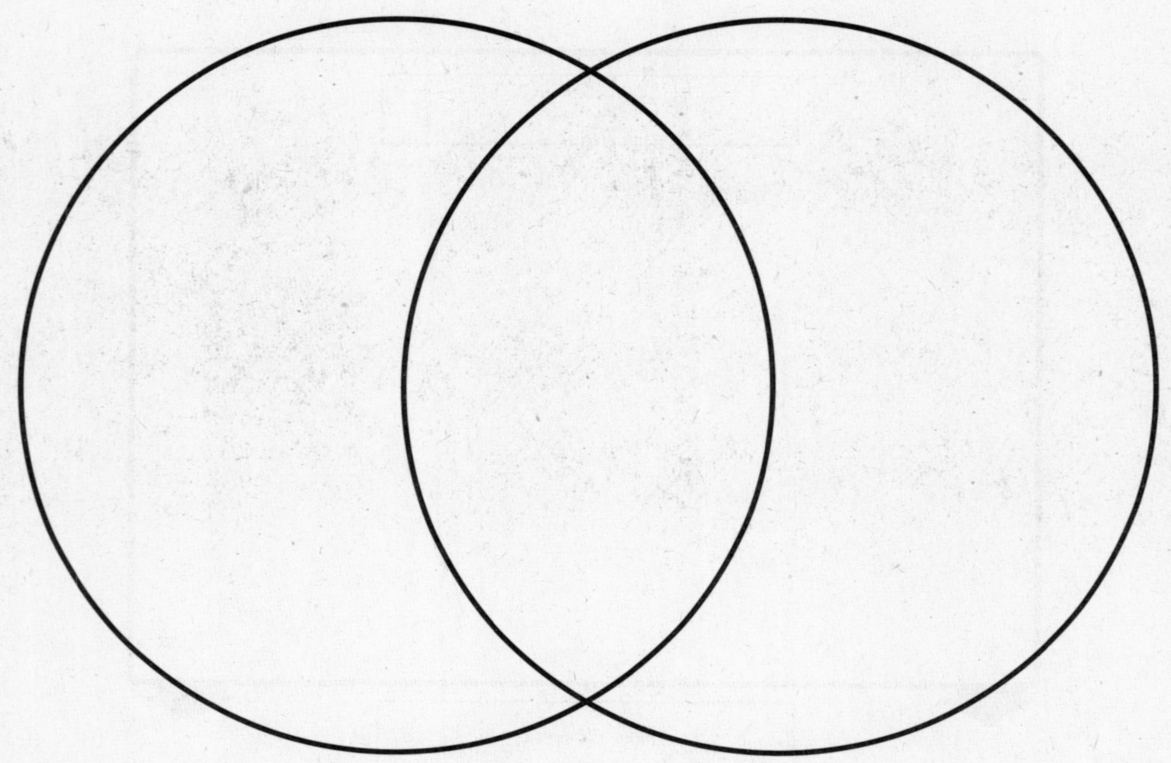

Name ______________________ Class ______________ Date ______________

# Triple Venn Diagram

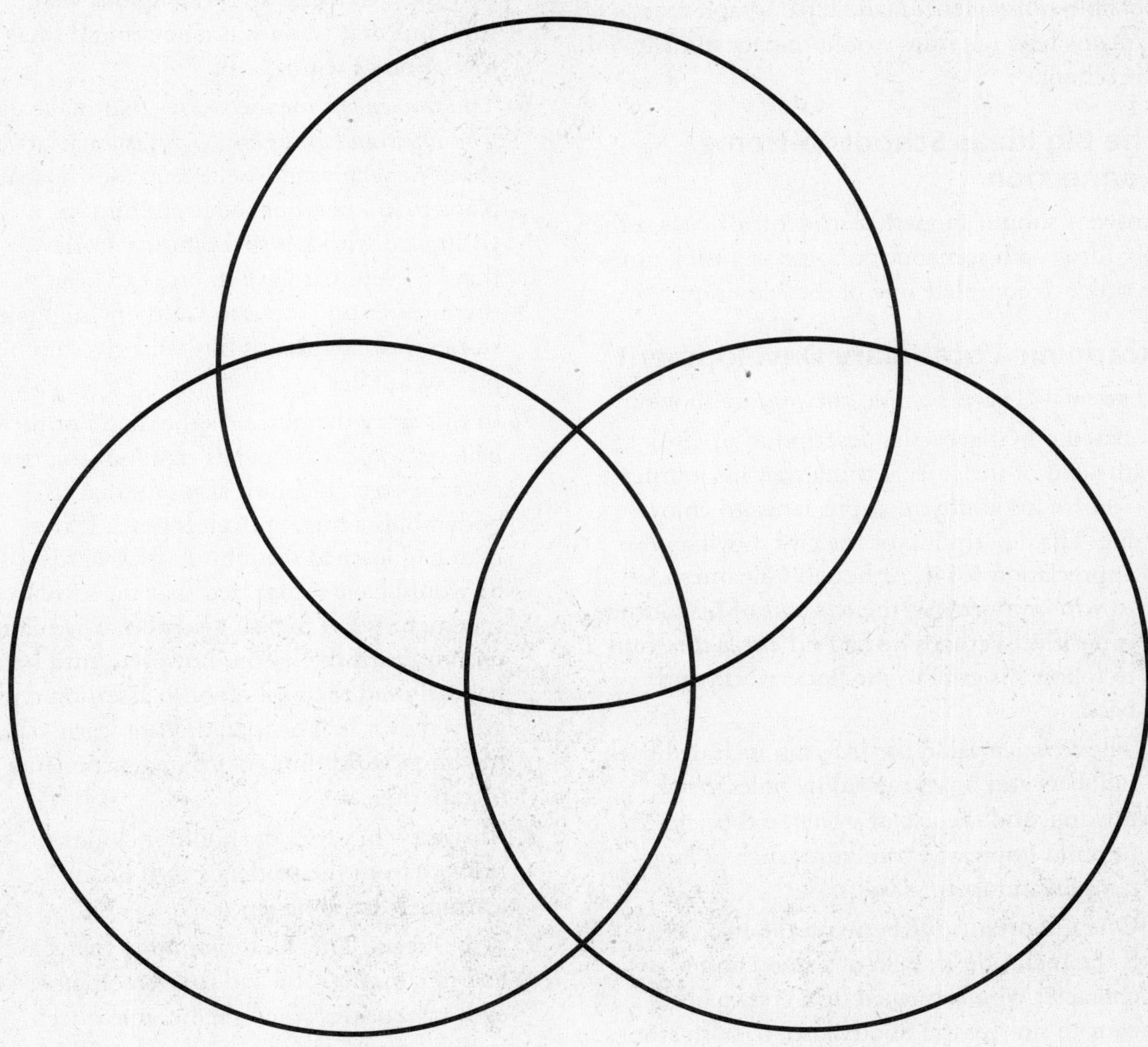

# Answers

## Unit 3 Answers

### Unit Introduction

Answers will vary but should contain three rules, possible consequences, and a paragraph that explains how the rules would impact students in the school.

### The Big Ideas School-to-Home Connection

Answers should show that students discussed the Big Ideas with someone at home and took notes in order to complete one of the activities.

### Academic Vocabulary Development

Answers will vary. Sample answers are shown:

1. Based on Gilgamesh's description of Uruk at the end of the story, I think that his journey *restored* his ability to appreciate and enjoy life. His description of the city shows a great appreciation for it. Although Gilgamesh failed to win immortality, the *outcome* of his journey is positive. Perhaps he had no *alternative* but to follow his grief to the underworld and back.
2. The *technologies* in use in Uruk included both sailboats and boats moved by poles, brick making, and the use of stones and bricks to build impressive structures such as large temples and fortress walls.
3. One important *link* between the two texts is the inclusion in each of a flood and a character who is warned by a god to build a boat to survive the flood. Also, in both stories, the god tells the human character to take all kinds of animals on board the boat so that the various species can survive the flood.
4. I do not think the father was fair or wise when he *restored* the prodigal son. It was not fair because the prodigal son did not suffer any consequences for his foolishness and his previous disrespect of his father. It was not wise because there were no consequences. I doubt that the prodigal son really learned anything or changed as a result of this episode.
5. Christianity is *linked* to Judaism because it grew out of Judaism. Islam is *linked* to both Judaism and Christianity because Mohammed, the founder of Islam, said that the teachings of both religions were valid but that Islam was a newer and final revelation of truth.
6. The *framework* for the stories that make up *The Thousand and One Nights* is a narrative about Scheherazade. Scheherazade's husband plans to kill her, but she keeps him so enthralled with her spellbinding stories that he keeps her alive in order to hear them. After one thousand and one nights of stories, Scheherazade's husband gives up his plan to kill her.
7. In this story the bird tells the man not to believe "foolish assertions" and not to grieve over the past. The bird also says that its body holds a huge, priceless pearl. If the man had learned from bird's first words, he would have recognized that the second statement was a foolish assertion. The man did not learn the lesson, however, until he had believed the bird's foolish assertion and grieved over it. The man did not learn via the bird's words but via his own experience of suffering.
8. Answers will vary but should include an *instance* from the student's own life of learning from experience.
9. Yes, Queen Rania had *inhibitions* that she had to conquer. She had to overcome her own insecurities when she became queen, and she sometimes questioned herself in the face of external criticisms about her lifestyle.
10. This episode shows me that both Rama and Ravana's brother are men of integrity. When Rama's *inspection* of Ravana's body revealed a scar on Ravana's back, Rama felt remorse about killing a retreating man. When Ravana's brother heard Rama's remorse, he was honest and *restored* Rama's confidence even though Rama had killed his brother.

# Answers

## Part 1: Southwest Asia, 3500 B.C.–Present

### English Language Coach, Part 1

1. f
2. h
3. j
4. d
5. b
6. c
7. i
8. a
9. e
10. g

### Gilgamesh: The Search for Everlasting Life; The Return

**Literary Element**

Answers may vary.

1. oversaw Enkidu's body for days
2. finds plant that restores youth
3. travels to Twin Peaks, crosses Waters of Death
4. faces scorpion people

**Reading Strategy**

1. sound
2. sight
3. feel
4. smell
5. feel
6. sight

**Selection Vocabulary Practice**

**EXERCISE A**

1. antidote
2. ravaged
3. prevail
4. treacherous

**EXERCISE B**

1. synonym
2. synonym
3. synonym
4. antonym

**EXERCISE C**

Answers will vary but should describe the adventures of an epic hero, and use all of the vocabulary words correctly.

**Vocabulary Strategy**

Answers will vary.

**Multiple–Meaning Word:** bright (p. 456)
**Meanings of Word:** intelligent; intense in color
**Correct Meaning:** intense in color
**Multiple–Meaning Word:** lie (p. 456)
**Meanings of Word:** rest on the ground; make a false statement
**Correct Meaning:** rest on the ground
**Multiple–Meaning Word:** plant (p. 462)
**Meanings of Word:** set one's foot down firmly; leafed organism
**Correct Meaning:** leafed organism
**Multiple–Meaning Word:** cast (p. 463)
**Meanings of Word:** to get rid of something; a group of actors in a play
**Correct Meaning:** to get rid of something
**Multiple–Meaning Word:** fit (p. 461)
**Meanings of Word:** suitable; conforming to one's body
**Correct Meaning:** suitable

**Grammar Practice**

1. tumbling
2. Going for weeks without proper rest
3. Prevented from seeing the king
4. punishing, shivering
5. Listening closely
6. whispering
7. Fearing the worst
8. Having lost his way
9. Disturbed by what he knew
10. challenging

# Answers

**Selection Quick Check**

1. Gilgamesh weeps bitterly.
2. Gilgamesh searches for Utnapishtim because he is afraid of death; Utnapishtim has been granted the gift of eternal life.
3. He must stay awake for six days and seven nights.
4. He reveals that if Gilgamesh finds and takes a certain underwater plant, his youth will be restored.
5. A serpent steals the plant while Gilgamesh bathes in a well.

**Grammar Workshop**

1. they
2. their
3. he
4. she
5. they
6. them
7. its
8. Sample answer: Gilgamesh cut off the stones, and his action made his body shoot up to the surface.
9. Sample answer: They sailed for three days and nights, even though the journey would take ordinary men six weeks.

**Literary History: Sacred Texts**

Answers will vary. Students' parables should be short, simple stories from everyday life that teach a deeper moral lesson.

## Genesis 6–9: The Flood *from the* King James Version of the Bible

**Literary Element**

Answers will vary.

1. **Theme:** Don't judge a book by its cover.
   **Explanation:** It is unwise to judge things only by the way they look.
   **Example(s):** "Cinderella"
2. **Theme:** Slow and steady wins the race.
   **Explanation:** It is better to do your best and be thorough than to rush to finish first.
   **Example(s):** "The Tortoise and the Hare"
3. **Theme:** No one will believe a liar, even when he's telling the truth.
   **Explanation:** If you are known for telling lies, no one will trust you when you tell the truth.
   **Example(s):** "The Boy Who Cried Wolf"
4. **Theme:** Brains often win over brawn.
   **Explanation:** It is better to be clever than strong.
   **Example(s):** "Brer Rabbit and Brer Bear"

**Reading Strategy**

Responses will vary but should state details and questions from the text as well as answers to those questions. Responses in final column of table should relate to leading a just life, acting responsibly, or seeking meaning in life.

**Selection Vocabulary Practice**

**EXERCISE A**

1. **word:** corrupt
   **etymology:** Latin *corruptus,* "to destroy, spoil, bribe"
   **sample sentence:** The corrupt president was sent to jail.
2. **word:** covenant
   **etymology:** Latin *convenire,* "come together"
   **sample sentence:** The covenant we have will protect us both.
3. **word:** abate
   **etymology:** Latin *ad,* "to" and *battuere,* "to beat"
   **sample sentence:** The hail should start to abate after midnight.

**EXERCISE B**

1. Yes; a covenant is an agreement.
2. Yes; abate means to lessen, not to increase.
3. No; if he is corrupt, he will act immorally or unjustly.

# Answers

### EXERCISE C

Answers will vary but should accurately reflect a conversation Noah and one of his sons might have had and should correctly use all of the vocabulary words.

### Vocabulary Strategy

Answers will vary.

2. bare; bear; bare: naked; bear: to carry
3. nights; knights; nights: evenings; knights: armed men on horseback from the Middle Ages
4. seen; scene; seen: noticed; scene: a spectacle or event
5. sent; scent; sent: gave; scent: an odor

### Grammar Practice

1. flooding, crafting a huge ship
2. carrying many animals
3. Sailing across an endless sea
4. seeing all of the people and animals
5. grunting
6. returning home
7. cleaning
8. hearing noises outside the ship
9. Consulting with others
10. inspiring

### Selection Quick Check

1. He regrets creating humankind. He find humans wicked and their plans evil.
2. God gives Noah specific instructions to build an ark.
3. Noah is instructed to take his wife, sons, and sons' wives, along with two of each living creature—a male and a female.
4. They are killed by the flood.
5. It brings back an olive leaf.

## The Book of Ruth *from the* King James Version of the Bible

### Literary Element

Answers will vary.

1. Thy people shall be my people, and thy God my God; where thou diest, will I die; and there will I be buried.
2. And she said unto them, 'Call me not Naomi, call me Mara.'
3. Tarry this night, and it shall be in the morning, that if he will perform unto thee the part of a kinsman, well; let him do the kinsman's part: but if he will not do the part of a kinsman to thee, then I will do the part of a kinsman to thee, as the Lord liveth: lie down until morning.
4. What day thou buyest the field of the hand of Naomi, thou must buy it also of Ruth the Moabitess, the wife of the dead, to raise up the name of the dead upon his inheritance.

### Reading Strategy

**Character:** Naomi

**Character's Words, Thoughts, or Actions:** She endures the deaths of her husband and sons, yet she is not too bitter. She provides guidance to Ruth. "Blessed be he of the Lord, who hath not left off his kindness to the living and to the dead."

**My Response:** What a strong, inspiring woman! A lot of people would have given up on life after all that, but she didn't. That's impressive.

**Character:** Ruth

**Character's Words, Thoughts, or Actions:** She is very loyal to Naomi. Her husband died.

**My Response:** I felt sad for her, but then found myself cheering her on. I'm glad she was able to become the wife of Boaz.

**Character:** Boaz

**Character's Words, Thoughts, or Actions:** "Go not to glean in another field, neither go from hence, but abide here fast by my maidens."

# Answers

**My Response:** Boaz did not know Ruth well enough to marry her.

**Selection Vocabulary Practice**

**EXERCISE A**

1. winnow
2. glean
3. redeem
4. sojourn

**EXERCISE B**

1. b
2. b
3. c
4. c

**EXERCISE C**

Answers will vary but should describe some of the things Ruth has experienced since moving to Bethlehem, and use at least three of the vocabulary words correctly.

**Vocabulary Strategy**

1. root: *testis,* "witness" + *facere,* "to make"; to make witness against
2. root: *afflictus,* "to cast down"; to be troubled or injured
3. root: *redimere,* "to take, buy"; to buy back
4. root: *confirmare,* "to make firm"; to ratify or strengthen
5. root: *nativus,* "born"; the place of birth
6. root: *morsus,* "to bite"; a small piece of food

**Grammar Practice**

1. to find a new home
2. to leave
3. to sell the cows
4. to be loyal to her child
5. to eat
6. To forgive those who had continually wronged her
7. to notice
8. to gather firewood
9. To traverse the river safely
10. to find that

**Selection Quick Check**

1. There is a famine in Bethlehem.
2. Naomi's husband dies, her two sons marry women from Moab, and then her sons also die.
3. Ruth refuses to leave Naomi; she is determined to leave her own people and go to Bethlehem with Naomi.
4. Boaz has heard of all that Ruth has done for Naomi.
5. She sleeps at his feet and declares herself Boaz's handmaid.

## The Prodigal Son *from the* King James Version of the Bible

**Literary Element**

1. Answers will vary. It is never a good idea to be greedy or to try to take advantage of another person.
2. It is important for people to learn to take care of themselves.

**Reading Strategy**

**Top box:** Theme: forgiveness

**Lower boxes:** Answers will vary but should support the stated theme.

**Grammar Practice**

**1.** SUB <u>When the father saw the prodigal son</u>, he ran toward him.

**2.** SUB <u>Although the son loved his father</u>, he wanted to leave home for a life of adventure.

**5.** SUB <u>After the famine swept the land</u>, the prodigal son realized his mistake.

Sentences 3 and 4 do not have subordinate clauses.

**Selection Quick Check**

1. The son wasted the money on "riotous living" in another country.

## Answers

2. The son had to work in a field as a servant to survive.
3. The father threw a feast for the son.
4. Sample answer: No, the father should have punished the son because the son acted foolishly.
   OR: Yes, regardless of how foolishly the son behaved, he is still the father's child, and it is important to forgive each other.
5. Sample answer: Yes, because even in the modern world people make bad decisions, waste money, or respond to situations oddly.

### The Exordium *and* Daylight *from* the Qu'ran

**Literary Element**

Answers may vary for students' explanations about whether a statement is an example of antithesis.

1. is an example of antithesis because it contrasts selfishness with generosity to emphasize what true happiness is.
2. is not an example of antithesis because no ideas or phrases are contrasted.
3. is an example of antithesis because it contrasts the effects of recklessly spoken words with the words of the wise to emphasize the power of words.

**Reading Strategy**

Answers will vary.

1. The image suggests that closely following Allah's word will lead to happiness.
2. The image suggests the connection between all people. Even the orphan is part of our larger family.
3. The image of the beggar suggests that the righteous will always reach out to the needy.

**Selection Vocabulary Practice**

**EXERCISE A**

1. inflict, harm
2. praise, soothe
3. love, respect
4. despise, hate
5. acquire, receive
6. reprimand, rebuke

**EXERCISE B**

1. chide
2. abhor
3. incur

**EXERCISE C**

Answers will vary but the poem should discuss the importance of peace in the world and use all of the vocabulary words correctly.

**Vocabulary Strategy**

**Word:** straight; **Denotation:** without bends or curves; **Connotation:** righteous, good, just, honorable

**Word:** shelter; **Denotation:** a building that provides protection; **Connotation:** a safe, loving place

**Word:** poor; **Denotation:** lacking in money or assets; **Connotation:** leading an empty, pointless, hopeless life

**Word:** prize; **Denotation:** something given to the winner of a contest; **Connotation:** a reward for good actions

**Grammar Practice**

1. compound
2. simple
3. compound
4. simple
5. compound
6. simple
7. compound
8. compound
9. simple

**Selection Quick Check**

1. He addresses Allah.
2. He asks to be guided "to the straight path."

# Answers

3. It holds a "richer prize" than the present life.
4. He urges the faithful to proclaim the goodness of the Lord.

## The Second Voyage of Sindbad the Sailor *from* The Thousand and One Nights

### Literary Element

Rewrites will vary but should clearly demonstrate third-person limited point of view. Comparisons should note that first-person point of view reveals Sindbad's thoughts and feelings. Comparisons should stress the excitement and immediacy of first person point of view, its potential unreliability, and the objectivity and global scope of third-person point of view.

### Reading Strategy

Answers will vary.

**Problem:** His ship and crew sail away, leaving Sindbad stranded on a deserted island.

**Solution:** Sindbad binds himself to a roc's talon, hoping that the bird will deposit him somewhere more promising.

**Problem:** The roc deposits Sindbad on a barren hilltop.

**Solution:** Sindbad loads himself down with diamonds and attaches a sheep carcass to his chest. A vulture flies away with the carcass and Sindbad and drops them when a man yells.

**Problem:** The man is frightened of Sindbad.

**Solution:** Sindbad reassures him and gives him some diamonds.

### Selection Vocabulary Practice

#### EXERCISE A

1. thicket
2. confound
3. tumult
4. fruitless

#### EXERCISE B

1. It will be a fruitless search.
2. He was in a thicket.
3. Tumult followed the collision.
4. He confounded the boy.

#### EXERCISE C

Answers will vary. The letter should contain at least three vocabulary words.

### Vocabulary Strategy

1. adjective
2. precipitously, adverb; precipitousness, noun
3. Latin
4. steep
5. definition a

### Grammar Practice

1. The moment Sindbad awoke and became aware of his situation, he threw himself on the sand and sobbed. C
2. Despite his terror, Sindbad immediately began searching the island for signs of life. C
3. When he discovered the roc, Sindbad made a plan, and he executed it perfectly. CC
4. The roc dropped Sindbad in a more inhospitable place, so that, ironically, he was worse off than before. C
5. A vulture saved the day for Sindbad, which amazed him and probably amazes readers, too. C
6. The karkadan was reported to have a horn that looked like a man, although that seems unlikely to modern-day readers. C
7. After he sold thousands of diamonds, Sindbad's thoughts turned toward home, and he started planning. CC
8. When he got back home, people treated Sindbad as a hero, and everyone wanted to be his friend. CC

### Selection Quick Check

1. He leads a joyful and carefree life.
2. He feels an irresistible longing to travel again and visit distant cities and islands.

# Answers

3. He falls asleep and the crew, not missing him, sails without him.
4. The deep valley is covered with diamonds.
5. He sees a rhinoceros.

## *from the* Rubáiyát

### Literary Element

Poems will vary but must follow the rhyme scheme of the *Rubáiyát: aaba* and address in some fashion the wisdom of living for the moment.

Many students will explain that writing rhymed poetry following a rhyme scheme is more difficult than writing unrhymed poetry because finding words that rhyme and also make sense is challenging. Some students may argue that having a strict structure limits the possibilities and thus makes writing rhymed poetry easier than writing unrhymed poetry.

### Reading Strategy

Explanations will vary slightly but should be similar to the following:

1. Wake up! It's morning.
2. Time moves quickly and unceasingly.
3. Individual beings are only a short-lived and insignificant part of nature.
4. A higher power determines people's fates.
5. If people could, they would change the world to be more to their liking.

### Vocabulary Strategy

1. Night
2. time
3. line
4. no
5. sow
6. buy

### Selection Quick Check

1. The Sultán's Turret is caught in a Noose of Light.
2. The speaker advises "take the Cash in hand and waive the Rest," or enjoy what one has in the present.
3. The Rose has the human quality of speech.
4. The speaker learns "I came like Water, and like Wind I go," meaning that all things are fleeting.
5. The speaker wishes that he and his love could remake life to suit their own desires.

## The Counsels of the Bird *from* The Masnavi

### Literary Element

Answers will vary.

1. **Maxim:** "Believe not foolish assertions of any one!" **Interpretation:** Don't believe anyone who says foolish things. **My version:** Don't believe foolish words, no matter who says them.
2. **Maxim:** "Do not grieve for what is past;/ When a thing is done, vex not yourself about it." **Interpretation:** What's done is done. **My version:** You can't change the past, so don't fret about it.
3. **Maxim:** "To give counsel to a sleepy ignoramus / Is to sow seeds upon salt land." **Interpretation:** Advice is wasted on a fool. **My version:** Advising an ignoramus is a waste of breath.

### Reading Strategy

Details and generalizations will vary. Sample responses follow.

### Details About the Man

captures bird with "wiles and snares"

cries and weeps

doesn't follow bird's advice

### Generalization

The man is smart enough to catch the bird but then is easily fooled by the bird.

# Answers

### Details About the Bird

promises good advice if man lets him go

invents a story about a pearl hidden inside his body

calls man a "sleepy ignoramus" and refuses to tell him the third piece of advice

### Generalization

The bird is smarter than the man but impatient when the man doesn't follow his advice.

### Selection Vocabulary Practice

**EXERCISE A**

1. assertion
2. deem
3. prosperity

**EXERCISE B**

1. deem
2. prosperity
3. assertion

**EXERCISE C**

Answers will vary but should be expressed in concise maxim form and include two of the vocabulary words.

### Vocabulary Strategy

Answers will vary. Possible answers are shown.

1. precious *pretium;* price of great value or high price
2. prosperity *prosperus;* favorable economic well-being
3. lamentations *lamentum;* lament acts of mourning
4. ignorance *ignorans;* to not know lack of knowledge, education

### Grammar Practice

1. In "The Counsels of the Bird," a man <u>who captures a bird</u> learns a lesson.
2. The bird, <u>whose fear of the man isn't evident</u>, offers him advice.
3. Has there ever been a bird <u>whose gift of gab was greater</u>?
4. Can you imagine anyone <u>who would trust the advice of a bird</u>?
5. The advice <u>that the bird gives</u> is excellent though.
6. The bird, <u>who must have made a plan</u>, tests the effect of his counsel.
7. He tempts the man with a story about a pearl, <u>which can't possibly be true</u>.
8. The man, <u>whose greed overcomes his common sense</u>, falls for the story.
9. The second counsel <u>that the man ignores</u> is to let bygones be bygones.
10. The bird has the final word in the story, <u>which is how it should be</u>.

### Selection Quick Check

1. The word refers to the three pieces of advice the bird gives to the man.
2. The bird says that the man has eaten the flesh of other animals and was not satisfied.
3. The bird claims the man will declare himself happy.
4. The bird claims that a precious pearl is inside his body.
5. The man is a sleepy ignoramus.

## Elegy for a Woman of No Importance

### Literary Element

Answers will vary. Sample answers are shown.

1. curtain "no curtain opened to air the room of grief" Curtain is given the human ability of being able to take action.
2. moon "The moon murmured sadly." The moon is able to speak and feel emotions.
3. night "Night, unconcerned, gave way to morning" The night can experience a lack of emotion.
4. wind "wind / which played about the rooftops / playing in deep forgetfulness" The wind is given the ability to play and to forget.

# Answers

**Reading Strategy**

Answers will vary. Sample answers are shown.

TONE: regretful

1. "When she died no face turned pale, no lips trembled"
2. "no eyes followed the coffin to the end of the road—"
3. "The moon murmured sadly."

**Selection Vocabulary Practice**

**EXERCISE A**

1. murmur; shout
2. shrill; soothing
3. vague; definite

**EXERCISE B**

1. vague
2. murmur
3. shrill

**EXERCISE C**

Elegies will vary but must include the vocabulary words.

**Vocabulary Strategy**

Answers will vary. Sample answers are shown.

1. **hovering:** remaining suspended; nagging at the memory, lingering almost unnoticeably
2. **vague:** unclear, without form, indistinct; borderless, smudged, nearly transparent
3. **scrap:** small, detached piece; worthless shred, tiny bit of something unimportant
4. **squabbling:** quarreling noisily over petty matters; play fighting, rolling and tumbling, quarreling for fun
5. **spilling:** allowing to flow unintentionally so as to be wasted; overflowing carelessly, being squandered

**Selection Quick Check**

1. A woman of no importance has died.
2. The moon murmurs sadly at the news of the woman's death.
3. With morning comes the call to fasting, the mewing of a hungry cat, the cries of street vendors, and the squabbling of boys.

## The Sound of Birds at Noon

**Literary Element**

Answers will vary. Sample answers are shown.

1. Example: They sing without giving us a thought / and they are as many / as the seed of Abraham.

Effect: Having the first idea on the first line separates it from the other idea in this passage. The second division emphasizes the word *many*.

2. Example: They have a life of their own, / they fly without thinking

Effect: These lines show a natural division of assertion and example.

3. Example: Their hearts aren't heavy / even when they peck at a worm.

Effect: This line division comes at a natural pause and maintains the conversational rhythm of the poem.

4. Example: Over the years / it even seems to have / a note of compassion.

Effect: This example maintains the rhythm of the poem and emphasizes the final line and the word *compassion*.

**Reading Strategy**

Answers will vary. Sample answers are shown.

**Main Purpose:** to describe

**Details:** chirping; many "as the seed of Abraham," "every wing is grace" peck at worms, touch branches

**Selection Vocabulary Practice**

**EXERCISE A**

Answers will vary. Possible synonyms are shown.

1. mean; evil
2. unusual; scarce
3. caring; empathy

# Answers

**EXERCISE B**

1. rare
2. compassion
3. malicious

**EXERCISE C**

Poems will vary, but the topic should be violence and all three vocabulary words should be included.

**Vocabulary Strategy**

1. c
2. b
3. a
4. b

**Selection Quick Check**

1. The chirping of birds is "not in the least malicious."
2. Whether the birds are common or rare, "every wing is grace."
3. She concludes that the birds' chirping even has a note of compassion.

## The Diameter of the Bomb

**Literary Element**

Answers will vary. Sample answers are shown.

1. the diameter of its effective range

The detached, technical word choice makes the poem begin as a report from a disinterested observer might. The beginning of the poem sets up a contrast with the ending.

2. two hospitals are scattered

The word *scattered* emphasizes the almost random effect of the violence.

3. solitary man mourning her death

Both the sound and the meaning of the words create a somber mood.

4. a circle with no end and no God

The words are short and blunt, echoing the finality of death. The despair lingers in the reader's mind.

**Reading Strategy**

1. cause: bomb blast; effect: four dead, eleven wounded
2. cause: young woman is buried; effect: man far away mourns her death
3. cause: orphans crying; effect: makes an endless, Godless circle of despair

**Selection Vocabulary Practice**

**EXERCISE A**

1. considerably
2. range
3. solitary

**EXERCISE B**

Sample Answers

1. You could measure the distance between where a bomb was launched and where it fell. *Range* refers to the extent that something travels.
2. You would be very unlikely to find a person who prefers to be solitary in a crowd. A solitary person is someone who has no companions.
3. Twins who look considerably different do not resemble each other closely. *Considerably* means "greatly."

**EXERCISE C**

Answers will vary but should respond to the poem and include the three vocabulary words.

**Vocabulary Strategy**

**bomb:** Greek *bombos;* deep hollow sound  an explosive device fused to detonate under certain conditions

**hospital:** Latin *hospitalis;* of a guest  institution where sick are given medical attention

**circle:** Greek *krikos;* ring  ring or halo

**solitary:** Latin *solus;* alone  being, living, or going alone

# Answers

### Selection Quick Check

1. The diameter of the bomb measures thirty centimeters.
2. Two hospitals and one graveyard are located in the larger circle.
3. The speaker says he "won't even mention the crying of orphans."

## Butterflies

### Literary Element

Answers will vary. Sample answers are shown.

1. a dusty mountain
2. an enraged dragon
3. an empty snail shell
4. crumpled paper

Poems will vary but must include one of the similes from the activity.

### Reading Strategy

Answers will vary but must cite three passages from one or more of the following poems: "Butterflies," "Elegy for a Woman of No Importance," "The Sound of Birds at Noon," or "The Diameter of the Bomb" and relate them to a personal experience.

### Selection Quick Check

1. The speaker didn't need an elegy.
2. She follows the path of the butterflies in her heart.
3. A bedouin knows how to trace the steps of his mare.

## The Letter, from Persepolis

### Literary Element

Answers will vary but may include some of the following:

| Symbol | Meaning |
|---|---|
| Cadillac | upper class or status |
| Mehri | peasant class |
| mark of the slap | anger and fear |

Paragraphs will vary. A sample answer is shown. The use of symbolism makes the story richer and more interesting than it would be otherwise. The use of symbolism contrasts with the simple illustration style and emphasizes the seriousness of the story.

### Reading Strategy

Answers will vary. Sample answers are shown.

1. The words and images are equally important in "The Letter."
2. Graphic novels look like long comic books printed with sturdier covers on better paper. They have panels like comic books, and like comic books, they follow the convention of speech balloons and thought balloons. However, their stories are not like the stories in comic books. They have complex plots and characters.
3. I was amused and moved by "The Letter." I felt as though I understood what Marjane was like and why she was upset with the way things were in Iran. I think the genre worked well with this story; the simple drawings and words seem just right for a story told by a child.

### Selection Vocabulary Practice

**EXERCISE A**

1. antonyms
2. synonyms
3. synonyms

**EXERCISE B**

1. demonstrate
2. clandestine
3. devoted

**EXERCISE C**

Pages will vary but should follow graphic novel conventions and include the three vocabulary words.

### Vocabulary Strategy

1. res, meaning "thing, wealth" and publica, meaning "public"

2. By combining the words for wealth and public, the etymology shows how valuable the Romans thought the republic was.
3. noun
4. 1b

**Grammar Practice**

Sentences 1, 2, 3, 7, 8, 10, and 12 have adverb clauses and should have an X on the line before them.

1. after she realized what it stood for
2. Because she was a sensitive child,
3. Even though they got along,
7. After Marjane's father found out about Hossein and Mehri,
8. Because she was easily persuaded,
10. When they got home at night,
12. when writing "The Letter."

**Selection Quick Check**

1. Darvishian tells sad, true stories about poor children.
2. Mehri is the maid who takes care of Marjane.
3. Marjane writes letters from Mehri to Hossein.
4. Marjane's father tells Hossein that Mehri is the family's maid, and Hossein loses interest in Mehri.
5. Marjane and Mehri attend a demonstration against the Shah.

## Regarding Rania

**Reading Strategy**

Answers will vary. Sample answers are shown.

**Issue:** women's dress in Arab countries

**Information:** In some Arab countries, all women are pressured into wearing modest clothing and headscarves. In other Arab countries, such as Egypt, women have greater latitude to wear what they want.

**Issue:** equality of women in Arab countries

**Information:** In Arab countries, women do not have the same legal rights as men do.

**Issue:** social role of women in Arab countries

**Information:** In some Arab countries, such as Saudi Arabia, most women remain at home and cannot pursue careers. In other Arab countries, such as Jordan and Egypt, many women have careers and participate in politics.

**Selection Quick Check**

1. Rania al Abdullah is the queen of Jordan.
2. She wants to show that the way women dress should be up to them.
3. She was celebrating Human Rights Day by reading a passage from the United Nation's Universal Declaration of Human Rights.
4. She is trying to establish social and political reforms to improve the lives of women.
5. She talked about improving women's rights.

## Part 2: South Central Asia, 3500 B.C.–Present

## English Language Coach, Part 2

1. yes
2. Substitutions will vary.
3. yes
4. yes
5. Substitutions will vary.
6. yes
7. Substitutions will vary.
8. yes

## *from the* Rig-Veda

**Literary Element**

1. Answers will vary but should include the idea that if two things are dark, one cannot hide the other. However, because of the seeming absurdity of the phrase, the writer is emphasizing the idea of complete and utter darkness.
2. Answers will vary but may include the idea that existence and non-existence are linked—you cannot know one without knowing the other.

# Answers

### Reading Strategy

Answers will vary but should be similar to the following:

1. meaning: water without a bottom; connotation: body of water so vast and deep that it is bottomless; image of a huge, endless ocean
2. meaning: declare publicly; connotation: saying with exuberance; image of a member of royalty speaking in public
3. meaning: part of a plant from which a new plant will grow; connotation: place of growth; idea of fertility, images of flowering plants and nature

### Selection Vocabulary Practice

#### EXERCISE A

1. b
2. d
3. a

#### EXERCISE B

1. proclaim
2. distinguishing
3. impulse

#### EXERCISE C

Student responses will vary but should include ideas about creation and the three vocabulary words.

### Vocabulary Strategy

Synonyms and connotations will vary. Possible synonyms and connotations are shown.

1. night: time from dusk till dawn
   gloom: dark or shadowy place
2. intelligence: mental acuteness
   knowledge: understanding of something
3. want: strong desire
   wish: wanting something that is perhaps unattainable

### Grammar Practice

1. DO; underline *that you shouldn't eat meat*
2. OP; underline *whichever verses are appropriate for a ritual*
3. OP; underline *whatever evil forces he encountered*
4. PN; underline *where you will find the sacred hymns of Hinduism*
5. S; underline *Whoever wrote this hymn*
6. PN; underline where *Hindus believe you will be released from the cycle of death and rebirth*

### Selection Quick Check

1. The first stanza describes conditions before creation.
2. Darkness was hidden by darkness.
3. Desire is the first seed of mind.

## Hundred Questions *from the* Mahabharata

### Literary Element

Answers will vary but should include the following ideas:

1. He interacts with the yaksha and answers his questions.
2. He finds courage to ask the voice why he killed his brothers.
3. When he comes upon his dead brothers, he analyzes the situation before acting. He answers all of the yaksha's seemingly endless questions.
4. Even though he is extremely thirsty, he finds the strength to keep from drinking the water and answers all of the yaksha's questions.
5. He sees it as his duty to help the brahmin. He chooses to save the life of the brother whose mother is different from his, out of respect for her, putting aside his own feelings for his own brothers. He knows the answers to the yaksha's questions, which reflect the values of his culture.

# Answers

**Reading Strategy**

1. sacred code of conduct or duty
2. carry out responsibilities based on station in life

**3.–5.** Answers will vary but should include the actions and thoughts of the brothers as they relate to the Hindu concept of *dharma* and preserving the natural order. Possible answers follow: the brothers performed austerities; Yudhistira prepared to perform rites for the dead; Yudhistira showed respect to the yaksha by doing what he was told; Yudhistira chose to save Nakula, in honor of his other mother.

**Selection Vocabulary Practice**

**EXERCISE A**

1. synonym: austerity; possible antonym: act of self-indulgence
2. synonym: fatuous; possible antonyms: wise, intelligent
3. synonym: poignancy; possible antonym: without deep feeling
4. synonym: avarice; possible antonyms: generosity, benevolence
5. synonym: inordinate; possible antonyms: moderate, little

**EXERCISE B**

1. b
2. b
3. a
4. a
5. b

**EXERCISE C**

Editorials will vary but should include an argument that agrees or disagrees with the yaksha's actions and give reasons to support the argument. Editorials should also use at least four vocabulary words.

**Vocabulary Strategy**

Words and their connotations will vary, but for each word, students should give the dictionary definition under *Denotation,* and a reasonable *Connotation.* Possible words, denotations, and connotations: ***searing:*** *very hot; so hot as to be unbearable;* ***lamented:*** *expressed sorrow or grief; suggests religious undertones, overwhelming grief;* ***vanquish:*** *to defeat or conquer; suggestion of defeating a noble, powerful warrior;* ***immense:*** *very large; so large as to be overwhelming*

**Grammar Practice**

1. imp.
2. int.
3. dec.
4. imp.
5. int.
6. exc.
7. dec.
8. dec.
9. int.
10. imp.

**Selection Quick Check**

1. Yudhistira feels it is his duty because he is a member of the warrior class.
2. The sound of cranes alerts them.
3. They ignore a voice telling them not to drink from the pool.
4. The voice materializes into a yaksha.
5. The yaksha is Yama, the God of Justice, and Yudhistira's father.

## *from* Homer in India

**Reading Strategy**

Answers will vary but should include the following ideas:

1. Because many were illiterate, *bhopas* learned the stories through oral storytelling.
2. The villagers placed a great deal of importance on attending the performance of the bhopas because they believed that the *bhopas* could invoke gods that would help them in their livelihoods.

# Answers

3. Young children began memorizing stories from their parents or other elders because it was so important to their culture.
4. The gods on which the villagers placed the most importance were those that could help them in their agricultural pursuits, and villagers attended the performances of the *bhopas*, whose stories included such gods. In addition, they prayed to local gods whom they believed would help them.

### Selection Quick Check

1. The epics were memorized and performed by a caste of wandering *bhopas*—shamans and bards.
2. She found a *bhopa* who knew the entire Dev Narayan epic and recorded his performance of the epic.
3. A *phad* is a large painted piece of cloth that the *bhopas* use as a backdrop while they recite the stories.
4. The villagers believe that Pajubi, who is very powerful at curing sick animals, enters Mohan as he recites the epic and that Pajubi helps their animals.
5. The poems were part of a religious ritual that was extremely important to local herders.

## Rama and Ravana in Battle *from the* Ramayana

### Literary Element

Conflicts will vary but may include the following:

1. Rama is conflicted about the chariot he is sent. He struggles with whether or not it is a trap or a gift from the gods; internal conflict.
2. Rama is in a physical conflict with Ravana throughout the story as they do battle; external conflict.
3. Ravana is conflicted when he notices ominous signs. He briefly struggles with whether or not he should be concerned with the omens; internal conflict.
4. Ravana is in a physical conflict with Rama throughout the story as they do battle; external conflict.

### Reading Strategy

Summaries may vary but should be similar to the following:

1. You could hear the cries of the warriors' widows over the courtiers' chants and songs of triumph.
2. Rama thought about which weapon to use next. He chose "Brahamasthra," which the Creator Brahma designed earlier. Shiva used the weapon to kill Tripura, a monster who wanted to destroy the world by taking on the forms of flying mountains and then crushing cities.
3. Ravana's and Rama's horses glared at each other. The flags on the chariots clashed. On Ravana's flag was the ensign of the Veena, a stringed musical instrument. Rama's flag showed the whole universe on it. The sound of the bow strings on both sides rose above all others.

### Selection Vocabulary Practice

#### EXERCISE A

Synonyms and connotations will vary but may include the following:

1. connotation: the utmost; synonym: greatness; connotation: super
2. connotation: of ancient times; synonym: original; connotation: first
3. connotation: in a perfect state; synonym: pure; connotation: unblemished

#### EXERCISE B

1. b
2. a
3. c

#### EXERCISE C

Stories will vary but should include elements that are referred to in the epic, such as that Ravana attacked the divine elephants that guard the four directions and was gored by one of their tusks. Stories should also include three vocabulary words.

**Vocabulary Strategy**

1. *spec:* see; do; *-or:* one who; definition: one who looks on or watches
2. *aero:* air; *-al:* relating to; definition: of or relating to the air
3. *a:* not: *vert:* turn; definition: turned away
4. *bene:* good; *dict:* say; *-ion:* quality of; definition: expression of good wishes
5. *de:* from, down; *ject:* throw; definition: acting down in spirits

**Grammar Practice**

Revisions of fragment will vary. Possible sentences are given.

1. F; Ravana shot arrows from a dozen bows.
2. F; Rama rode in a chariot sent by the gods.
3. S
4. F; Rama and his army of monkeys defeated Ravana.
5. F; Could Ravana ever win the battle?
6. S
7. F; Rama was unsure of what to do next.
8. F; Although he had prayed for his arms and heads to be indestructible, Ravana forgot to strengthen his heart.
9. S
10. F; Rama was surrounded by his brothers and all his other war chiefs.

**Selection Quick Check**

1. Ravana joins the battle because he can no longer stand for the destruction of his army.
2. He intends to kill or be killed by Rama.
3. The gods send Rama a special chariot to help him defend himself against Ravana.
4. They fight with bows and arrows at first. They later use supernatural powers to fight each other.
5. Rama tells Vibishana to make grand funeral arrangements and to honor Ravana's memory so that he can go to heaven.

**Comparing Literature Graphic Organizer**

1. Beginning—foolish, man with no scholarship; wise, three learned men
   End—foolish, three learned men; wise, man with no scholarship
2. Beginning—foolish, wolf; wise, dog
   End—foolish, dog; wise, wolf
3. Beginning—foolish, reed; wise, oak
   End—foolish, oak; wise, reed
4. Beginning—foolish, all animals; wise, elephant
   End—foolish, elephant; wise, termite

## The Lion-Makers *from the* Panchatantra

**Literary Element**

1. d
2. c
3. b
4. a

Experiences will vary but should clearly illustrate each lesson being taught.

**Reading Strategy**

Answers may vary but should be similar to the following:

1. This must be a fable because there is a moral at the beginning and ending of the text. This means that the story teaches a lesson about right and wrong.
2. This saying is the moral of the fable. It means that common sense is more important than learning. I can use it as a guide as I read the story to see how the moral is taught.
3. The illustrations are very colorful and look Indian in style. There are animals interacting with people, and a fierce lion is depicted in both illustrations.

4. There is a moral at the beginning and the same moral at the end, set off in italics. Because it is set off and repeated, its importance is magnified.

**Selection Vocabulary Practice**

**EXERCISE A**

Words will vary but may include the following.

1. friendship, citizenship; *-ship* means "state or quality of"
2. amazement, amusement; *-ment* means "result of"
3. rarity, scarcity; *-ity* means "state or quality of"

**EXERCISE B**

1. b
2. c
3. a

**EXERCISE C**

Letters will vary but should include a reasoned argument about why common sense is more important than what you learn in books.

**Vocabulary Strategy**

1. b
2. a
3. a
4. b
5. b
6. stationery
7. miner
8. meddle
9. principal
10. wring

**Grammar Practice**

Revisions will vary. Possible corrections are given.

1. The *Panchatantra* is a collection of Indian fables; they contain lessons about living wisely.
2. The stories in the *Panchatantra* were written down around 200 B.C. They were passed down through oral tradition.
3. The fourth Brahman had sense; however, he found scholarship distasteful.
4. Scholarship is less than sense; therefore seek intelligence.
5. They traveled in the forest and came upon a lion's skeleton.
6. Three of the Brahmans wanted to bring the lion to life, but the fourth Brahman did not.
7. The *Panchatantra* was translated into many languages. It was translated into English in 1570.
8. The lion came to life, but the fourth Brahman did not die.
9. The first three Brahmans were great scholars; the fourth had sense.
10. The fourth Brahman warned the others, but they did not listen.

**Selection Quick Check**

1. Three of them have high academic achievement but no sense.
2. They think accomplishments should be used for travel, winning the favor of kings, and acquiring money.
3. He has sense but no scholarship.
4. He says the fourth Brahman is their friend.
5. He warns them that if they bring the lion to life, the lion will kill them all.

## The Kabuliwallah

**Literary Element**

Responses will vary but should include the following ideas:

1. He is good with children. He is kind and generous.
2. Mini is an outgoing, brave girl who enjoys the company of others.
3. Mini's mother is an anxious person who worries and doesn't trust people she doesn't know.
4. The narrator is compassionate and understanding of his fellow humans.

# Answers

### Reading Strategy

Answers will vary but might include some of the following:

1. Mini was afraid of the Kabuliwallah at first.
2. Some people felt it was acceptable to cheat the Kabuliwallah because he was of lower social status.
3. Mini prepared for her wedding and for her departure from her father's house.
4. The young Mini doesn't understand what "going to her father-in-law's house" means, and so assumes it means going to jail.
5. He arranges his daughter's wedding according to Hindu beliefs and traditions.
6. He views meeting a "criminal"—the Kabuliwallah—as a bad omen for the day of the wedding.

### Selection Vocabulary Practice

**EXERCISE A**

1. formidable
2. fettered
3. arid
4. demur

**EXERCISE B**

1. formidable
2. demur
3. fettered
4. sordid
5. arid

**EXERCISE C**

Journal entries will vary but should include the thoughts and feelings of the character and three of the vocabulary words.

### Vocabulary Strategy

1. adjective
2. Three meanings are given. Tagore uses the third meaning, because the hero and heroine are in a dangerous position.
3. It is from the Latin word that means "obtained by prayer or begging." This helps my understanding because someone in a precarious position may pray or beg to be delivered from harm.

### Grammar Practice

1. enjoyed
2. laughing
3. realized
4. prepared
5. wrapped
6. imagining
7. married
8. recognized

### Selection Quick Check

1. She cannot live without chattering.
2. He gives her almonds and raisins.
3. They share many jokes and laughter.
4. She reminds him of his own daughter.
5. The narrator gives him money so that he may return to his own daughter in Afghanistan.

## Like the Sun

### Literary Element

Responses will vary but should include the following ideas:

1. The analogy doesn't work, because hearing a painful truth is not pleasant or soothing, like listening to pleasant music would be.
2. The analogy does work, because a punch in the stomach is painful and takes your breath away, similar to hearing a painful truth.
3. The analogy does work, because diving into ice-cold water would be shocking to your body and might take your breath away, just as hearing a painful truth might.
4. The analogy does not work, because gazing at the stars is something that is relaxing and enjoyable, unlike hearing a painful truth.

# Answers

### Reading Strategy

Answers will vary but should include background knowledge that is relevant to students' understanding of the events listed. Sample answers are given.

1. My mother asked me how a new outfit looked. I didn't think it was very flattering, but I lied so I wouldn't hurt her feelings.
2. I put off writing a book report until the last minute, and I felt dread and anxiety over finishing it in time.
3. When my brother told me I wouldn't make the team because I wasn't good enough, I was so angry with him that I hid his favorite CD.

### Selection Vocabulary Practice

**EXERCISE A**

1. b
2. a
3. a

**EXERCISE B**

1. shirk
2. scrutinize
3. stupefied

**EXERCISE C**

Journal entries will vary but should include interactions with people during which the student tells them the truth and should include the people's responses.

### Vocabulary Strategy

1. a grade in a British school or some private American schools
2. created and wrote a piece of music
3. a man in charge of the staff at a private school; principal
4. involving attention to detail in preparation or implementation

Sentences will vary, but should include the use of the correct meaning of the jargon, based on the field from which it comes.

### Grammar Practice

1. chose
2. sought
3. sung
4. became
5. given
6. seen
7. known
8. drove

### Selection Quick Check

1. He compares it to the sun.
2. People temper the truth so it does not shock.
3. He says it can't be helped.
4. He has avoided grading a hundred test papers.
5. He feels worried that there will be consequences for telling the truth.

## By Any Other Name

### Literary Element

Responses will vary but should include the following ideas:

1. Most likely she felt she had less worth than the English children.
2. It reminds me of when the United States had racial segregation in our schools, and on public transportation, and the injustice of it.
3. It shows how Indians were treated under British rule.
4. She watches as her older sister quickly wants to conform.
5. I feel sorry for Premila because she wants to be like the others when she doesn't have to be.
6. It shows how children so desperately want to conform—want to be like other children—and will do so even if it means giving up part of their culture.
7. It meant that Santha could resume her life before "Cynthia," a life she enjoyed very much.

# Answers

8. I felt proud of Premila to have so much courage and conviction. It made me happy that the girls could go back to their normal lives without having to deal with the prejudices of other people.
9. It shows that you don't have to stand for being put down by other people for no other reason than you are from a different culture.

**Reading Strategy**

Answers will vary but should include examples from the text and contemporary times that illustrate each issue. Following are sample answers.

1. Premila's teacher thinks that Indian children cheat.
2. Stores owned by certain ethnic groups are vandalized because people mistrust and are angry at others from different cultures.
3. Premila leaves school because she believes she has been mistreated when the Indian children are forced to sit a desk apart. Their English teachers think that they cheat on tests.
4. People sued a major airline when they were banned from boarding a plane based on how they looked.
5. The headmistress renames the girls with British names, implying that those names are "prettier" or better.
6. Muslim girls in France are forbidden to wear headscarves and are forced to adopt Western clothing.

**Selection Vocabulary Practice**

**EXERCISE A**

1. provincial
2. insular
3. tepid

**EXERCISE B**

1. incomprehensible
2. sedately
3. tepid

**EXERCISE C**

Entries will vary but should include descriptions of the events that led up to Premila's leaving school, from her point of view, as well as her thoughts and feelings.

**Vocabulary Strategy**

1. a
2. b
3. a
4. b
5. a
6. a
7. b
8. a

**Grammar Practice**

1. ate
2. remembers
3. will play *or* shall play
4. told
5. had
6. will write *or* shall write
7. wears

**Selection Quick Check**

1. The younger sister, Santha, is the narrator.
2. The headmistress renames them Cynthia and Pamela.
3. Premila and Santha have Indian food for lunch, whereas the other students bring sandwiches.
4. She doesn't understand the concept of competitive games and allows the other children to catch her.
5. She is able to put the experience "happily away" because it happened to a girl named Cynthia, not to her.

# Answers

## The Wagon

### Literary Element

Responses will vary but should include the following ideas:

1. The narrator believes something terribly sinister is in the muck-wagon and becomes so ill he vomits. Someone writes an article about not allowing the garbage carts to pass through city streets.
2. The narrator is hallucinating or imagining things—it doesn't seem that others are bothered by the muck-wagon.
3. The three men instill fear in the heart of the narrator, and he thinks they know some awful truth. No one else from the story seems to have encountered these men.
4. The men don't exist; they are only in the narrator's mind.
5. The narrator thinks the cityfolk have become immune to the smell, but it still torments him.
6. The smell is gone; the narrator is completely irrational at this point.

### Reading Strategy

Ambiguities should be similar to the following. Explanations for the ambiguities may vary but should make sense based on the passage.

1. The men had noticed the strange sunset, but none of the others had.
2. People were too busy with their lives to notice; it didn't affect them.
3. The narrator is overcome with pain because of the smell, but his own wife can't smell it at all.
4. The smell is in the narrator's head, or the narrator is more susceptible to the smell.
5. The city people are not bothered by the smell anymore, but the narrator is tormented by it.
6. The narrator has become deranged, and the smell is only in his head. OR The cityfolk are different from the narrator; they choose to ignore the smell and go on with life, not dwelling on the negative.

### Selection Vocabulary Practice

**EXERCISE A**

1. pungent
2. impervious
3. surge

**EXERCISE B**

1. b
2. b
3. a

**EXERCISE C**

Entries will vary but should include descriptions of what is in the wagon and the narrator's response to it.

### Vocabulary Strategy

Synonyms will vary. Possible synonyms are given. Definitions should match chosen synonyms.

**1.–2.** trudged: shambled, shuffled, plodded, slogged

**5.–6.** uncanny: eerie, mysterious, creepy, weird, odd, peculiar

**9.–10.** odor: smell, scent, aroma, fragrance

### Grammar Practice

1. underline *had trudged*; past perf.
2. underline *have become*; present perf.
3. underline *will have died*; future perf.
4. underline *has skyrocketed*; present perf.
5. has fallen
6. had become
7. will have been
8. have decided

### Selection Quick Check

1. They are watching the sunset.
2. The sky continues to glow red, even after the sun sets.
3. He often stops at the bookshop, which is owned by an old friend of his.
4. The odor becomes especially unbearable.

# Answers

**5.** He sees them again at the end of the story, chasing after the wagon.

## Spelling Practice

**1.** fatuous—treacherous
**2.** pristine—clandestine
**3.** restore—redeem
**4.** demur—murmur
**5.** pugnacious—pungent
**6.** inexorable—incur
**7.** abate—abandoned

## Writing Workshop

Answers will vary. Students should include specific details related to the personal experience.

## Speaking, Listening, and Viewing

Answers will vary. Students should include thoughtful evaluations of students' presentations.